Reinhold Chemistry Textbook Series

CONSULTING EDITORS

Harry H. Sisler
University of Florida
Gainesville, Florida

Calvin A. VanderWerf
Hope College
Holland, Michigan

Bonner and Castro—*Essentials of Modern Organic Chemistry*
Day and Selbin—*Theoretical Inorganic Chemistry*
Drago—*Physical Methods in Inorganic Chemistry*
Fairley and Kilgour—*Essentials of Biological Chemistry, Second Edition*
Fieser and Fieser—*Advanced Organic Chemistry*
Fieser and Fieser—*Topics in Organic Chemistry*
Heftmann—*Chromatography, Second Edition*
Heftmann and Mosettig—*Biochemistry of Steroids*
Klingenberg and Reed—*Introduction to Quantitative Chemistry*
Lingane—*Analytical Chemistry of Selected Metallic Elements*
Luder—*A Different Approach to Thermodynamics*
Meyer—*Food Chemistry*
Mortimer—*Chemistry: A Conceptual Approach*
Neckers—*Mechanistic Organic Photochemistry*
Reid—*Principles of Chemical Thermodynamics*
Sanderson—*Chemical Periodicity*
Sanderson—*Inorganic Chemistry*
Smith—*Chemical Thermodynamics: A Problems Approach*
Smith and Cristol—*Organic Chemistry*

Selected Topics in Modern Chemistry

Brey—*Physical Methods for Determining Molecular Geometry*
Cheldelin and Newburgh—*The Chemistry of Some Life Processes*
Eyring and Eyring—*Modern Chemical Kinetics*
Hildebrand—*An Introduction to Molecular Kinetic Theory*
Kieffer—*The Mole Concept in Chemistry*
Moeller—*The Chemistry of the Lanthanides*
Morris—*Principles of Chemical Equilibrium*
Murmann—*Inorganic Complex Compounds*
O'Driscoll—*The Nature and Chemistry of High Polymers*
Overmann—*Basic Concepts of Nuclear Chemistry*
Rochow—*Organometallic Chemistry*
Ryschkewitsch—*Chemical Bonding and the Geometry of Molecules*
Sisler—*Electronic Structure, Properties, and the Periodic Law*
Sisler—*Chemistry in Non-Aqueous Solvents*
Sonnessa—*Introduction to Molecular Spectroscopy*
Strong and Stratton—*Chemical Energy*
VanderWerf—*Acids, Bases, and the Chemistry of the Covalent Bond*
Vold and Vold—*Colloid Chemistry*

i

Consulting Editors' Statement

An understanding of the principles of thermodynamics and their application to chemical systems is fostered by the development of facility in the solution of numerical problems based on these principles. Professor Norman O. Smith has included many carefully worked out problems in this text and through the theoretical development of important concepts has enabled the student to acquaint himself with the fundamental ideas necessary to solve these meaningful and illuminating problems. Thus he has provided an excellent text to help the student achieve this understanding and facility. The Reinhold Publishing Corporation is proud to add this title to its Chemistry Textbook Series.

HARRY H. SISLER

C. A. VANDERWERF

ii

Chemical Thermodynamics

A PROBLEMS APPROACH

NORMAN O. SMITH

Professor of Chemistry
Fordham University
New York, New York

REINHOLD PUBLISHING CORPORATION

A subsidiary of Chapman-Reinhold, Inc.

NEW YORK   AMSTERDAM   LONDON

"A theory is the more impressive the greater the simplicity of its premises is, the more different kinds of things it relates, and the more extended is its area of applicability. Therefore the deep impression which classical thermodynamics made upon me. It is the only physical theory of universal content concerning which I am convinced that, within the framework of the applicability of its basic concepts, it will never be overthrown......"

Albert Einstein

Excerpt from Albert Einstein, "Autobiographical Notes," appearing in *Albert Einstein: Philosopher—Scientist*, 1949, now published by The Open Court Publishing Company, LaSalle, Illinois.

Preface

This book is intended to assist the student at both the college and early graduate level who is struggling for a comprehension of elementary thermodynamics, the backbone of physical chemistry. The seemingly abstract nature, the unavoidable rigor, and the many ramifications of the subject present a hurdle that is surmounted easily only by a few. At the same time a grasp of the subject and its implications can be a most rewarding and satisfying experience.

Thermodynamics is an old subject, but the recent appearance of many texts on it, besides testifying to its importance and difficulty, indicates considerable disagreement on how it should be presented, even making allowance for different levels of preparation. Some treatments, for example, introduce the reader first to entropy and later to free energy—others do the reverse. At the college level thermodynamics is usually taught as part of a course in general physical chemistry, the textbook for which cannot devote much space to illustrative problems, so the student, for whom the latter are a great aid, may be left behind. At the graduate level there is little or no time for reviewing college material and the student who never really understood the concepts as an undergraduate finds that he has to go back and assimilate them. At all levels the illustration of the use of relationships by means of worked numerical examples is helpful to most students. The writing of the present volume was undertaken primarily with this in mind. It is intended to supplement any standard physical chemistry or thermodynamics text, although it can be used by itself. Worked examples serve as a major teaching tool. These are, for the most part, straightforward, as they are intended to be instructive rather than challenging or subtle. Because of this the student should make an effort to study each one as it is presented. Every chapter concludes with a set of problems. These, too, have worked solutions which will be found at the end of the book. The practice of presenting a numerical problem without giving the method of solution and the final result, or even of providing a numerical answer without indicating how it was obtained, has not been followed. In the author's experience it is frustrating to the student not to have access to the solution. It is especially so if he is studying the subject without the benefit of an instructor.

The order of treatment of the various topics is what is believed to be the most logical and pedagogically sound. It corresponds generally to that in current texts. Special attention has been given to the entropy increase in isolated systems undergoing irreversible processes, and how this is related to the Kelvin-Planck statement of the second law. Only a brief reference to the statistical aspects of thermodynamics is made, and this is in connection with entropy. The need for and meaning of partial

v

39755

molal properties is discussed in detail, and methods of evaluating them included. The concept of chemical potential plays a prominent role. Certain habitual student errors are indicated. Sometimes a point, which in the author's opinion is not covered in sufficient detail elsewhere, is elaborated. This is particularly true in connection with the second law. No apologies are made for the occasional repetition of important ideas. The inadequacies of the "idealized" Clausius-Clapeyron equation are discussed more thoroughly than usual. There are sections on the calculation of ideal phase diagrams for vaporization and fusion, for both complete miscibility and simple eutectic types. The temperature dependence of the state functions for pure solids, liquids and gases is shown graphically. The distinction between standard state and reference state for components in solution is clarified. The importance of the isobaric restriction in Henry's law is illustrated. The symbol G for free energy, and definitions of q and w as the heat absorbed *by* and the work done *by* the system on the environment have been adopted as being the most widely used at present. New terms are printed in bold-face type as they are introduced. The table of physical constants lists the values most recently (1963) recommended by the National Academy of Science and the National Research Council. There is a set of "teasers" to challenge the better student and possibly the professor!

I am grateful to the office of the Director of Research and Program Development of Fordham University for assistance in the typing of part of the first draft of the manuscript. Finally, I wish to acknowledge with gratitude the patience of my wife, Ann, who spent many hours either in silence or listening to the typewriter or calculating machine, but without whose encouragement the task of writing could not have been completed.

N. O. S.

Contents

Introduction—
meaning of fundamental terms

HEAT, WORK, ENERGY AND TEMPERATURE

Thermodynamics, sometimes called **energetics**, is the study of the relationship between heat and other forms of energy. In spite of its name, classical thermodynamics deals with differences between systems "at rest." A **system** is a portion of matter set aside by real or imaginary boundaries for purposes of study. The system is said to be **closed** if no matter is allowed to enter or leave it, and **open** if this is permitted. It is **isolated** when neither matter nor energy is allowed to enter or leave. This includes the elimination of all work done on the system by the environment or by the system on the environment. Frequently we may choose to consider not only "the system" but also its immediate environment (that part of the environment which is affected by the given change). Homogeneous portions of systems are called **phases**.

The above statements require definitions of several terms in order to be understood. **Work** done by a system in thermodynamics is work done by the system *on* the environment and can always be translated into the raising of weights against the force of gravity or the coiling of a spring. The two most common kinds of work are (1) work of expansion and (2) electrical work. In **work of expansion**, often called **P-V work**, the system expands against the environment; this involves a mechanical force acting through a distance. By a suitable arrangement such work could be used, e.g., to cause the rotation of a shaft, as in the operation of an engine. In **electrical work** an electric charge moves from a point of higher to one of lower potential. (Electrical work can always be translated di-

1

rectly into the raising of weights and so is recognized as thermodynamic work.) Other kinds occasionally considered are that done by the decreasing of surface area, that done by a moving magnetic pole, etc. In this book we shall use the symbol w to stand for the work done *by* the system on the environment. With this understanding it is clear that w is negative when work is done on the system by the environment. (Admittedly this convention is not adopted universally: a minority of authors represent the work done by the system on the environment by $-w$ instead of by w. It is unfortunate that this difference exists, but it is one that can be easily tolerated as long as it is recognized!)

Energy is the ability to do work. **Kinetic energy**, the most obvious form of it, is the energy possessed by a moving mass as a result of its motion. There are, however, many other kinds of energy. **Heat energy**, or simply **heat** can do work by causing the matter into which it flows to expand against a force. A pair of molecules in close proximity to each other possess a **negative potential energy** if work is required against the force of intermolecular attraction to separate them by an infinite distance where the potential energy is arbitrarily taken to be zero. Analogously, mutual repulsion corresponds to **positive potential energy**. A mixture of hydrogen and oxygen is said to have **chemical energy** because, in the process of their chemical union to give water, work can be obtained. A charged capacitor may be said to have **electrical energy** because it has the potential for doing electrical work. Clearly, all forms of energy are expressible in the same units, whether the unit be the erg, joule, calorie, liter-atmosphere, electron-volt, etc. (The relationships which exist among these units are given in the appendix.) It should be noted that, since electrical quantities can be measured more accurately than thermal quantities, it is now common to define the calorie in terms of electrical energy. When 1 international coulomb falls through a potential of 1 international volt, 1 international joule of work is done, or 1.000165 absolute joules of work. The calorie most widely used in chemical thermodynamics is the **defined calorie**, equal to 4.1840 absolute joules. With this definition the calorie differs very slightly (negligibly for most purposes) from the various calories based on the heat required to raise the temperature of 1 g of liquid water through 1°C.

Heat energy is that form of energy which passes from one body to another solely as the result of a difference in temperature between the two bodies. The term **temperature**, however, is often defined as that quality of a body which determines its ability to give up heat to, or receive heat from, another body with which it is placed in contact. It is, of course, circuitous to define heat in terms of a temperature difference and temperature in terms of heat flow, but the difficulty may be avoided in the following way. Let us suppose that we are totally unfamiliar with the idea of temperature. We keep a sample of matter, such as a gas A, in a container at constant pressure and are mystified by the fact that its volume changes unpredictably with time. We observe the same sort of behavior with two other samples of gas, B and C. The pressures of all three samples are not necessarily the same, but are held constant. We now place A in contact with B and record their respective volumes, V_A and V_B. We then place A in contact with C instead of with B and wait for conditions under which the volume of A is again V_A, and at the same time record the volume of C, which we call V_C. We can now observe that, whenever B and C are in contact, and the volume of B is V_B, the volume of C is always V_C. We are thus led to recognize the existence of a quality of a system X, which is the same for any other system Y, when X and Y are in contact. This quality is the **temperature**, and the experimental result just described is known as the **zeroth law of thermodynamics**. Whenever two objects are kept in contact until no further transfer of energy takes place between them, the one quality—it may be the only one—that is the same for both objects is their temperature. The means whereby temperature is measured will be discussed later in this Introduction.

Both heat and work are thus energy in transit. We may not speak of a system as possessing a certain amount of work, or a certain amount of heat, for these quantities are meaningful only when an energy transfer is occurring.

THERMODYNAMIC EQUILIBRIUM

Any closed system, subject to a constant and uniform pressure and held at a constant and uniform temperature, will eventually, and frequently quickly, attain a condition in which no further detectable change in its properties occurs with the passage of time. In order to guarantee that such a system has "gone as far as it can go" and is not merely in a condition where changes are possible but are occurring too slowly for detection, the further restriction must be imposed that the same condition be reproducible when attained by a different procedure, e.g., by approaching the given temperature from lower and from higher temperatures. This implies a sensitivity on the part of the system to changes in the imposed conditions. In such systems the uniformity of pressure and consequent lack of net motion of matter is referred to as a condition of **mechanical equilibrium**; the uniformity of temperature and consequent lack of net transfer of heat is called a condition of **thermal equilibrium**; the absence of any further net chemical changes in any of the phases or between the phases of the system, e.g., between liquids and solids, and the consequent constancy in the chemical composition of every phase is considered a condition of **chemical equilibrium**. When a system is simultaneously in mechanical, thermal and chemical equilibrium, it is in **thermodynamic equilibrium**, and it is to such systems that the term "at rest," used earlier, refers. Classical thermodynamics is concerned with the energy changes involved in taking a system from one such state to another.

THERMODYNAMIC STATE

When the energy changes involved in passing from one equilibrium state to another are discussed, the states must be described unambiguously. This can be done by specifying certain macroscopic properties because we are dealing with matter in bulk. These are of two kinds: **intensive properties**—those which are independent of the mass of the material, such as temperature, pressure, density, molar volume and molar heat capacity—and **extensive properties**—those which do depend on the mass of material, such as volume, mass, energy. The conventional macroscopic properties used in describing the state of a system are chosen from the following: composition, temperature, pressure and volume. The state of a pure, homogeneous substance is defined by specifying any two of the variables of temperature, pressure and volume, and such specification fixes all the intensive properties, of the substance. In order to fix the extensive properties, the mass or the number of moles of the substance must be fixed. Consider, e.g., the change from an initial system consisting of solid $CaCO_3$ at 300°K and 1 atm to a final system consisting of solid CaO and CO_2 gas, both at 300°K and 1 atm. Such a specification of the substances present and their temperature and pressure is said to define the initial and final systems. It should be noted, however, that for purposes of evaluating the energy effects associated with the above change, one must know how much material is present in the systems. In this connection, then, the extensive properties are also required. The degree to which a knowledge of extensive properties plays a role in describing the state of the system will clearly depend on the object in mind and is usually evident from the context.

TEMPERATURE SCALES

The observation that two objects which are in thermal equilibrium with a third object are also in thermal equilibrium with each other permits quantitative measurement of temperature. We imagine that one of these objects is a fixed mass of a pure substance, which is called the **thermometric substance**, and utilize one of its properties such as its volume, V, as the **thermometric property**. Two readily reproducible environmental temperatures, such as the freezing point of water saturated with air at 1 atm and the normal boiling point of water, are chosen as **fixed or reference temperatures or points**, and the value of V when the substance is in thermal equilibrium with each environment is recorded. These particular temperatures are known as the **ice point** and **steam point**, respectively. Calling these volumes V_i and V_s, and arbitrarily calling the fixed temperatures 0° and 100°, we could define any other temperature, t, where the volume of the thermometric substance is V_t, by the following relation:

$$ t = \frac{(V_t - V_i)}{\frac{1}{100}(V_s - V_i)} = \frac{100(V_t - V_i)}{(V_s - V_i)} $$

This is because one-hundredth of the increase in volume in going from 0° to 100° represents 1°, and dividing this into the increase from 0° to $t°$ gives the number of degrees difference between 0° and $t°$, and therefore the temperature t known as **centigrade temperature**. Thus a plot of V_t vs. t must be linear.

It is possible, however, to find a thermometric property which is independent of the thermometric substance. This is the value of the limit of the product of pressure and volume, PV, for a gas as P approaches zero (or the value of PV for an ideal gas). We will indicate this limiting value at a given temperature t' by $(PV)_{t'}^\circ$. If we were to use the same two fixed points as in the preceding discussion, viz. the ice and steam points, and continue to assign these the values of $0°$ and $100°$, respectively, the temperature would be given by

$$t' = \frac{100[(PV)_{t'}^\circ - (PV)_i^\circ]}{(PV)_s^\circ - (PV)_i^\circ}$$

where $(PV)_i^\circ$ and $(PV)_s^\circ$ are the limiting values of PV when the temperatures are those of the ice and steam points, respectively. The values of t' so obtained would be **centigrade ideal gas temperatures**. This relation between $(PV)_{t'}^\circ$ and t' is linear, as before. When $(PV)_{t'}^\circ = 0$, $t' = 273.15$. Letting T stand for $t' + 273.15$ gives

$$T = 273.15 + \frac{100[(PV)_T^\circ - (PV)_i^\circ]}{(PV)_s^\circ - (PV)_i^\circ}$$

where $(PV)_T^\circ$ is the value of $(PV)^\circ$ at temperature T. The new temperatures, T, so obtained are called **absolute ideal gas temperatures**, and $T = 0$ when $(PV)_T^\circ = 0$, an extrapolated quantity. It follows by substitution of zero for both T and $(PV)_T^\circ$ that $(PV)_s^\circ - (PV)_i^\circ$ equals $100(PV)_i^\circ/273.15$. Replacing this value in the above expression for T gives, on simplification,

$$T = 273.15[(PV)_T^\circ/(PV)_i^\circ]$$

Now this is not only a linear relation but a direct proportion.

It will be realized that the accuracy of the important extrapolated quantity 273.15 in the above relations depends on the accuracy of the measured $(PV)_i^\circ$ and $(PV)_s^\circ$. Improvements in techniques might conceivably require a small change in the extrapolation, and this could require revision of previously determined temperatures. Moreover, it has been discovered that the triple point temperature of water is a more precise fixed point than the normal freezing point in the presence of air. The former is $0.01°$ higher than the latter. These difficulties were obviated by international agreement in 1960 according to which (1) the ice point was replaced by the water triple point temperature as a fixed point and (2) the temperature of the latter was fixed at $273.1600°$ on the absolute scale, so that we now have:

$$T = 273.1600 \; [(PV)_T^\circ/(PV)_{t.p.}^\circ]$$

where $(PV)_{t.p.}^\circ$ is the value of $(PV)^\circ$ at the water triple point. Adoption of this procedure means that henceforth (1) centigrade temperatures based on the ice point are converted to absolute temperatures by adding $273.15°$ to them and (2) gas thermometers no longer need to be calibrated at the steam point. The only effect of any revision of the extrapolation to absolute zero would be to change the size of a degree by a few thousandths of a per cent at most, thus making only a negligible change in most accepted temperatures up to several hundred degrees centigrade.

STATISTICAL NATURE OF THERMODYNAMICS

Thermodynamics has developed from experimental observations of the behavior of matter in bulk, involving colossal numbers of molecules. It is thus the average behavior of large numbers of particles which are under study. Exceptions to the laws of thermodynamics can be expected when only a few molecules are considered.

The first law of thermodynamics—energy

WORK OF EXPANSION AND COMPRESSION

The most common kind of work connected with elementary thermodynamics is work of expansion (or compression). This is frequently called p-V work. Work is the action of a force through a distance and is therefore expressed, e.g., in dyne-centimeters or ergs. Since dyne-cm = (dyne cm^{-2})(cm^3), work can also be expressed as the product of pressure and volume units. Thus a volume change of 1 liter for a pressure of 1 atm is 1 liter-atm* of work. Since 1 atm = $1.0132(10^6)$ dyne cm^{-2} and 1 cal = $4.184(10^7)$ ergs, 1 liter-atm = $1.0132(10^6)(10^3)/4.184(10^7)$ = 24.22 cal and 1 cal = 0.04129 liter-atm.

It is important to realize that, since work is conventionally defined and measured as work that is done by or on the surroundings, it is the external pressure, the pressure of the environment, which is used in evaluating work, whether it be expansion or compression which the system is undergoing. This will be indicated by the subscript "ex" for "external."

---

*The preferred unit of volume is the cubic centimeter (cm^3). However, we shall follow the common practice of calling 1000 cm^3 a liter. Similarly, the work done when a volume change of 1000 cm^3 is made against a pressure of 1 atm will be called a liter-atmosphere (liter-atm). The difference between 1000 cm^3 and 1 liter is negligible.

If, as is the most common usage, we let w stand for the work done *by* the system *on* the surroundings, then we have:

$$w = \int_{V_1}^{V_2} p_{ex} dV \qquad (1\text{-}1)$$

where V_1 and V_2 are the initial and final volumes, respectively. To evaluate w, p_{ex} has to be expressed as a function of V. However, if p_{ex} is constant during the volume change, w becomes $p_{ex}(V_2 - V_1)$ or $p_{ex}\Delta V$.

The pressure, P, within the system is often appreciably different from p_{ex}. If $V_1 < V_2$, $w > 0$ and work is done *by* the system, whereas if $V_1 > V_2$, $w < 0$ and work is done *on* the system.

Example 1-1 If a gas under a pressure of 10 atm, occupying 8 liters, is expanded against a constant external pressure of 1 atm to a volume of 80 liters at a pressure of 1 atm, find w.

Ans. Since p_{ex} is constant, $w = 1(80 - 8) = 72$ liter-atm.

Note A constant p_{ex} of 1 atm would correspond to normal atmospheric pressure on the outside of the piston head, and is thus a condition commonly encountered. The piston has moved until $P = p_{ex}$, so no further expansion is possible.

Example 1-2 Find w in Example 1-1 if p_{ex} were 0.5 atm instead of 1 atm, but the final gas pressure were still 1 atm.

Ans. $w = 0.5(80 - 8) = 36$ liter-atm.

Note While the gas may have suffered a change in temperature, this has nothing to do with the evaluation of w.

Example 1-3 Two moles of ideal gas at 3.0 atm and 300°K, in a cylinder fitted with a piston, are compressed isothermally to one-half the volume by an external pressure of 7.0 atm. Find w.

Ans. Let V_1 and V_2 be the initial and final volumes of the gas. $V_1 = nRT/P = 2.0(0.082)(300)/3.0 = 16.4$ liters, and $V_2 = V_1/2 = 8.2$ liters. Therefore $w = p_{ex}\Delta V = 7.0(8.2 - 16.4) = -57.4$ liter-atm.

Example 1-4 Find w for the vaporization of 1 mole of water at 100°** and 1 atm, assuming the density of the liquid to be 1 g cm^{-3} and the vapor to be ideal.

*Ans.**** $\bar{V}_1 = 18$ $cm^3 = 0.018$ liter. $\bar{V}_2 = nRT/P = 1(0.082)(373)/1 = 31$ liters. Since $p_{ex} = 1$ atm throughout, $w = 1(31 - 0.018) = 31$ liter-atm.

**Throughout this book temperatures are understood to be in degrees centigrade unless otherwise stated.
***A bar over the symbol for an extensive property will be used to mean that property of *one mole* of material.

CONSERVATION OF ENERGY AND THE FIRST LAW
OF THERMODYNAMICS

A property of a state which depends only on the temperature, pressure and composition, and not on any other factors such as previous history, is a **state function**. State functions used in thermodynamics are called **thermodynamic functions**. When one equilibrium state is converted to another, the thermodynamic functions change to the values for the new state, and the change in any one function (the difference between the values for the two states) is independent of how the change was performed. This chapter introduces a particular state function—the internal energy, or simply the energy.

Energy is manifested only when it is in transit, i.e., when it is converted into work or heat. Suppose a mole of water vapor at 34° and 25 mm pressure is to be converted into water vapor at 100° and 25 mm. Such a conversion can be effected in an infinite number of ways. One may, e.g., heat the vapor at constant pressure from 34° to 100°. It can be readily determined by experiment that about 600 cal of heat enter the water vapor and about 135 cal of work of expansion are performed. Suppose, however, one were to conduct the same change by a quite different route. We may find that a net quantity of 2500 cal of heat is absorbed and a net quantity of work amounting to 2035 cal is performed. By still another route we may find that 1750 cal of heat are absorbed and 1285 cal of work are done. We now observe that the difference between the net heat absorbed and the net work done is 465 cal in all three cases. Similar studies on many changes of state have shown beyond doubt that regardless of the path taken, of the various kinds of work performed in conducting the change, or of the extent of frictional losses, if the *net* work (w) done by the system is subtracted from the *net* heat (q) gained by the system, the result is the same for all paths. Furthermore, if the final state is identical to the initial state, it is found that $q = w$.

These experimental results lead to the conclusion that there is some property of a system, with the dimensions of energy, that depends only on state, and which therefore changes with change in state; the difference between the energy absorbed as heat (q)[†] and that lost as work (w)[†] appears as an increase in the value of this energy property. In other words, that part of the q which does not appear as w goes toward increasing the value of this property. Moreover, if the heat q is provided by the immediate surroundings and the work w is done on those same immediate surroundings the net energy lost by the surroundings, viz. $q - w$, equals the gain in the energy property of the system.

The energy property referred to in the preceding paragraph is called the **internal energy** and given the symbol E. We cannot measure its absolute value, but we can measure the changes it undergoes as shown earlier. If ΔE stands for the *increase* in the energy in a given change, i.e., for

---

[†]This is the convention used by most, but not all, present day authors.

$E_{final} - E_{initial}$, it is equal to $q - w$. We thus arrive at the mathematical formulation of the **first law of thermodynamics**, $\Delta E = q - w$, or:

$$q = \Delta E + w \qquad (1\text{-}2)$$

Notice that ΔE includes all changes other than those which involve heat transfer and work accomplished. This is true whether the change be a physical one, a chemical one, or both.

The equality of ΔE (the net energy gained by the system) and $q - w$ (the net energy lost by the surroundings), as given by Eq. (1-2), is equivalent to a statement of the **principle of the conservation of energy**. It is thus often said that the first law of thermodynamics *is* the principle of the conservation of energy.

Although there can be no destruction or creation of energy, there can be conversion of energy from one form into another, as long as the total remains constant. This total must include all energy in transit, i.e., all heat gained or lost, and all work done. We may, e.g., convert the energy of a graphite and oxygen mixture into the energy of carbon dioxide plus the energy dissipated in such forms as heat and light, and work done on the surroundings, but there must be no change in the total amount.

Example 1-5 Verify the statement made previously that the work done in heating 1 mole of water vapor at 34° to 100°C under a constant pressure of 25 mm is about 135 cal. (Assume the vapor to be ideal.)

Ans. $\overline{V}_1 = 0.082(307)(760)/25 = 770$ liters; $\overline{V}_2 = \overline{V}_1(373/307) = 940$ liters. Therefore $w = (25/760)170 = 5.6$ liter-atm $= 136$ cal.

Example 1-6 One gram atom of zinc is placed in excess dilute H_2SO_4 at 25° contained in a cylinder fitted with a weightless, frictionless piston of cross section area 490 cm^2. As the reaction proceeds the piston moves outward against the external pressure of 1 atm. The liberated heat of reaction is allowed to dissipate and eventually the temperature of 25° is restored. The total amount of heat lost by the reaction mixture during this time is found to be 36.43 kcal, and the piston has moved outward a distance of 50 cm. Find ΔE for the contents of the cylinder.

Ans. $w = p_{ex}\Delta V = 1(50)(490)/1000 = 24.5$ liter-atm $= 593$ cal. $q = -36,430$ cal. Therefore $\Delta E = q - w = -37,020$ cal.

Example 1-7 A $2:1$ mixture of H_2 and O_2 gases was ignited and exploded in a bomb (constant volume) and the temperature rose 20° before any energy had time to escape. What are the values of q, w, ΔE?

Ans. No heat entered or left the system in this time interval so $q = 0$. Moreover $w = 0$, for the volume of the contents of the bomb remained constant. Therefore $\Delta E = 0$.

REVERSIBLE PROCESSES AND MAXIMUM WORK

The term "reversible process" in thermodynamics has a very special meaning. A thermodynamically reversible process is actually one for which the conditions are so strict that it cannot be completely realized in practice. Let us see what is meant.

Imagine a gas in a cylinder being compressed from an initial pressure of P_1 to a final pressure of P_2 by a weightless, frictionless piston. (We are already in the realm of fiction!) The cylinder is immersed in a constant temperature bath. As the gas is compressed the work being done upon it would appear as a rise in temperature of the gas except for the fact that the heat is discharged into the constant temperature bath. Even though the temperature of the gas shows no change, its pressure rises because of decreased volume. Now if the pressure on the outside of the piston is maintained only infinitesimally greater than the pressure of the gas *throughout the compression*, the gas will be compressed and its temperature will not change but remain infinitesimally higher than that of the bath (thus maintaining the heat flow to the bath). Notice that the outside pressure and the gas pressure are both increasing but that the former is always infinitesimally larger than the latter. Such a process will take an infinite time for completion. The important thing is that *if* at any time, the external pressure on the piston were to be diminished by only an infinitesimal amount, the direction of motion of the piston and the direction of the heat flow would be reversed: the whole process would be reversed and one could recover *all* the work performed in the compression, leaving the surroundings virtually unchanged. Furthermore the system under these conditions (uniform temperature, uniform pressure) is at all times only infinitesimally removed from equilibrium. A process which can be reversed in every respect by an infinitesimal change in any of the forces (mechanical, thermal, electrical, etc.) is a **reversible process.** In retracing a reversible path in the opposite direction, both the system and its immediate surroundings are returned to their initial states without changing the rest of the universe in any way. This is another earmark of a truly reversible process. Processes which are not proceeding reversibly are said to be **irreversible.** All naturally occurring processes are irreversible.

Similarly, if two storage cells held at the same temperature and delivering emfs differing by an infinitesimal amount are connected in opposition, the one with the larger emf will charge the other one reversibly, for an infinitesimal change in the emf of one of the cells could reverse the whole process.

We now observe that, when such reversible processes are **isothermal,** i.e., at constant temperature throughout the process, the maximum amount of work for the given change is performed. In the expansion described earlier, had p_{ex} (of necessity less than P) differed from P by *more than* an infinitesimal amount at any stage the change would still have occurred, but less work would have been done than when they differed only infinitesimally. Similarly, in the illustration of the charging of a cell, had the opposing emf of the cell (B) being charged (of necessity less than that of the cell (A) doing the charging) differed from the emf of A by *more than* an infinitesimal amount at any stage, the change in A would still have occurred, but less electrical work of charging would have been done. Thus any relaxing of the conditions of reversibility results in less work being done. Hence the important conclusion is reached that in a given change at constant temperature, w is a maximum when that change is carried out reversibly. Moreover, since in such a given change ΔE or $q - w$ is fixed, and since $w_{irrev} < w_{rev}$, then $q_{irrev} < q_{rev}$. (Cf. Examples 1-18 and 4-2.) This principle will be proved in Chapter 2. If w happens to be negative, as it would be in the above examples had they been reversed by an infinitesimal change in the driving force, w is still the maximum for the given reversed change; although $|w_{rev}|$ is now numerically less than $|w_{irrev}|$, w_{rev} is still greater algebraically than w_{irrev}, for both are negative. This will be illustrated in Example 1-11.

It is desirable at this point to recommend that the student exercise care in his use of the words "change" and "process." When attention is focused on the initial and final states one should use the word "change," as in discussing the values of ΔE or $q - w$. When, on the other hand, attention is focused on the method whereby the change is effected one should use the word "process," as in discussing the value of q or the value of w.

While the temperature must remain the same everywhere in the system in all reversible processes, it need not remain constant throughout the process. Consider a gas undergoing an expansion against an external pressure which is only infinitesimally less than the gas pressure, but under conditions where no heat is allowed to enter or leave the gas, i.e., $q = 0$. As the gas expands its pressure P drops and so does its temperature, but p_{ex} is controlled so as to be always infinitesimally smaller than P. This is still a reversible process but it is no longer isothermal. Because of this the concept of maximum work for the change from the given initial to the given final state now has no meaning. One could accomplish the given change by an infinite number of paths, all reversible, and do a different amount of work for each path. For example, instead of going from state A to state B by a single reversible expansion as described, one could go from state A to some state C by a reversible isothermal expansion, then from state C to some state D by a reversible non-isothermal expansion, and then from state D to state B by a reversible isothermal compression. A different amount of work would have been performed in following the path A $\longrightarrow$ C $\longrightarrow$ D $\longrightarrow$ B than in going directly from A to B (see Problem 4 at the end of this chapter). In summary, while the concept of reversibility can be applied to all changes, it is only meaningful to say that w is a maximum for those which are at the same temperature for the duration of the process.

REVERSIBLE ISOTHERMAL EXPANSION AND COMPRESSION OF IDEAL GAS

If n moles of an ideal gas expand reversibly from volume V_1 to volume V_2 while the temperature remains constant at $T°K$ then $w = \int_{V_1}^{V_2} p_{ex} dV =$

$\int_{V_1}^{V_2} P\,dV$, since p_{ex} and P differ infinitesimally. Since $P = nRT/V$,

$$w = \int_{V_1}^{V_2} (nRT/V)\,dV = nRT \ln (V_2/V_1) = nRT \ln (P_1/P_2), \qquad (1\text{-}3)$$

P_1 and P_2 being the initial and final pressures. For reversible isothermal *compression* $V_2 < V_1$ or $P_2 > P_1$, so $w < 0$.

Example 1-8 Find w when 2 moles of ideal gas at 6 atm and 300°K are expanded reversibly and isothermally to double the volume.

Ans. The final volume of the gas is twice the initial, so $V_2/V_1 = 2$. Therefore $w = nRT \ln (V_2/V_1) = 2.0(0.082)(300)(2.3) \log 2 = 34$ liter-atm.[††]

Example 1-9 Find w for the change described in Example 1-8 in which, however, the process is one of expansion against a constant external pressure of 3 atm.

Ans. The initial volume, $V_1 = nRT/P = 2.0(0.082)(300)/6.0 = 8.2$ liters. Similarly $V_2 = 16.4$ liters. Therefore $w = p_{ex}\Delta V = 3(16.4 - 8.2) = 24.6$ liter-atm.

Note This process accomplished less work than the reversible one even though the initial and final states of the gas were the same.

Example 1-10 Find w for the isothermal reversible compression of 2.00 moles of ideal gas at 300°K to one-half its volume.

Ans. $w = nRT \ln (V_2/V_1) = nRT \ln \left(\frac{1}{2}\right)$. Therefore $w = 2.00(0.0821)(300) \times (2.303) \log 0.500 = -34.1$ liter-atm.

Note Work is done *on* the gas *by* the surroundings.

SPECIAL NOTE The usual error made in problems of this kind is in the mathematics, simple as it is. The student who is not thoroughly familiar with common logarithms of numbers less than unity should become so before proceeding further.

Let us work out the arithmetic for Example 1-10 in detail:

$$w = 2.00(0.0821)(300)(2.303) \log 0.500$$
$$= 113.4 \log 0.500$$
$$= 113.4(9.699 - 10) \text{ or, as it is often written, } 113(\overline{1}.699)$$
$$= 113.4(-0.301)$$
$$= -34.1 \text{ liter-atm.}$$

It is clearly erroneous to say that $113 \log (0.500) = -113(0.699) = -79.0$, but many students try to do it this way!

[††]The function $RT \ln x = RT(2.303) \log x$ occurs so frequently that it is useful to remember that, when R is in calories per degree per mole, $RT(2.303) = 4.576T$. This in turn equals 1364.3 when $T = 298.15°$K.

Example 1-11 Find w for the isothermal compression in Example 1-10 by means of a constant external pressure of 7 atm.

Ans. $w = p_{ex}\Delta V = 7(8.2 - 16.4) = -57.4$ liter-atm.

Note Comparing Example 1-11 with Example 1-10 we see that in the reversible process the gas still does more work than in the irreversible process, -34.1 being greater (algebraically) than -57.4.

EXACT AND INEXACT DIFFERENTIALS

The concept of state functions brings one inevitably to the subject of exact differentials. If P, Q and R are all continuous functions of x, y and z, and if there is a function $U = f(x, y, z)$ such that its total differential, $dU = Pdx + Qdy + Rdz$, then dU is said to be an **exact differential**. It is evident that $P = (\partial U/\partial x)_{y,z}$, $Q = (\partial U/\partial y)_{x,z}$ and $R = (\partial U/\partial z)_{x,y}$, and it can be readily shown that $(\partial P/\partial y)_{x,z} = (\partial Q/\partial x)_{y,z}$, $(\partial Q/\partial z)_{x,y} = (\partial R/\partial y)_{x,z}$ and $(\partial R/\partial x)_{y,z} = (\partial P/\partial z)_{x,y}$. Now *the differentials of all state functions* such as volume and energy *are exact*. Moreover, the volume of homogeneous systems of pure substances depends only on the pressure, the temperature and the number of moles of substance, so $V = f(P, T, n)$, and $dV = (\partial V/\partial P)_{T,n}dP + (\partial V/\partial T)_{P,n}dT + (\partial V/\partial n)_{P,T}dn$. If the number of moles is fixed the term with dn disappears so $V = f(P, T)$ and $dV = (\partial V/\partial P)_T dP + (\partial V/\partial T)_P dT$, dV being an exact differential. For one mole of an ideal gas the function $f(P, T)$ is particularly simple, viz. $\overline{V} = RT/P$, so $(\partial \overline{V}/\partial P)_T = -RT/P^2$, $(\partial \overline{V}/\partial T)_P = R/P$ and $d\overline{V} = -(RT/P^2)dP + (R/P)dT$. We note that $[\partial(-RT/P^2)/\partial T]_P = [\partial(R/P)/\partial P]_T = -R/P^2$. On the other hand, the quantities q and w are not functions of state, i.e., no function can be found for which $q = f(P, T, n)$ or for which $w = f(P, T, n)$. The differentials of q and w are therefore said to be **inexact**. To distinguish them from exact differentials we shall write them Dq and Dw, rather than dq and dw. Furthermore we write: $\int_{\text{initial state}}^{\text{final state}} Dq = q$, not $q_{\text{final state}} - q_{\text{initial state}}$, and similarly for w.

HEAT EFFECTS AT CONSTANT VOLUME

For all changes at constant volume no P-V work is done on or by the surroundings. Moreover, if no electrical or other work is performed (a condition easy to meet) then $w = 0$. Since $q = \Delta E + w$, $q = \Delta E$ or, as it is usually written,

$$q_V = \Delta E \tag{1-4}$$

Notice that the subscript "V" makes clear the absence of P-V work but that the absence of other forms of work is only *implied*.

This gives us an operational meaning for ΔE: we may state that ΔE for a given change is the heat absorbed by the system when that change takes place under conditions in which no work is done at all. Internal energy could thus be defined as *that property of a system the increase in which, for a given change, is equal to the heat absorbed by the system in that change, provided that no work is done.*

Example 1-12 A quantity of gas absorbs 50 cal of heat without change in volume. In so doing its temperature rises from 30 to 32°. Find ΔE for the gas.

Ans. Since $w = 0$, $\Delta E = q = 50$ cal.

Note The absence of all kinds of work, not merely *P-V* work is implied. The rise in temperature did not enter the calculation.

Example 1-13 A sample of benzoic acid was sealed in a bomb calorimeter (constant volume) along with excess oxygen at high pressure, and the whole brought to 25° in a thermostat. On ignition the acid was converted completely into liquid water and carbon dioxide gas, and the temperature rose briefly to 28° before any heat had an opportunity to escape to the thermostat. The temperature of the bomb and its contents then returned to 25° on standing, during which time 6000 cal of heat passed into the thermostat. Find (a) ΔE for the change: bomb and reactants at 25° $\longrightarrow$ bomb and products at 28°. (b) ΔE for the change: bomb and reactants at 25° $\longrightarrow$ bomb and products at 25°.

Ans. (a) Since $w = 0$, $\Delta E = q = 0$, since no heat had as yet left the bomb. (b) Since $w = 0$, $\Delta E = q = -6000$ cal.

Note It is the latter answer which is the more important.

Since $q_V = \Delta E$, the heat required to raise the temperature of a system 1° while held at constant volume will be $Dq_V/dT = (\partial E/\partial T)_V$. This is called the **heat capacity** of the system at **constant volume**, usually quoted in calories per degree and denoted by the symbol C_V. Thus:

$$C_V = (\partial E/\partial T)_V \tag{1-5}$$

If only 1 mole of a substance is being raised 1°, it is called the **molar heat capacity at constant volume** and is given in calories per degree per mole. For 1 g of material it is called the **specific heat at constant volume** (cal deg^{-1} g^{-1}). It is ordinarily understood that *all* the heat referred to in the above definition of C_V is **sensible**, i.e., heat which results in a temperature change. **Latent** heat, which produces phase transformations without temperature changes, is therefore excluded, for then C_V would be infinite. C_V for a given substance depends chiefly upon the temperature and negligibly upon the pressure. The heat required to raise the temperature of a system from T_1 to T_2 at constant volume would be found from $q_V = \Delta E = \int_{T_1}^{T_2} (\partial E/\partial T)_V dt = \int_{T_1}^{T_2} C_V dT$. If C_V can be taken to be independent of temperature, then this simplifies to $q_V = C_V(T_2 - T_1)$.

Example 1-14 If C_V for $Cl_2(g)$ is 6.2 cal deg^{-1} mole^{-1} at 300°K how much heat is required to raise the temperature of 4 moles of $Cl_2(g)$ from 299°K to 301°K at constant volume?

Ans. C_V is 6.2 cal deg^{-1} for 1 mole or 4(6.2) cal deg^{-1} for 4 moles. Therefore $q = q_V = 4(6.2)\Delta T = 4(6.2)(2) = 49.6$ cal.

HEAT EFFECTS AT CONSTANT PRESSURE. ENTHALPY

When a change occurs at constant pressure an ambiguity may arise. Is the pressure of the system constant, or is the pressure of the environment constant? Usually one means that both are equal and constant, but failure to recognize the distinction may sometimes lead to trouble!

The **enthalpy** or **heat content**, H, is defined as:

$$H = E + PV \tag{1-6}$$

where P is the pressure of the system itself, and E and V are its energy and volume. Since, for a given state, E, P and V are all defined, H is also defined, and thus becomes a thermodynamic function. It follows that ΔH for a given change is independent of path. Now the above definition of H is made with an eye to convenience, so that ΔH will be readily measurable. This is shown as follows. *If* only P-V work is permitted the first law becomes, in differential form, $Dq = dE + p_{ex}dV$. But, for any change, $dH = dE + d(PV)$, from the definition of H. *If* P is held constant, $dH = dE + PdV$. Furthermore, *if* $P = p_{ex}$, $dH = dE + p_{ex}dV$. Since Dq and dH both equal $dE + p_{ex}dV$, they equal each other, or $Dq = dH$ when only P-V work is permitted and $P = p_{ex}$ = constant. The value of q with all these provisos is called q_P. Thus we obtain:

$$q_P = \Delta H \ (P = p_{ex} = \text{constant, only } P\text{-}V \text{ work}) \tag{1-7}$$

The temperature may or may not change. Enthalpy is thus *that property of a system the increase in which, for a specified change at constant pressure, and for* $P = p_{ex}$, *with only P-V work being permitted, is equal to the heat absorbed when that change occurs.* Fortunately these restrictions can often be easily realized by leaving the system open to the atmosphere and making no arrangements to do electrical work.

We may think of the enthalpy of a system as the intrinsic energy it possesses (E) plus its energy as a result of occupying space (PV), i.e., the work which must have been done against an environmental pressure P to create the volume V occupied by it.

Since $q_P = \Delta H$, the heat required to raise the temperature of a system $1°$ while held at constant pressure will be $Dq_P/dT = (\partial H/\partial T)_P$, called the **heat capacity** of the system **at constant pressure** and denoted by the symbol C_P. Thus we have:

$$C_P = (\partial H/\partial T)_P \tag{1-8}$$

The units are the same as for C_V. For 1 g of material C_P is called the **specific heat at constant pressure** (cal deg^{-1} g^{-1}). When the constant pressure used is 1 atm, a superscript zero is appended to the symbol. As for C_V, only sensible heat is ordinarily included in the definition of C_P.

Heat effects at constant pressure usually fall into one of two categories: those involving primarily a temperature change, and those resulting from a change in composition at constant temperature, the latter group lying in the domain of thermochemistry.

Example 1-15 If 10 liters of 0.01N HCl at 25° are mixed with 10 liters of 0.01N NaOH at 25° in an open vessel and the resulting solution restored to 25°, 1,336 cal of heat are found to have been given up to the surroundings. Find ΔH.

Ans. $q = q_P = \Delta H = -1,336$ cal.

Attention may be drawn to the fact that, in equating C_P to a heat input at constant pressure divided by the resulting temperature rise, the implication, rarely stated explicitly, is that the heat input occurs so slowly that P remains the same at all points within the system. Too rapid heating could create local temperature and pressure differences which could upset the required equality of P and p_{ex}. Similarly, evaluating ΔH from q_P for chemical reactions implies a sufficiently slow heat absorption or evolution that pressure excursions, however temporary, do not occur.

The appreciable temperature dependence of C_P (and C_V), and the need to integrate expressions like Eqs. (1-5) and (1-8) require that heat capacity be expressed as a function of T. Thus we commonly find the following forms:

$$\overline{C}_P = a + bT + cT^2 + dT^3 \ldots \tag{1-9}$$

and

$$\overline{C}_P = a' + b'T + c'T^{-2} \ldots \tag{1-10}$$

where the parameters are determined by fitting the equations to the experimental data. A given set of such parameters applies only to a limited temperature range, which must be stated in tabulations. Since C_P (and C_V) depends to a small extent on the pressure, the pressure should, strictly, be stated. A pressure of 1 atm is indicated by a superscript zero. For a gas the symbol C_P° means not only a pressure of 1 atm but the value of C_P *if the gas were ideal* at 1 atm. The difference between C_P at 1 atm and C_P° is so small, however, that we will not consider it further.

Example 1-16 By how much does the enthalpy of 3 moles of $Cl_2(g)$ change when its temperature is increased at a constant pressure of 1 atm from 300 to 400°K? Its heat capacity at a constant pressure of 1 atm in this temperature range is $7.5755 + 2.4244(10^{-3})\,T - 9.650(10^{-7})\,T^2$ cal deg^{-1} mole^{-1}.

Ans.

$$\Delta H = q_P = \int_{T_1}^{T_2} C_P\,dT = 3 \int_{T_1}^{T_2} \overline{C}_P\,dT$$

$$= 3 \int_{300}^{400} [7.5755 + 2.4244(10^{-3})\,T - 9.650(10^{-7})\,(T^2)]\,dT$$

$$= 3 \left[7.5755(400 - 300) + 2.4244(10^{-3}) \left(\frac{400^2 - 300^2}{2} \right) \right.$$

$$\left. - 9.650(10^{-7}) \left(\frac{400^3 - 300^3}{3} \right) \right] = 2491.5 \text{ cal}$$

Note A common error is to write factors such as $(T_2^2 - T_1^2)$ as $(T_2 - T_1)^2$.

INTERNAL PRESSURE

Joule's classic experiment, in which a gas was expanded into a vacuum, whereupon no heat effects were observed, leads to the concept of internal pressure. Since no work of expansion is done on the surroundings and no heat effect detected, both q and w are zero, so $\Delta E = 0$. Subsequent work has shown this to be strictly true only for ideal gases. Since the volume of the gas changes with no change in temperature or internal energy, $(\partial E/\partial V)_T = 0$, i.e., the internal energy of an ideal gas is independent of its volume if its temperature is kept constant. This quantity, $(\partial E/\partial V)_T$, is called the **internal pressure**. (Notice that it *has* the dimensions of pressure.) Do not confuse internal pressure with internal energy. While zero for *ideal* gases, the internal pressure is small but not zero for *real* gases, and is quite large for liquids and solids. Furthermore, since $\Delta H = \Delta E + \Delta(PV)$, and since, for ideal gases, $\Delta(PV)$ is zero at constant temperature (Boyle's law), ΔH is also zero at constant temperature. It follows that $(\partial H/\partial V)_T = 0$ too, for an ideal gas. Alternatively one may say $(\partial E/\partial P)_T = (\partial H/\partial P)_T = 0$ for ideal gases, since at constant temperature a change in volume implies a change in pressure.

Example 1-17 Two moles of liquid water at 100° and 1 atm were vaporized to water vapor at the same temperature and pressure, by the addition of 19,400 cal of heat. Find ΔE, assuming the water vapor to be ideal. Did the internal pressure increase, decrease, or remain constant?

Ans. $q = 19,400$ cal $= q_P = \Delta H$. By the first law, however, $q = \Delta E + w$, so $19,400 = \Delta E + w$. But $w = p_{ex}\Delta V = P\Delta V = P(V_2 - V_1) = 1[2(0.0821) \times (373)/1 - 2(0.018)] = 61.2$ liter-atm $= 1481$ cal. Therefore $\Delta E = 19,400 - 1481 = 17,920$ cal. The internal pressure must have decreased considerably (from the value for the liquid to practically zero).

Example 1-18 Find ΔE, ΔH and q for the gas in Examples 1-8 and 1-9.

Ans. Since the ideal gas suffered no temperature change, both ΔE and ΔH are zero in both examples. For the reversible expansion in Example 1-8, $q = q_{rev} = w_{max} = 34$ liter-atm $= 820$ cal. For the irreversible expansion of Example 1-9, $w = q = 24.6$ liter-atm $= 595$ cal.

Note Observe that $q_{irrev} < q_{rev}$ in the isothermal expansion.

The fact that both E and H are independent of V and P at constant temperature *for ideal gases* has the consequence that $C_V = (\partial E/\partial T)_V$ and $C_P = (\partial H/\partial T)_P$ can now be written $C_V = dE/dT$ and $C_P = dH/dT$, or

$dE = C_V dT$ and $dH = C_P dT$. For ideal gases, then, $\Delta E = \int_{T_1}^{T_2} C_V dT$ and $\Delta H = \int_{T_1}^{T_2} C_P dT$ for a change in temperature from T_1 to T_2 and both of these apply whether or not volume or pressure is kept constant. Actually, C_V and C_P are often taken to be independent of temperature, too, for ideal gases, and so $\Delta E = C_V \Delta T$ and $\Delta H = C_P \Delta T$.

JOULE-THOMSON EFFECT

When a nonideal gas is forced through a porous plug in a well-insulated cylinder as illustrated in Fig. 1-1, so that its pressure is kept constant but different on both sides of the plug, the temperature T_2 is found to be $>$ or $< T_1$ depending on the gas used, the values of P_1 and P_2 and the value of T_1 itself. If a volume V_2 liters appears on the right-hand side for every V_1 liters that disappears on the left, V_2 being measured at pressure P_2 and V_1 at pressure P_1, the work done by the gas entering the low pressure side, on the gas already there, is $P_2 V_2$, and the work done on the same gas leaving the high pressure side, by the gas behind it, is $P_1 V_1$. The net work done by the gas passing through the plug is therefore $w = P_2 V_2 - P_1 V_1 = -\Delta E = E_1 - E_2$, since $q = 0$. It follows that $E_1 + P_1 V_1 = E_2 + P_2 V_2$, so $H_1 = H_2$. Thus, in the change, $\Delta H = 0$. Whether $T_2 <$ or $> T_1$ depends on whether $E_2 <$ or $> E_1$, which in turn depends on whether $P_2 V_2 >$ or $< P_1 V_1$, i.e., on whether PV increases or decreases in the change. One cannot decide this merely by examining, e.g., a PV-P graph for the temperature T_1, because $P_1 V_1$ and $P_2 V_2$ are for different temperatures. In other words, the sign of the effect is not determined only by the sign of $(\partial PV / \partial P)_T$.

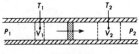

Fig. 1-1

The quantitative measure of the effect is given by the **Joule-Thomson coefficient**, $\mu = (\partial T / \partial P)_H$, which can be shown to equal $(-1/C_P)[(\partial E / \partial V)_T \times (\partial V / \partial P)_T + (\partial (PV) / \partial P)_T]$. Since $(\partial E / \partial V)_T$ is usually positive and $(\partial V / \partial P)_T$ is always negative, $(\partial E / \partial V)_T (\partial V / \partial P)_T$ is usually negative. If $(\partial (PV) / \partial P)_T$ is also negative μ will be positive, so cooling will be observed. However, when $(\partial (PV) / \partial P)_T$ is positive, μ may be positive or negative. Temperatures at which $\mu = 0$ are called **inversion temperatures**.

Example 1-19 Taking μ for CO_2 as approximately constant at 1.30 in the range of pressure 2 to 15 atm find the final temperature attained by CO_2 when it is subjected to a Joule-Thomson expansion from $P = 15$ atm to $P = 2$ atm, if its initial temperature is $20°$.

Ans. $\mu = (\partial T / \partial P)_H = 1.25$. Therefore $\Delta T = \int_{15}^{2} (\partial T / \partial P)_H \, dP = (\partial T / \partial P)_H \times$

$\int_{15}^{2} dP = 1.30(2 - 15) = -17°$. The final temperature is thus $20 - 17 = 3°C$.

Note   Actually μ varies from 1.37 at 15 atm to 1.21 at 2 atm.

RELATIONS BETWEEN C_P AND C_V: $C_P - C_V$ AND C_P/C_V

For gases, C_P and C_V can both be measured readily, but for liquids and solids only C_P is easily determined directly. It thus becomes desirable to be able to convert one into the other. Both their difference and ratio are of significance.

Now $C_P - C_V = (\partial H / \partial T)_P - (\partial E / \partial T)_V$ as shown already. But $H = E + PV$, so $(\partial H / \partial T)_P = (\partial E / \partial T)_P + P(\partial V / \partial T)_P$. Therefore $C_P - C_V = (\partial E / \partial T)_P + P(\partial V / \partial T)_P - (\partial E / \partial T)_V$. For a pure substance, however, $E = f(T, V)$. It follows that $dE = (\partial E / \partial T)_V dT + (\partial E / \partial V)_T dV$, so $(\partial E / \partial T)_P = (\partial E / \partial T)_V + (\partial E / \partial V)_T (\partial V / \partial T)_P$. Substitution in the expression for $C_P - C_V$, and cancellation of $(\partial E / \partial T)_V$ gives:

$$C_P - C_V = (\partial E / \partial V)_T (\partial V / \partial T)_P + P(\partial V / \partial T)_P \qquad (1\text{-}11)$$

The quantities E and V refer to whatever amount of material C_P and C_V refer to, e.g. one mole or one gram. Each of the two terms on the right of the equation has real physical meaning. Heating at constant volume does nothing but raise the temperature: heating at constant pressure has three effects: (1) a rise in temperature, (2) the work of pushing back the environment, (3) the extension of the substance against the intermolecular forces. For a given rise in temperature the difference between C_P and C_V is determined by effects (2) and (3). Effect (2) is measured by the last term on the right, $P(\partial V / \partial T)_P$. Effect (3) is measured by $(\partial E / \partial V)_T (\partial V / \partial T)_P$. This is the energy required to pull the molecules apart in a vacuum so that the substance occupies the increased volume that has resulted from the rise in temperature. For liquids and solids the term $P(\partial V / \partial T)_P$ is usually negligible. For gases, however, the other term is negligible.

Example 1-20   The specific heat of $CCl_4(l)$ at 25° is 0.20 cal deg^{-1} g^{-1} at a constant pressure of 1 atm. Find its specific heat at constant volume at 25° if, at this temperature, its internal pressure is 3340 atm, its density is 1.584 g cm^{-3} and its coefficient of expansion, $(1/V)(\partial V / \partial T)_P$, is 0.00124 deg^{-1}.

Ans.   Considering 1 g of CCl_4, the volume will be $1/1.584 = 0.631$ cm^3 g^{-1}. Therefore $(\partial V / \partial T)_P = 0.00124(0.631) = 0.000782$ cm^3 deg^{-1} g^{-1}, and $(\partial E / \partial V)_T (\partial V / \partial T)_P + P(\partial V / \partial T)_P = (3340 \text{ atm})(0.000782 \text{ cm}^3 \text{ deg}^{-1} \text{ g}^{-1}) + (1 \text{ atm})(0.00078 \text{ cm}^3 \text{ deg}^{-1} \text{ g}^{-1}) = (2.60 + 0.00078) \text{ atm cm}^3 \text{ deg}^{-1} \text{ g}^{-1} = 2.60(24.2)/1000$ cal deg^{-1} g^{-1}, neglecting the second term, $= 0.0629$ cal deg^{-1} $g^{-1} = C_P - C_V = 0.20 - C_V$. Therefore $C_V = 0.14$ cal deg^{-1} g^{-1}.

For ideal gases, since $(\partial E/\partial V)_T = 0$ and $(\partial V/\partial T)_P = nR/P$ (from $V = nRT/P$), $C_P - C_V = (0)(nR/P) + (P)(nR/P) = nR$, or

$$\overline{C}_P - \overline{C}_V = R \tag{1-12}$$

which is nearly true for real gases.

Example 1-21 If C_P for $CH_4(g)$ varies with temperature ($T°K$) in the following way: $\overline{C}_P$ (cal deg^{-1} mole^{-1}) $= 3.381 + 18.044(10^{-3})\,T - 43.00(10^{-7})\,T^2$, find $\overline{C}_V$ as a function of T.

Ans. $\overline{C}_V = \overline{C}_P - R = 1.394 + 18.044(10^{-3})\,T - 43.00(10^{-7})\,T^2$ cal$^-$ deg^{-1} mole^{-1}.

For gases of simple molecular constitution it is often possible to estimate C_V, and therefore C_P. According to classical theory every "square term" needed to describe the energy of a molecule contributes $\frac{1}{2}R$ to $\overline{C}_V$. On this basis the *approximate* values listed in Table 1-1 are commonly found. These "classical" values should only be used when better data are not available. A notable exception among diatomic gases is Cl_2 with $\overline{C}_V \cong 6$ and $\overline{C}_P \cong 8$ at room temperature.

Table 1-1

Kind of Gas	$\overline{C}_V$(cal deg^{-1} mole^{-1})	$\overline{C}_P$(cal deg^{-1} mole^{-1})	$\overline{C}_P/\overline{C}_V$
Monatomic	3	5	1.67
Diatomic	5	7	1.40
Linear Polyatomic	5	7	1.40
Nonlinear	6 or >6	8 or >8	1.33 or <1.33

As molecular complexity increases $\overline{C}_P/\overline{C}_V$, or γ, as it is abbreviated, decreases, as seen in the last column. The use of this ratio will be referred to later.

ADIABATIC PROCESSES

Processes in which $q = 0$ are said to be **adiabatic**. For them, $\Delta E = -w$ by the first law. If only P-V work is permitted we have $dE = -p_{ex}dV$. For ideal gases undergoing adiabatic processes, since $dE = C_V dT$, we have $C_V dT = -p_{ex}dV$. If C_V is independent of T and p_{ex} is constant, $C_V\Delta T = -p_{ex}\Delta V = -w$. In these relations C_V refers to all the material undergoing the change in volume ΔV.

Example 1-22 Two moles of ideal gas at 400°K occupying a volume of 7 liters are expanded adiabatically against a constant pressure of 1 atm until the final pressure is 2 atm. Find the final temperature and volume if $\overline{C}_V$ for the gas is 5 cal deg^{-1} mole^{-1}, independent of temperature.

Ans. As $q = 0$ and C_V is independent of T, $C_V\Delta T = -p_{ex}\Delta V$. Since there are 2 moles, $C_V = 2(5) = 10$ cal deg^{-1}. Substitution gives $10(T_2 - 400)$ cal =

$-1(V_2 - 7)$ liter-atm $= -1(V_2 - 7)(24.2)$ cal. However, T_2 and V_2 are also related through the gas law, $P_2V_2 = nRT_2$. Substitution gives $2V_2 = 2(0.0821)(T_2)$. We thus have two equations in two unknowns permitting both T_2 and V_2 to be determined. The solutions are $T_2 = 348°K$ and $V_2 = 28.6$ liters.

Note This expansion, although adiabatic, was not reversible. The usual difficulty in solving problems such as this is the failure to recognize that the ideal gas law still applies to the initial and final states and thus the second relation between T_2 and V_2 is overlooked.

Example 1-23 Find ΔE and ΔH for the change described in the preceding example.

Ans. Since the gas is ideal, $\Delta E = C_V \Delta T = 10(348 - 400) = -520$ cal, and $\Delta H = C_p \Delta T = 2(7)(348 - 400) = -728$ cal, for $\overline{C}_p = \overline{C}_V + R$.

Note ΔH could have been calculated by use of the relation $\Delta H = \Delta E + \Delta(PV) = \Delta E + (P_2V_2 - P_1V_1)$. A common erroneous approach to this problem is to say that, since p_{ex} is constant, $q = \Delta H$, and since $q = 0$, ΔH must be zero too. The fallacy lies in inferring that $P = p_{ex} = $ constant, whereas only $p_{ex} = $ constant, P varying from 9.38 to 2 atm.

REVERSIBLE ADIABATIC PROCESSES

When an adiabatic process occurs reversibly $P = p_{ex}$, so dE is not only given by $-p_{ex}dV$ but also by $-PdV$. If at the same time the substance is an ideal gas we have

$$C_V dT = -PdV = -(nRT/V)dV$$

where C_V refers to all n moles of the gas. Dividing both sides by n gives:

$$\overline{C}_V dT = -(RT/V)dV$$

where $\overline{C}_V$ is for one mole. Rearranging and integrating gives:

$$\int_{T_1}^{T_2} C_V d \ln T = - \int_{V_1}^{V_2} R d \ln V$$

or,

$$-R\ln (V_2/V_1) = \overline{C}_V \ln (T_2/T_1)$$

taking $\overline{C}_V$ to be independent of T. This is the same as:

$$\ln (V_2/V_1) = \ln (T_2/T_1)^{\overline{C}_V/R}$$

If we now take the antilogarithm of both sides we have:

$$V_1 T_1^{\overline{C}_V/R} = V_2 T_2^{\overline{C}_V/R} \tag{1-13}$$

Replacing T_1 by P_1V_1/nR and T_2 by P_2V_2/nR, and recalling that $\overline{C}_P - \overline{C}_V = R$, gives:

$$P_1 V_1^{\gamma} = P_2 V_2^{\gamma} \tag{1-14}$$

where $\gamma = \overline{C}_P/\overline{C}_V$.   Replacing V_1 by nRT_1/P_1 and V_2 by nRT_2/P_2 in Eq. (1-14) gives:

$$T_1{}^{\gamma}P_1{}^{1-\gamma} = T_2{}^{\gamma}P_2{}^{1-\gamma} \qquad (1\text{-}15)$$

These relations are used to determine any one of P_1, V_1, T_1, P_2, V_2, T_2 from three others.   Notice that $P_1V_1 = nRT_1$, and $P_2V_2 = nRT_2$, even though the process is adiabatic.

It is common to indicate expansions and contractions graphically by p_{ex}-V plots or P-V plots.   For reversible processes these are identical. Fig. 1-2 contrasts the behavior in submitting an ideal gas to a reversible isothermal expansion from (P_1, V_1) to (P_2, V_2) with that of a reversible adiabatic expansion from the same initial state to (P_2, V_3).   Curve *a* fol-

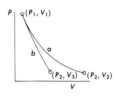

Fig. 1-2

lows the relation PV = constant, Boyle's law, whereas curve *b* follows PV^{γ} = constant.   Notice that *b* is the steeper.   The temperature at (P_2, V_2) is, of course, the same as that at (P_1, V_1) but higher than that at (P_2, V_3).

Example 1-24 Two moles of an ideal monatomic gas at 37° and 1 atm are compressed reversibly and adiabatically until the pressure is doubled. What final temperature is attained?

Ans. Since the gas is monatomic $\overline{C}_p/\overline{C}_V$ is 1.67.   Using Eq. (1-15) we have $310^{1.67}(1^{1-1.67}) = T_2{}^{1.67}(2^{1-1.67})$.   Taking the logarithms of both sides yields 1.67 log 310 = 1.67 log T_2 – 0.67 log 2, the solution of which is $T_2 = 409°\mathrm{K}$.

Note C_V was assumed to be independent of T; this is permissible for ideal gases.   The number of moles of gas did not enter the calculation. The final temperature would have been the same, in fact, had a different number of moles of gas been used.

Example 1-25 Find w, q, ΔE and ΔH for the change in Example 1-24.

Ans. Since the process was adiabatic, $q = 0$, so $w = \int_{V_1}^{V_2} p_{ex}dV =$

$-\Delta E = -C_V \Delta T = -2\,(3)\,(409 - 310) = -594$ cal. $\Delta H = -C_p \Delta T = -2\,(5)\,(409 - 310) = -990$ cal.

Note A frequent source of error in a problem of this kind is failure to recognize that C_V in $\Delta E = C_V \Delta T$ is not just for one mole but for all the gas.

THERMOCHEMISTRY

Thermochemistry is the study of the heat effects attending chemical changes, although so-called physical changes, being no different thermodynamically, are usually included.   The basic experimental tool is the calorimeter, which gives values of either q_p or q_V for the change reactants $\longrightarrow$ products, both being at the same temperature. As shown earlier q_p is identified with ΔH, and q_V with ΔE. The dependence of ΔH or q_p (but not of q) on only the initial and final states, and thus the independence of the path, is expressed in **Hess's law of constant heat summation.** Data involving ΔH are far more common because of their greater relevance to everyday experimental work. Thermochemical equations describe the reactants and their states, the products and their states, and ΔH or ΔE. A subscript on the latter quantities tells the temperature in degrees Kelvin, and a superscript zero, when used on a ΔH value, indicates that each substance was at 1 atm pressure. This superscript is often omitted because ΔH is almost independent of the pressure as long as that pressure is constant. The letters g, l and s (or c) are used to indicate the state of aggregation of each substance. Needless to say, the equation must be balanced.   Fractional coefficients may be used. The magnitude of the ΔH or ΔE must correspond to the amounts designated by the coefficients stated in the equation. There must be no ambiguity regarding the state of each substance; e.g., when indicating 2 g atoms of atomic oxygen (monatomic) in an equation one must write $2O(g)$ and not $O_2(g)$, which would mean 1 mole of diatomic oxygen. Whether $H_2O(l)$ or $H_2O(g)$ is meant must, similarly, be clearly stated.   Substances in hypothetical states, e.g., H_2O (g, 298°K, 1 atm), may be used. Whether the reaction as written goes to completion by itself or goes at all is irrelevant, for we are here concerned only with the difference between the enthalpies of the products and reactants.

Heats of reaction are, of course, meaningless unless associated with a given equation for a given change. Moreover, to say, e.g., that for the reaction $Ag_2O(s) + 2HCl(g) \longrightarrow 2AgCl(s) + H_2O(l)$, ΔH_{298}° is -78.1 cal mole^{-1}, is ambiguous. The heat of reaction is simply $\Delta H_{298}^{\circ} = -78.1$ kcal for the reaction as written.

When one mole of a given substance appears by itself on the right side, and when only the elements which comprise it appear on the left in their stable states, the value of ΔH° is called the **standard heat of formation** of that substance.   Thus from the equation $H_2(g) + \frac{1}{8}S_8(\text{rhombic}) + 2O_2(g) \longrightarrow H_2SO_4(l)$, $\Delta H_{298}^{\circ} = -193.91$ kcal, the standard heat of formation of $H_2SO_4(l)$ is said to be -193.91 kcal mole^{-1} at 298°K, the word "standard" often being omitted, but implied. We may replace $\frac{1}{8}S_8$ by S(rhombic), since the latter describes an unambiguous state. The symbol ΔH_f is often used for heat of formation. Heats of formation of the elements in their stable states are obviously zero.

The values of ΔH associated with various reaction types are given corresponding names such as heats of combustion, heats of hydrogenation, heats of esterfication. But it is in the form of heats of formation that thermochemical data are usually provided, and these most commonly for 25°C. From these, ΔH for any other reaction type can be determined (at the temperature of the given data), since ΔH for given change = Sum of heats of formation of products – Sum of heats of formation of reactants, i.e.,

$$\Delta H = \sum_{\text{products}} \Delta H_f - \sum_{\text{reactants}} \Delta H_f \qquad (1\text{-}16)$$

where ΔH_f stands for heat of formation. That this is so is evident from the fact that the right-hand side is:

$(H_{\text{products}} - H_{\text{elements comprising}})$ –
$\qquad\qquad$ products

$\qquad\qquad\qquad (H_{\text{reactants}} - H_{\text{elements comprising}})$
$\qquad\qquad\qquad\qquad\qquad\qquad$ reactants

The elements comprising products and reactants are the same, however, and so this reduces to

$$H_{\text{products}} - H_{\text{reactants}}$$

which, of course, equals ΔH.

Thermochemical equations can be manipulated in the same way as algebraic equations. For example, terms may be transposed, or equations may be added or subtracted or multiplied through by a factor. The bulk of simple thermochemical problems involves finding ΔH for a reaction from given thermochemical data. A good procedure is to write the given data as thermochemical equations, making certain that they are correct in every detail. These are then examined to determine what substances in the provided data do, and what substances do not, appear in the reaction for which ΔH is to be found. It is now merely a question of manipulating the given data so that the unwanted substances cancel. Frequently this involves merely using Eq. (1-16).

Example 1-26 Find ΔH°_{298} for $C_2H_6(g) + 3\frac{1}{2}O_2(g) \longrightarrow 2CO_2(g) + 3H_2O(l)$ if the standard heats of formation of $C_2H_6(g)$, $CO_2(g)$ and $H_2O(l)$ are -20.24, -94.05 and -68.32 kcal mole^{-1}, respectively, at 25° and 1 atm.

Ans. $\Delta H^{\circ}_{298} = [2(-94.05) + 3(-68.33)] - [(-20.24) + 3\frac{1}{2}(0)] = -372.82$ kcal.

Note It is important to remember to multiply each heat of formation by the number of moles of that substance appearing in the equation.

Example 1-27 Find ΔH°_{298} for $Na_2O(s) + 2HCl(g) \longrightarrow 2NaCl(s) + H_2O(l)$ from the following information.

Standard heats of formation of $NaOH(s)$ and $H_2O(l)$ at 25° are $\Delta H^{\circ}_{298} = -102.0$ and -68.3 kcal mole^{-1}, respectively.

$$Na_2O(s) + H_2O(l) \longrightarrow 2NaOH(s), \qquad \Delta H^{\circ}_{298} = -36.3 \text{ kcal}$$
$$Na(s) + HCl(g) \longrightarrow NaCl(s) + \tfrac{1}{2}H_2(g), \qquad \Delta H^{\circ}_{298} = -76.1 \text{ kcal}$$

Ans. From the standard heats of formation we have:

$$Na(s) + \tfrac{1}{2}O_2(g) + \tfrac{1}{2}H_2(g) \longrightarrow NaOH(s), \qquad \Delta H^{\circ}_{298} = -102.0 \text{ kcal}$$

and

$$H_2(g) + \tfrac{1}{2}O_2(g) \longrightarrow H_2O(l), \qquad \Delta H^{\circ}_{298} = -68.3 \text{ kcal.}$$

Surveying these and the two other given equations we observe that the following substances are to be eliminated: $NaOH(s)$, $Na(s)$, $H_2(g)$ and $O_2(g)$. We therefore arrange the equations as follows, with the substances to be retained placed on the left or right depending on where they appear in the desired equation:

$$Na_2O(s) + H_2O(l) \longrightarrow 2NaOH(s), \qquad \Delta H^{\circ}_{298} = -36.3 \text{ kcal} \quad (1)$$
$$Na(s) + HCl(g) \longrightarrow NaCl(s) + \tfrac{1}{2}H_2(g), \qquad \Delta H^{\circ}_{298} = -76.1 \text{ kcal} \quad (2)$$
$$NaOH(s) \longrightarrow \tfrac{1}{2}H_2(g) + \tfrac{1}{2}O_2(g) + Na(s), \qquad \Delta H^{\circ}_{298} = 102.0 \text{ kcal} \quad (3)$$
$$H_2(g) + \tfrac{1}{2}O_2(g) \longrightarrow H_2O(l) \qquad \Delta H^{\circ}_{298} = -68.3 \text{ kcal} \quad (4)$$

We double eqs. (2), (3) and (4) and add them to (1) to give:

$$Na_2O(s) + 2HCl(g) \longrightarrow 2NaCl(s) + H_2O(l) \quad \Delta H^{\circ}_{298} = -36.3 + 2(-76.1)$$
$$+ 2(102.0) + 2(-68.3)$$
$$= -121.1 \text{ kcal}$$

All the manipulations of ΔH described above are applicable in principle to ΔE but the usual procedure for the calculation of ΔE values is to calculate ΔH as described previously and then to convert it to ΔE.

RELATION BETWEEN $q_P(\Delta H)$ AND $q_V(\Delta E)$

It is easy to overlook the fact that in comparing reactions at constant pressure on the one hand and at constant volume on the other we are not only comparing different *processes* but also different *changes*. Even if the reactants are in the same states for both, the products will be in different states. For example, in $C(graphite) + \tfrac{1}{2}O_2(g) \longrightarrow CO(g)$, at $25°$, if the C and the $\tfrac{1}{2}O_2$ are both at 1 atm, the resulting CO will be also at 1 atm for the constant pressure change but will be at about 2 atm for the constant volume change. CO at 1 atm and $25°$ is in a different state from CO at 2 atm and $25°$, so the two processes involve different changes.

Suppose that we wish to find, e.g., ΔH for the reaction $C_6H_6(l) + 7\tfrac{1}{2}O_2(g) \longrightarrow 6CO_2(g) + 3H_2O(l)$ at $25°$ from the measured value of q_V or ΔE. As carried out experimentally, a bomb of 300 cm^3 capacity containing 1 g of benzene and excess O_2 under a pressure of 20 atm, let us say, would be used. The reaction would be allowed to take place and the heat effect, including restoration of the bomb and contents to $25°$, measured. The heat absorbed in the overall change is q_V, q_V being less than zero here. The total pressure, it should be noted, decreases during the reaction from 20 atm to roughly 18 atm because of the reduction in the number of moles of gas. The change (1) in the accompanying scheme denotes the reaction just described. If the reactants had been decompressed from a pressure of 20 atm to only 1 atm their energy would have changed negligibly. The same is true if the products had been decompressed to 1 atm.

$$C_6H_6(l) + 7\tfrac{1}{2}O_2(g) \xrightarrow{(1)} 6\,CO_2(g) + 3\,H_2O(l)$$

at 20 atm and 25°	at 18 atm and 25° Cv
in vol. of 300 cm^3	in vol. of 300 cm^3
$\downarrow\ \Delta E \sim 0$	$\downarrow\ \Delta E \sim 0$

$$C_6H_6(l) + 7\tfrac{1}{2}O_2(g) \xrightarrow{(2)} 6\,CO_2(g) + 3\,H_2O(l)$$

at 1 atm and 25°	at 1 atm and 25° Cp
in vol. of about 6600 cm^3	in vol. of about 5700 cm^3

Thus, by measuring ΔE for change (1) we have, in effect, measured ΔE for change (2). We wish, however, to find ΔH for (2), or q_p. Now ΔH (for (2)) = $\Delta E + \Delta(PV)$ (for (2)) = $\Delta E + P\Delta V$ (for (2)), since P is constant, viz. 1 atm. The ΔV in change (2) is almost entirely the result of the replacement of $7\tfrac{1}{2}O_2$ by $6\,CO_2$, since liquids (and solids) occupy such a small volume by comparison with gases. Since $PV \cong nRT$ for gases, $P\Delta V \cong \Delta nRT$, where Δn is the increase in the number of moles of *gas* occurring on reaction, $6 - 7\tfrac{1}{2} = -1\tfrac{1}{2}$ in this case. Thus ΔH (for (2)) = $\Delta E + \Delta nRT$ (for (2)) $\cong \Delta E + \Delta nRT$ (for (1)) = $q_V + \Delta nRT$. Since H varies only slightly with P, q_P at all reasonable pressures would be the same. In the same way q_V would be practically the same regardless of the volume used. Thus we write:

$$q_P = q_V + \Delta n_{\text{gases}}RT \qquad (1\text{-}17)$$

without having to state what constant pressure is used for q_P or what constant volume is used for q_V.

Example 1-28 If, in the constant volume combustion of 1.000 g of benzene(l) to form $CO_2(g)$ and $H_2O(l)$, 9.985 kcal were evolved at 25°, find ΔH_{298} for this combustion per mole of benzene. The molecular weight of benzene is 78.11.

Ans. The combustion is represented by the equation $C_6H_6(l) + 7\tfrac{1}{2}O_2(g) \longrightarrow 6\,CO_2(g) + 3\,H_2O(l)$, for which $q_V = -9.985$ kcal g^{-1}, or $-9.985(78.11) = -779.9$ kcal mole^{-1}. But $\Delta H = \Delta E + \Delta nRT = q_V + \left(-1\tfrac{1}{2}\right)RT$; therefore $\Delta H_{298} = -779,900 + \left(-1\tfrac{1}{2}\right)(1.99)(298) = -780,800$ cal mole benzene^{-1}.

Note Only the *gases* are considered in evaluating Δn. The use of R in calories required q_V to be expressed in calories, not kilocalories. The difference between q_P and q_V represents the work done by the environment as it closed in on the system.

HEATS OF IONIC REACTIONS

Thermochemical reactions involving ions most commonly take place in aqueous solution. Since the enthalpy of ions depends not only on the temperature and pressure but also on their concentration one would have to include a statement of this in the thermochemical equation. It is usual, however, to consider only ions at infinite dilution, which means, in effect, that their concentration is so small that further dilution would make no difference in their enthalpy or energy. Infinite dilution is often indicated by (aq) placed after the formula. The principles underlying thermochemical ionic equations are the same as already described except that the heat of formation of ions, defined as for non-charged species, involves free electrons. For example, the heat of formation of OH^- ion is $\Delta H°$ for $\frac{1}{2}O_2(g) + \frac{1}{2}H_2(g) + e \longrightarrow OH^-(aq)$, and that for Zn^{2+} is $\Delta H°$ for $Zn(s) \longrightarrow Zn^{2+}(aq) + 2e$. Such heats of formation cannot be measured, for the ionic species cannot be isolated for study. We therefore assign some arbitrary value to some one of such ion formation reactions and calculate all other values on that basis. The conventional arbitrary choice is $H^+(aq)$, for which *the standard heat of formation is assigned the value zero*. One can then find, e.g., the heat of formation of $Zn^{2+}(aq)$ by measuring ΔH for $Zn(s) + 2H^+(aq) \longrightarrow Zn^{2+}(aq) + H_2(g)$, which presents no problem, since this reaction occurs on dissolving zinc in very dilute acid. $\Delta H°_{298}$ for this change is found to be:

$$-36.43 \text{ kcal} = \sum_{\text{products}} \Delta H°_f - \sum_{\text{reactants}} \Delta H°_f =$$

$$(\Delta H°_f \text{ for } Zn^{2+}(aq) + 0) - (0 + 0)$$

Thus the standard heat of formation of $Zn^{2+}(aq)$ is -36.43 kcal mole^{-1}.

Example 1-29 If the standard heats of formation of $HCl(g)$ and $Cl^-(aq)$ are -22.06 and -40.02 kcal mole^{-1}, respectively, at 25°, find $\Delta H°_{298}$ for $HCl(g) \longrightarrow H^+(aq) + Cl^-(aq)$.

Ans. $\Delta H°_{298} = \sum_{\text{products}} H°_f - \sum_{\text{reactants}} H°_f = (0 - 40.02) - (-22.06) = -17.96$ kcal.

HEATS OF SOLUTION

When solutions occur in thermochemical equations their concentrations must be indicated. A solution of 1 mole of KCl in 50 moles of water is designated $KCl \cdot 50 H_2O$ or $KCl \cdot 50 Aq$, being careful to place the dot *above* the line to avoid ambiguity. An infinitely dilute solution of 1 mole of KCl would be designated $KCl \cdot \infty H_2O$ or $KCl(aq)$. The value of ΔH for the solution of 1 mole of solute in as much solvent as is needed to give the stated concentration is said to be the **total** or **integral heat of solution** of that solute for that specified concentration. Heats of solution depend not only on the solute, solvent, temperature and pressure (the last to a very minor extent) but also on concentration. Since for $H_2SO_4(l)$ + $4 H_2O(l) \longrightarrow H_2SO_4 \cdot 4 H_2O$, $\Delta H_{298} = -12.92$ kcal, one may say that the total heat of solution of $H_2SO_4(l)$ in water at 25° is $\Delta H = -12.92$ kcal mole^{-1} in an aqueous solution with a mole fraction of H_2SO_4 of 0.20. This quantity is to be distinguished from the **partial** or **differential heat of solution** of H_2SO_4 in water at this concentration, to be discussed in Chapter 6.

Example 1-30 The total heat of solution of $H_2SO_4(l)$ in $0.555m$ aqueous solution is $\Delta H_{298} = -17.68$ kcal mole^{-1}. Find (a) how much heat will be evolved when enough water at 25° is added to 2.00 moles H_2SO_4 at 25° to give a $0.555m$ H_2SO_4 solution at 25° and (b) the total heat of solution of water in $0.555m$ H_2SO_4 solution.

Ans. (a) Since 1 mole of H_2SO_4 dissolved in sufficient water to give $0.555m$ solution causes the evolution of 17.68 kcal at 25°, 2 moles will cause the evolution of 2(17.68), or 35.36 kcal (when dissolved in twice as much water). (b) A $0.555m$ solution has 0.555 moles of acid to every 1000 g or 55.5 moles of water, or 1 mole of acid to every 100 moles of water. Thus we may write:

$$H_2SO_4(l) + 100 H_2O(l) \longrightarrow H_2SO_4 \cdot 100 H_2O, \qquad \Delta H_{298} = -17.68 \text{ kcal}$$

The value of ΔH is therefore $-17.68/100 = -0.1768$ kcal per mole H_2O, which is the total heat of solution of water in $0.555m$ H_2SO_4 at 25°.

Total heats of solution of solute may be combined to give **heats of dilution** as illustrated below.

Example 1-31 The total heat of solution of $C_2H_5OH(l)$ in water at 25° is $\Delta H = -1,122$ cal mole^{-1} for a solution for which $X_{C_2H_5OH} = 0.166$, and -1678 cal mole^{-1} for a solution for which $X_{C_2H_5OH} = 0.100$. Find the heat of dilution from the more concentrated to the more dilute solution, per mole of ethanol.

Ans. We are given:

$$C_2H_5OH + 5 H_2O(l) \longrightarrow C_2H_5OH \cdot 5 H_2O, \qquad \Delta H_{298} = -1122 \text{ cal}$$

and

$$C_2H_5OH + 9 H_2O(l) \longrightarrow C_2H_5OH \cdot 9 H_2O, \qquad \Delta H_{298} = -1678 \text{ cal}$$

Subtracting gives:

$$C_2H_5OH \cdot 5 H_2O + 4 H_2O(l) \longrightarrow C_2H_5OH \cdot 9 H_2O, \qquad \Delta H_{298} = -556 \text{ cal}$$

which is the desired heat of dilution.

BOND ENERGIES

The heat effects in chemical reactions at constant volume are a manifestation of the energies required when chemical bonds are broken and energies lost when other bonds are formed, in addition to any energy changes

associated with intermolecular forces. The chemist, to exploit thermochemistry to the full, inquires what contribution each of the bonds involved makes to the net result. To do this he must first minimize the
effects of intermolecular attraction and repulsion by reducing all his
thermochemical data to reactions involving only gases.

The **bond energy** of the bond between elements A and B in the gaseous
compound AB is the energy required at $25°$ to convert $AB(g)$ into $A(g)$ and
$B(g)$, and is indicated by the symbol $D_{A—B}$. (Strictly, this dissociation
should be carried out at constant volume, but data for constant pressure
are commonly used, since we have seen that q_V and q_P do not differ
greatly.) If elementary A and B are diatomic gases, $D_{A—B}$ could be found
from the ΔH's for $A_2(g) \rightarrow 2A(g)$, $B_2(g) \rightarrow 2B(g)$ and $AB(g) \rightarrow \frac{1}{2}A_2(g) + \frac{1}{2}B_2(g)$.

Bond energies in polyatomic molecules present more of a problem. The
value of $D_{C—H}$ may be estimated as being one-fourth the value of ΔH for
$CH_4(g) \rightarrow C(g) + 4H(g)$, so it is really an average bond energy; $D_{O—H}$ is
estimated as one-half of ΔH for $H_2O(g) \rightarrow 2H(g) + O(g)$, etc. Notice
that the first of these equations requires experimental data involving
$C(g)$. Since the only form of carbon ordinarily used for calorimetry is the
solid, the heat of sublimation has had to be determined to provide the
necessary link in determining bond energies involving carbon. Finally it
must be observed that even for a given pair of elements the bond energy
will depend upon whether the bond is single, double or triple, etc.

Example 1-32 Estimate ΔH_f for ethane gas if $D_{C—C}$, $D_{C—H}$, and $D_{H—H}$
are taken to be 80, 99 and 103 kcal mole^{-1}, respectively, and if the heat
of sublimation of graphite is 171.7 kcal mole^{-1}.

Ans. We wish to find ΔH for $2C(\text{graphite}) + 3H_2(g) \rightarrow C_2H_6(g)$. We are
given

$$2C(\text{graphite}) \rightarrow 2C(g), \qquad \Delta H = 2(171.7) \text{ kcal} \qquad (1)$$

and

$$H_2(g) \rightarrow 2H(g), \qquad \Delta H = 103 \text{ kcal} \qquad (2)$$

and

$$2C(g) + 6H(g) \rightarrow C_2H_6(g), \qquad \Delta H = -[(1(80) + 6(99)] \qquad (3)$$

since, in the formation of ethane from isolated atoms one C—C and six
C—H bonds are formed. Multiplying eq. (2) by 3 and adding the equations gives:

$$2C(\text{graphite}) + 3H_2(g) \rightarrow C_2H_6(g), \qquad \Delta H = -22 \text{ kcal}$$

VARIATION OF HEAT OF REACTION WITH TEMPERATURE

It is often desirable to find ΔH or ΔE at one temperature from ΔH or ΔE
at another. The relationship is determined readily by differentiating

$$\Delta H = \sum_{\text{products}} H - \sum_{\text{reactants}} H$$ with respect to T at constant P. Thus we

obtain:

$$(\partial \Delta H / \partial T)_P = \left(\partial \sum_{\text{products}} H / \partial T\right)_P - \left(\partial \sum_{\text{reactants}} H / \partial T\right)_P$$

$$= \sum_{\text{products}} (\partial H / \partial T)_P - \sum_{\text{reactants}} (\partial H / \partial T)_P$$

Since $(\partial H / \partial T)_P = C_P$, the right-hand side of the previous equation becomes

$$\sum_{\text{products}} C_P - \sum_{\text{reactants}} C_P = \Delta C_P.$$

Therefore we have:

$$(\partial \Delta H / \partial T)_P = \Delta C_P \qquad (1\text{-}18)$$

known as the **Kirchhoff relation.** If all the substances are at 1 atm, $(\partial \Delta H° / \partial T)_P = \Delta C_P°$ but, as explained earlier, the value of the pressure is unimportant as long as it is constant. This gives the *rate of change of the change* of enthalpy with temperature at constant pressure, and ΔC_P is the heat capacity of *all* the products minus that of *all* the reactants. Analogously, by differentiating $\Delta E = \sum_{\text{products}} E - \sum_{\text{reactants}} E$ with respect to temperature at constant volume we obtain the following:

$$(\partial \Delta E / \partial T)_V = \Delta C_V \qquad (1\text{-}19)$$

It follows from Eq. (1-18) that $d\Delta H = \Delta C_P dT$, so we have:

$$\int_{T_1}^{T_2} d\Delta H_P = \int_{T_1}^{T_2} \Delta C_P dT$$

or

$$\Delta H(\text{at } T_2) - \Delta H(\text{at } T_1) = \int_{T_1}^{T_2} \Delta C_P dT \qquad (1\text{-}20)$$

In this way ΔH at one temperature can be found from ΔH at another. As a result of the restriction noted earlier that C_V and C_P do not involve the latent heat of phase changes, Eq. (1-20) and the analogous result obtained from integration of Eq. (1-19) do not apply when any one of the reactants or products undergoes a phase change in the temperature interval of interest. When ΔC_P may be taken as *independent of T* we have:

$$\Delta H(\text{at } T_2) - \Delta H(\text{at } T_1) = \Delta C_P(T_2 - T_1) \qquad (1\text{-}21)$$

This is an acceptable assumption if $T_2 - T_1$ is small or if data to the contrary are not available.

Example 1-33 If the standard heat of formation of HCl(g) is $\Delta H° = -22.06$ kcal mole^{-1} at 25° estimate its value at 55°.

Ans. For $\frac{1}{2}H_2(g) + \frac{1}{2}Cl_2(g) \longrightarrow HCl(g)$, $\Delta H^{\circ}_{298} = -22.06$ kcal. Since no data for C_P's are provided we are forced to estimate them. We observe that H_2, Cl_2 and HCl are all diatomic gases, so would expect $\overline{C}_P$ to be about 7 cal mole^{-1} deg^{-1} for each. This means that $\Delta C_P = C_P$ for HCl $- [\frac{1}{2}\overline{C}_P$ (for H_2) $+ \frac{1}{2}\overline{C}_P$ (for Cl_2)$] = 7 - (3.5 + 3.5) = 0$, so $(\partial \Delta H/\partial T)_P = 0$ and ΔH is independent of T. Therefore it is estimated that the standard heat of formation of HCl(g) at $55° = \Delta H^{\circ}_{328} = \Delta H^{\circ}_{298} = -22.06$ kcal mole^{-1}.

When the temperature dependence of ΔC_P is considered, we must express ΔC_P as a function of T. This is done by first expressing C_P for each substance in some form such as Eq.(1-9) and then combining these to give ΔC_P: $\Delta C_P = \Delta a + \Delta bT + \Delta cT^2 + \ldots$, where

$$\Delta a = \sum_{\text{products}} a - \sum_{\text{reactants}} a,$$

$$\Delta b = \sum_{\text{products}} b - \sum_{\text{reactants}} b, \text{ etc.}$$

Eq.(1-18) then becomes:

$$d\Delta H = (\Delta a + \Delta bT + \Delta cT^2 + \ldots)\,dT.$$

For a particular temperature interval, T_1 to T_2, this integrates to give:

$$\Delta H \text{ (at } T_2) - \Delta H \text{ (at } T_1) = \Delta a(T_2 - T_1) + (\Delta b/2)(T_2{}^2 - T_1{}^2)$$
$$+ (\Delta c/3)(T_2{}^3 - T_1{}^3) + \ldots$$

To give an expression for ΔH at any temperature (within the range of validity of the parameters a, b, c, etc.) we use the indefinite integral $\Delta H = \Delta aT + (\Delta b/2)T^2 + (\Delta c/3)T^3 + \ldots + \text{constant}$. We shall indicate this constant of integration by ΔH_I, so we have:

$$\Delta H_T = \Delta H_I + \Delta aT + (\Delta b/2)T^2 + (\Delta c/3)T^3 + \ldots \quad (1\text{-}22)$$

A superscript zero is added when the pressure is 1 atm.

Example 1-34 Find the latent heat of vaporization of water at $27°$ and 1 atm if the value at the normal boiling point is 9720 cal mole^{-1}, if $\overline{C}^{\circ}_P$ for $H_2O(l)$ is taken to be constant at 18.06 cal deg^{-1} mole^{-1} and if $\overline{C}^{\circ}_P$ for $H_2O(g)$ varies with the temperature according to $\overline{C}^{\circ}_P$ (cal deg^{-1} mole^{-1}) $= 7.219 + 2.374(10^{-3})T + 2.67(10^{-7})T^2$.

Ans. We are given that, for $H_2O(l) \longrightarrow H_2O(g)$, $\Delta H^{\circ}_{373} = 9720$ cal. But

$$\Delta C^{\circ}_P = \overline{C}^{\circ}_P \text{ for } H_2O(g) - \overline{C}^{\circ}_P \text{ for } H_2O(l)$$
$$= 7.219 + 2.374(10^{-3})T + 2.67(10^{-7})T^2 - 18.06$$
$$= -10.84 + 2.374(10^{-3})T + 2.67(10^{-7})T^2.$$

Therefore

$$\Delta H^{\circ}_{373} - \Delta H^{\circ}_{300} = \int_{300}^{373} [-10.84 + 2.374(10^{-3})\,T + 2.67(10^{-7})\,T^2]\,dT$$

$$= -735, \text{ so } 9720 - \Delta H^{\circ}_{300} = -735, \text{ or } \Delta H^{\circ}_{300} = 10{,}455$$
$$\text{cal mole}^{-1}.$$

Note This is a "physical" change, but the method is applicable to chemical changes as well.

STANDARD ENTHALPY CHANGE FOR GASES

We have seen that the enthalpy change at a given temperature is indicated by the symbol ΔH° when every substance involved is at a pressure of 1 atm. Actually this means, in addition, that for gases not only is the pressure 1 atm but that each gas is behaving as if it were ideal (cf. the meaning of C_P°). It is thus desirable to be able to correct values of ΔH measured at 1 atm to ΔH° values, which requires knowing the difference between $\overline{H}$ at 1 atm and $\overline{H}^{\circ}$ for each gas in the reaction.

To show how this (small) difference, $\overline{H} - \overline{H}^{\circ}$, may be measured, let us examine the following changes:

$$\text{Real gas (1 atm, } T_1) \xrightarrow{\;(1)\;} \text{Ideal gas (1 atm, } T_1)$$
$$\downarrow (2) \qquad\qquad\qquad \uparrow (4)$$
$$\text{Real gas (} P^* \text{ atm, } T_2) \xrightarrow{\;(3)\;} \text{Ideal gas (} P^* \text{ atm, } T_2)$$

$\overline{H}^{\circ} - \overline{H}$, the negative of the desired quantity, is given by ΔH in step (1), which equals the sum of the ΔH values in steps (2), (3) and (4). P^* is some very small pressure. Step (2) is a Joule-Thomson expansion in which the temperature changes from T_1 to T_2. Thus ΔH in (2) is zero. ΔH is also zero in (3), for at a pressure as small as P^* the gas is ideal, and so the initial and final states are identical. In (4) ΔH is given by

$$\int_{T_2}^{T_1} \overline{C}_P\,dT = \int_{T_2}^{T_1} \overline{C}_P^{\circ}\,dT$$

for $\overline{C}_P$ is independent of P for ideal gases. We therefore have:

$$\overline{H}^{\circ} - \overline{H} = 0 + 0 + \int_{T_2}^{T_1} \overline{C}_P^{\circ}\,dT \qquad \text{or} \qquad \overline{H} - \overline{H}^{\circ} = \int_{T_1}^{T_2} \overline{C}_P^{\circ}\,dT$$

where T_1 is the temperature of interest (to which $\overline{H} - \overline{H}^{\circ}$ refers) and T_2 is the final temperature which would be attained in a Joule-Thomson expansion to very low pressure. Applying this procedure to each gas of a given reaction yields $\Delta(H - H^{\circ}) = \Delta H - \Delta H^{\circ}$, from which ΔH° may be found.

PROBLEMS

1. (a) Three moles of an ideal gas ($\overline{C}_V$ = 4.97 cal deg^{-1} mole^{-1}) at 10.0 atm and 0° are converted to 2.0 atm at 50°. Find ΔE and ΔH for the change.

   (b) Why cannot the value for w be calculated from these data?

2. If the change described in Problem (1) is carried out in two stages, (a) a reversible adiabatic compression to 50° and (b) a reversible isothermal expansion, find ΔE, ΔH, w and q for each stage and also for the overall process. Compare ΔE and ΔH with the answers to Problem 1.

3. If the change described in Problem 1 is carried out in two stages, (a) an adiabatic compression to 50° using a constant external pressure of 18.1 atm and (b) an isothermal expansion against a constant external pressure of 2.0 atm, find ΔE, ΔH, w and q for each stage and also for the overall process. Compare the overall values with those of Problem 2. Why is $q \neq \Delta H$ in (a) even though p_{ex} was constant?

4. When 1 mole of ideal gas [$\overline{C}_V$ = (5/2) R] at 300°K, occupying 2.40 liters (state A), expands reversibly and adiabatically until its volume is 5.00 liters its pressure drops to 3.67 atm (state B).

   (a) Show that the pressure of the gas in state A is 10.26 atm.

   (b) Confirm that the final pressure is 3.67 atm when the final volume is 5.00 liters.

   (c) Find the temperature of the gas in state B.

   (d) Find w for the above process.

   (e) Imagine that the above change (A $\longrightarrow$ B) be carried out via an intermediate state C, where A $\longrightarrow$ C is a reversible isobaric heating at a pressure of 10.26 atm and the volume in state C is 5.00 liters, and where C $\longrightarrow$ B is a reversible isochoric cooling at a volume of 5.00 liters. Find w for A $\longrightarrow$ C and for C $\longrightarrow$ B and thence w for A $\longrightarrow$ B by the two-stage process.

   (f) Compare this last result with that for (d) and comment.

5. (a) If, for the hypothetical diatomic gas A_2, $\overline{C}_P$ (cal mole^{-1} deg^{-1}) = $6.000 + 2.5000(10^{-3}) T$, find the heat necessary to raise the temperature of 1 mole of it from 200°K to 300°K at constant pressure.

   (b) If, for the hypothetical monatomic gas, A, $\overline{C}_P$ (cal mole^{-1} deg^{-1}) = 5.000, find the heat necessary to raise the temperature of 2 moles of it from 200°K to 300°K at constant pressure.

   (c) Suppose that the reaction $A_2(g) \longrightarrow 2A(g)$ is complete at all temperatures and that ΔH°_{200} = -10.000 kcal. Find ΔH°_{300}.

   (d) Calculate ΔH for the change $A_2(g, 200°K, 1$ atm) $\longrightarrow 2A(g, 300°K,$ 1 atm) by (i) imagining that A_2 at 200° is heated to 300° and then allowed to decompose at 300° and (ii) imagining that A_2 decomposes at 200° and the resulting A is heated to 300°.

6. Find ΔE_{298} for the reaction $B_2(g) \longrightarrow 2B(g)$ if q_P is 10.000 kcal at that temperature.

7. If the heat of combustion at constant volume of $C_2H_5OH(l)$, to give $CO_2(g)$ and $H_2O(l)$, is $q_V = -326.106$ kcal mole^{-1} at 25°, and if the standard heats of formation of $CO_2(g)$ and $H_2O(l)$ are $\Delta H^{\circ}_{298} = -94.052$ and -68.317 kcal mole^{-1}, respectively, find the standard heat of formation of $C_2H_5OH(l)$ at 25°.

8. Estimate ΔH for $Cl_2(g) + CH_4(g) \rightarrow CH_3Cl(g) + HCl(g)$ given the following bond energies: $D_{Cl-Cl} = 58$, $D_{C-Cl} = 77$, $D_{C-H} = 99$, $D_{H-Cl} = 103$ kcal mole^{-1}.

9. Fifty ml of $0.10N$ NaOH contained in a Dewar flask is titrated with 50 ml of $0.10N$ HCl. Both solutions are initially at 25°. If $\Delta H^{\circ}_{298} = -13.5$ kcal for $H^+(aq) + OH^-(aq) \rightarrow H_2O(l)$, find the rise in temperature of the resulting solution on reaching the end point, assuming that the heat capacity of the latter is the same as that of water, and that all solutions involved are infinitely dilute.

10. Find ΔH°_{298} for $MnO_4^-(aq) + 5\,Fe^{2+}(aq) + 8\,H^+(aq) \rightarrow Mn^{2+}(aq) + 4\,H_2O(l) + 5\,Fe^{3+}(aq)$ if the standard heats of formation of the ions (kcal mole^{-1}) are as follows at 298°K: $MnO_4^-(aq)$, -123.9; $Mn^{2+}(aq)$, -52.3; $Fe^{3+}(aq)$, -11.4; $Fe^{2+}(aq)$, -21.0. (Cf. Problem 7.)

11. The internal pressure of $CCl_4(l)$ at 25° and 1 atm is 3340 atm. If α, its coefficient of thermal expansion, $(1/V)(\partial V/\partial T)_P$, is $12.4(10^{-4})$ deg^{-1}, and its volume is 97.1 cm^3 mole^{-1} under these conditions, find (a) the difference between the heat capacities per mole of $CCl_4(l)$ at constant pressure and at constant volume and (b) the fraction of this difference that represents work of expansion against the atmosphere in constant pressure heating. What does the remaining fraction represent?

12. The integral heat of solution of NaOH in $4m$ solution is $\Delta H_{293} = -10,235$ cal mole^{-1}, and in an infinitely dilute solution it is $\Delta H_{293} = -10,100$ cal mole^{-1}. If a solution containing 4 moles of NaOH in 1000 g of water is diluted by a very large quantity of water find ΔH_{293}.

13. If the standard heat of formation of $HCl(g)$ is $\Delta H^{\circ} = -22.063$ kcal at 25°, find its value at 55° given the following data: $\overline{C}^{\circ}_P$ (cal deg^{-1} mole^{-1})

$$\text{for }\ H_2(g) = 6.9469 - 0.1999(10^{-3})\,T + 4.808(10^{-7})\,T^2$$
$$\text{for }\ Cl_2(g) = 7.5755 + 2.4244(10^{-3})\,T - 9.650(10^{-7})\,T^2$$
$$\text{for }\ HCl(g) = 6.7319 + 0.4325(10^{-3})\,T + 3.697(10^{-7})\,T^2$$

2

The second law of thermodynamics—entropy

HEAT ENGINES AND THE SECOND LAW

Apart from the important limitations of the first law there are no restrictions on the conversion of other forms of energy into heat. The conversion of heat into work, on the other hand, is subject to the limitations of the second law of thermodynamics which is a statement of observation.

According to the **Kelvin-Planck statement of the second law of thermodynamics**, *it is impossible, by means of a cyclic process, to remove heat from a reservoir and produce no effect on the surroundings other than the performance of work*. A **heat reservoir** is any isothermal portion of matter the specific purpose of which is to act as a source or as an acceptor of heat, and which has such a large heat capacity that it loses or gains heat without detectable change in temperature. Since a **heat engine** is a cyclic device for converting heat into work, it follows that a heat engine cannot operate with only one heat reservoir. It may be remarked that a gas in contact with a single heat reservoir, withdrawing heat from the reservoir and simultaneously expanding against an external pressure, does not contravene the second law, for that is not a *cyclic* process. A heat engine, it is true, converts heat from a reservoir into work, but only part of the heat acquired is used in this way—the remainder is discharged into another heat reservoir at a lower temperature. Since the second law requires that there be a "remainder" discharged, there must be at least two reservoirs, one providing heat and the other accepting the "remainder." Naturally, the reservoir which provides the heat must be at a different temperature (e.g., T_2) from that of the other reservoir, T_1—otherwise we would have the equivalent of only one reservoir, which according to the second law, would not work. Furthermore, T_2 must be greater than T_1— if it were not, one could, after the completion of a cycle, permit the heat lost by reservoir T_2 to be restored by direct conduction of heat from the T_1 reservoir. The net result would be that the work done during the cycle was provided, in effect, solely by the T_1 reservoir. The second law says this would not work either. Still another possibility would be for both reservoirs to provide heat. Again, restoration of the heat lost by the cooler reservoir by conduction from the hotter one would contradict the second law. In view of all this, T_2 must be greater than T_1, where T_2 is the temperature of the heat source (**boiler**) and T_1 is the temperature of the heat receiver (**condenser** or **sink**).

If q_2 is the heat absorbed per cycle from T_2, and q_1 is the heat absorbed per cycle from T_1 (q_1 is negative), the work done per cycle, $w = q_2 + q_1$, (since $\Delta E = 0$), for the working substance has undergone a complete cycle. The **thermodynamic efficiency**, η, is given by $w/q_2 = (q_2 + q_1)/q_2$. Since $w < q_2$, $\eta < 1$.

In the heat engine designed by **Carnot** and bearing his name, each cycle consists of the following four steps. The **working substance** is n moles of an ideal gas.

Step (1) The gas, at temperature T_2, expands reversibly and isothermally from volume V_1 to volume V_2 (Fig. 2-1), and does work w_1 while absorbing heat q_2 from the reservoir at T_2.

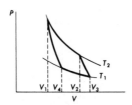

Fig. 2-1

Step (2) The gas expands reversibly and adiabatically to V_3 and does work w_2 while its temperature drops to T_1.

Step (3) The gas is compressed reversibly and isothermally at T_1 from V_3 to V_4, and does work w_3 while absorbing heat q_1 from T_1 ($w_3 < 0$, $q_1 < 0$).

Step (4) The gas is compressed reversibly and adiabatically to V_1 and does work w_4 while its temperature rises to T_2 ($w_4 < 0$).

The T_2 and T_1 isotherms in Fig. 2-1 are plots of $P = nRT_2/V$ and $P = nRT_1/V$, respectively. The two adiabatics are plots of $PV^\gamma = $ constant and $PV^\gamma = $ constant', respectively (cf. Fig. 1-2).

In step (1), since $\Delta E = 0$, $w_1 = q_2 = nRT_2 \ln (V_2/V_1)$.
In step (2), since $q = 0$, $w_2 = -C_V \Delta T = -C_V (T_1 - T_2)$.
In step (3), since $\Delta E = 0$, $w_3 = q_1 = nRT_1 \ln (V_4/V_3)$.
In step (4), since $q = 0$, $w_4 = -C_V \Delta T = -C_V (T_2 - T_1)$.
For the whole cycle, since $\Delta E = 0$, we have

$$
\begin{aligned}
w_{total} = q_{total} &= q_2 + q_1 \\
&= nRT_2 \ln (V_2/V_1) - C_V(T_1 - T_2) + nRT_1 \ln (V_4/V_3) \\
&\qquad\qquad\qquad\qquad\qquad\qquad\qquad - C_V(T_2 - T_1) \\
&= nRT_2 \ln (V_2/V_1) - nRT_1 \ln (V_3/V_4)
\end{aligned}
$$

But since V_2 and V_3 are on the same adiabatic,

$$
V_2 T_2^{C_V/R} = V_3 T_1^{C_V/R}
$$

Similarly

$$
V_1 T_2^{C_V/R} = V_4 T_1^{C_V/R}
$$

for the other adiabatic. Therefore $V_2/V_3 = V_1/V_4$ or $V_2/V_1 = V_3/V_4$. Substitution gives:

$$
\begin{aligned}
q_2 + q_1 &= nRT_2 \ln (V_2/V_1) - nRT_1 \ln (V_2/V_1) \\
&= (T_2 - T_1) nR \ln (V_2/V_1)
\end{aligned}
$$

It follows that:

$$
(q_2 + q_1)/q_2 = (T_2 - T_1)/T_2 \tag{2-1}
$$

or

$$
1 + q_2/q_1 = 1 - T_2/T_1 \qquad \text{or} \qquad q_1/T_1 + q_2/T_2 = 0
$$

Example 2-1 If a Carnot engine, operating between two heat reservoirs at $500°K$ and $300°K$, absorbs 1000 cal from the $500°$ reservoir per cycle how much heat is discharged into the $300°K$ reservoir and how much work is done per cycle? What is the efficiency of the engine?

Ans. By Eq. (2-1) $(1000 + q_1)/1000 = (500 - 300)/500$, or $q_1 = -600$ cal, so 600 cal are discharged into the $300°$ reservoir. $w = q_2 + q_1 = 1000 - 600 = 400$ cal. $\eta = (500 - 300)/500 = 0.400$.

A commonly found shorthand designation for heat engines is illustrated in Fig. 2-2 for the Carnot engine of the preceding example.

The second law is stated in a variety of ways but there is generally no demonstration that the various statements mean effectively the same thing. The Kelvin-Planck statement has been given earlier. The Clausius statement says that *heat will not flow from a colder to a warmer body without the expenditure of work.* To show that one statement is a consequence of the other let us *assume* that heat *will* flow from a colder to a warmer body without the expenditure of work. Imagine the Carnot engine.

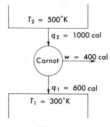

Fig. 2-2

of Example 2-1 (Fig. 2-2) at the end of one cycle. Now let the 600 cal discharged into T_1 be allowed to flow through some heat conductor from T_1 into T_2. No work is required. Thus T_1 suffers no net heat change; yet T_2 has lost 1000 − 600 = 400 cal of heat which have been converted into 400 cal of work. This contravenes the Kelvin-Planck statement. Our assumption is therefore wrong and the Clausius statement true.

We may now show that the validity of $(q_2 + q_1)/q_2 = (T_2 - T_1)/T_2$ is not confined to the use of ideal gases as working substances, or to the nature of the particular steps used in the Carnot cycle. To do this we imagine another engine, E, which may have any mode of operation as long as it is reversible and uses two heat reservoirs. Letting $T_2 = 500°K$ and $T_1 = 300°K$ as before, we run the Carnot, for which $\eta = 0.400$, in reverse so that, for every cycle, 400 cal of work done *on* the Carnot, 600 cal from T_1 are removed and 1000 cal are discharged into T_2 (Fig. 2-3). In this way the Carnot becomes a heat pump. We now couple E to the Carnot so that the work needed to run the Carnot pump is provided by E. If we suppose that E is more efficient than the Carnot, e.g., η for E is 0.500, only 800 cal will have to be removed from T_2 in order to do 400 cal work, the remaining 400 cal being discharged into T_1. The net result of this coupling is that T_2 gains 200 cal, T_1 loses 200 cal and no net work is done. Thus, by assuming E to be more efficient than the Carnot, we have contravened the Clausius statement. E, therefore, cannot be more efficient than the Carnot.

If, on the other hand, E is supposed to be less efficient than the Carnot, we may, by coupling the two as before, but running the Carnot forward and E in reverse, show that, again, heat is transferred from T_1 to T_2 without

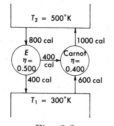

Fig. 2-3

any net expenditure of work. Thus E cannot be less efficient than the Carnot. It has therefore been shown that *all* reversible two-reservoir heat engines have the same efficiency.

Example 2-2 How much work is done in 10^3 cycles of a reversible heat engine operating between $1000°K$ and $200°K$ if, in each cycle, 900 cal are withdrawn from the high temperature reservoir and if the working substance is a nonideal gas?

Ans. $w/q_2 = (T_2 - T_1)/T_2 = (1000 - 200)/1000 = 0.800$, regardless of the working substance. If $q_2 = (900)(10^3)$ cal for every 10^3 cycles, $w = (0.800)(900)(10^3) = 720,000$ cal.

Example 2-3 If the engine in Example 2-2 is reversed so that it behaves as a heat pump, how much work is needed to remove 5000 cal from the low temperature reservoir?

Ans. It is still true that $w/q_2 = (T_2 - T_1)/T_2$, but now both w and q_2 are negative. Since $w = q_2 + q_1$ and $q_1 = 5000$ cal, $q_2 = (w - 5000)$ cal. Therefore $w/(w - 5000) = (1000 - 200)/1000$, giving $w = -20,000$ cal, so 20,000 cal of work are needed.

HEAT ENGINES WITH MORE THAN TWO HEAT RESERVOIRS

It has been shown that, for any reversible, two-reservoir heat engine, $w/q_2 = (T_2 - T_1)/T_2$ or $(q_1/T_1) + (q_2/T_2) = 0$ or $\Sigma(q/T) = 0$. This may be made more general by considering engines in which heat transfers occur at more than two temperatures. The heavy P-V curves of Fig. 2-1 now become, in general, the closed curve of Fig. 2-4. Several reversible iso-

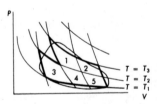

Fig. 2-4

thermal and adiabatic paths for an ideal gas are drawn across this area, and by selecting appropriate portions of these one can approximately reproduce the closed curve, as shown by the heavier lines. Each smaller area bounded by two adjacent isothermals and two adjacent adiabatics represents a Carnot cycle. Thus the overall cycle is represented approximately by the sum of a number of Carnot cycles, at least as far as the areas are concerned. We can go further than this, however, as follows:

$$\sum_{\text{cycle 1}} q/T + \sum_{\text{cycle 2}} q/T + \sum_{\text{cycle 3}} q/T + \sum_{\text{cycle 4}} q/T + \sum_{\text{cycle 5}} q/T$$

$$= \frac{q_{2(1)}}{T_3} + \frac{q_{1(1)}}{T_2} + \frac{q_{2(2)}}{T_3} + \frac{q_{1(2)}}{T_2} + \frac{q_{2(3)}}{T_2} + \frac{q_{1(3)}}{T_1}$$

$$+ \frac{q_{2(4)}}{T_2} + \frac{q_{1(4)}}{T_1} + \frac{q_{2(5)}}{T_2} + \frac{q_{1(5)}}{T_1}$$

where the numbers in parentheses refer to the particular Carnot cycle. This lengthy sum is zero, since, for each Carnot $\Sigma\ q/T = 0$. We observe at this point that $q_{1(1)} = -q_{2(4)}$ and that $q_{1(2)} = -q_{2(5)}$, for identical paths are traversed in opposite directions for Carnot cycles on opposite sides of a common isotherm. The resulting cancellation gives:

$$\frac{q_{2(1)}}{T_3} + \frac{q_{2(2)}}{T_3} + \frac{q_{1(5)}}{T_1} + \frac{q_{1(4)}}{T_1} + \frac{q_{1(3)}}{T_1} + \frac{q_{2(3)}}{T_2} = 0$$

Now the left-hand side of this last equation is close to $\Sigma\ q/T$ for the over-all cycle. If we had followed this same procedure but with an infinitely large number of isothermals and adiabatics, the result of such a cancellation would have been not close to but equal to $\Sigma\ q/T$ for the overall cycle, which is therefore also zero, and is written:

$$\oint \mathrm{D}q_{\text{rev}}/T = 0 \tag{2-2}$$

where $\oint$ symbolizes the line integral around a cyclic path.

ENTROPY

We here define a property of the working substance known as its entropy S, such that

$$dS = \mathrm{D}q_{\text{rev}}/T \tag{2-3}$$

(At this stage entropy has no readily visualized meaning, and one must be content with an abstract mathematical definition. A more concrete concept of it will develop later.) If a portion of matter (a system) at temperature T absorbs an amount of heat $\mathrm{D}q$ *reversibly* without change of temperature, we say its entropy increases by $\mathrm{D}q_{\text{rev}}/T$. If a finite quantity of heat is absorbed reversibly *at a constant temperature* T, the increase in entropy of the system, $\Delta S = \int dS = \int \mathrm{D}q_{\text{rev}}/T = q_{\text{rev}}/T$. If the temperature of the system *changes* from T_1 to T_2 during the heat absorption then the increase in its entropy is

$$\Delta S = \int_{T_1}^{T_2} \mathrm{D}q_{\text{rev}}/T.$$

Clearly Dq_{rev} must be positive and therefore heat must be absorbed to produce an increase in entropy in this way. It is most important to remember that only q_{rev} values may be used to calculate such entropy changes.

Before proceeding further we must show that entropy is a state function. Referring to Fig. 2-5, we take a system from A to B by path (1) and return it to A by path (2), *both paths being reversible*. Since in the complete

Fig. 2-5

cycle $\oint Dq_{rev}/T = 0$, it follows that $\oint dS = 0$ too, by the given definition of entropy. But:

$$0 = \oint dS = \underbrace{\int_A^B dS}_{\text{Path (1)}} + \underbrace{\int_B^A dS}_{\text{Path (2)}},$$

so we have

$$\underbrace{\int_A^B dS}_{\text{Path (1)}} = -\underbrace{\int_B^A dS}_{\text{Path (2)}} = \underbrace{\int_A^B dS}_{\text{Path (2)}}$$

Thus the change in S in going from A to B by either path is the same. Since *any* two reversible paths could have been chosen, the difference between S in state B and S in state A is independent of the path used, so entropy *is a state function*. (Observe that although Dq is an inexact differential, Dq_{rev}/T is exact.) It follows that if any system or portion of matter is taken through a series of changes and returned to its original state by reversible and/or irreversible processes, its entropy will be unchanged. This means that $\oint dS = 0$ for all cyclic changes. Since entropy is a ratio of energy to temperature, it is measured in units of energy per degree, most commonly cal deg^{-1}, abbreviated "eu" (for entropy units).*

It may be noted here that just as the first law gave rise to the energy function, so also the second law gives rise to the entropy function. We

*There is a growing tendency to use the term "gibbs" instead of "entropy unit." Thus 1 gibbs = 1 eu = 1 cal deg^{-1}.

have so far accumulated the following extensive thermodynamic functions: V, E, H, S. We shall see later in this chapter that the entropy function leads to a most important use of thermodynamics for the chemist: when properly employed it provides a means of deciding whether proposed chemical reactions are possible or not.

THE CALCULATION OF ΔS FOR TYPICAL CHANGES

Clearly a knowledge of q_{rev} is required if the relation $\Delta S = \int Dq_{rev}/T$ is to be used. This means that one must seek some process whereby the given change occurs reversibly. *The resulting* ΔS *is, however, quite independent of the path taken*, since ΔS is a state function. We thus use the concept of a reversible process as a means to an end, and having gained that end usually drop the restriction of reversibility.

When the initial and final states are at the same temperature, they are often also in equilibrium with each other. For example, if we wish to determine ΔS for $H_2O(s, 0°, 1 \text{ atm}) \longrightarrow H_2O(l, 0°, 1 \text{ atm})$, we imagine that the system is only infinitesimally removed from equilibrium regardless of how far the change has progressed, that the temperature is constant at $0°$, and that $P = p_{ex} = 1$ atm throughout the change. The heat required is thus automatically q_{rev}, so $\Delta S = \Delta H^{\circ}_{fusion}/273$. This ΔS is called the **entropy of fusion** although it is not really an entropy but an entropy *change*.

Example 2-4 If the heat of vaporization of water is 9710 cal mole^{-1} at $100°$ and 1 atm, find ΔS for $H_2O(g, 100°, 1 \text{ atm}) \longrightarrow H_2O(l, 100°, 1 \text{ atm})$.

Ans. $q = q_{rev} = -\Delta H^{\circ}_{vap} = -9710$ cal, so $\Delta S_{H_2O} = -9710/373 = -26.0$ eu.

Note Since, here, $\Delta S < 0$, the liquid has less entropy than the vapor. The value of ΔS for the reverse of the above change is the **entropy of vaporization**. For most liquids the latter quantity is a little over 21 eu mole^{-1}. The student who recalls **Trouton's rule** will see here its entropy basis. The method of calculation illustrated here applies, of course, to the determination of entropy changes for fusion, sublimation and transition *provided* the temperature and pressure of the two forms of the substance are those for which they are in equilibrium.

Suppose, now, that a substance experiences a change in pressure without a change in temperature or a phase change. Clearly, its volume must change. For liquids and solids the effect is only a very slight one, so the method will be illustrated by reference to a gas. To find ΔS for Gas $(T°K, P_1 \text{ atm}) \longrightarrow$ Gas $(T°K, P_2 \text{ atm})$, where, e.g., $P_2 < P_1$, we must visualize a reversible isothermal expansion. If the gas is ideal $q = q_{rev} = nRT \ln (V_2/V_1) = nRT \ln (P_1/P_2)$, so $\Delta S_{gas} = nR \ln (V_2/V_1) = nR \ln (P_1/P_2)$. Thus entropy increases with volume.

Example 2-5 By how much does the entropy of 3 moles of ideal gas change in going from a pressure of 2 atm to a pressure of 1 atm at $27°$ without change in temperature?

Ans. $\Delta S_{gas} = nR \ln (P_1/P_2) = 3(1.99) \ln (2/1) = 4.14$ eu.

If the final and initial states are different in temperature we proceed as follows. Let us suppose that the substance is to have its temperature raised without having its pressure changed. Such a condition can usually be realized, at least for solids and liquids, by slow heating of the substance while it is open to the atmosphere. Under these conditions $P = p_{ex}$ = constant and $Dq = Dq_P = C_P dT$ (cf. discussion of C_P in Chapter 1). In such slow heating Dq is, at the same time, indistinguishable from Dq_{rev}, for only a temperature change is involved and, provided $P = p_{ex}$ = constant, the same quantity of heat will be required to produce a given change in T whether the heat enters the substance reversibly or not! Thus $Dq_{rev} = C_P dT$, so

$$\Delta S = \int_{T_1}^{T_2} Dq_{rev}/T = \int_{T_1}^{T_2} C_P dT/T.$$

If C_P is independent of T this simplifies to $\Delta S = C_P \ln (T_2/T_1)$, which is valid for any pure substance.

By a similar argument the change in entropy of a pure substance undergoing a change in temperature at constant volume will be $\Delta S = \int_{T_1}^{T_2} C_V dT/T$, which becomes $\Delta S = C_V \ln (T_2/T_1)$ if C_V is independent of temperature.

Example 2-6 Find the change in entropy for $H_2O(s, -10°, 1 \text{ atm}) \longrightarrow H_2O(s, 0°, 1 \text{ atm})$, if $\overline{C}_P$ for ice is 9 cal deg^{-1} mole^{-1}.

Ans. The implication is that C_P is independent of T, so that $\Delta S = C_P \ln (T_2/T_1) = 9 \ln (273/263) = 0.33$ eu mole^{-1}.

Example 2-7 Find ΔS for $H_2O(s, -10°, 1 \text{ atm}) \longrightarrow H_2O(l, 10°, 1 \text{ atm})$, given that $\overline{C}_P$ is 9 and 18 cal deg^{-1} mole^{-1} for $H_2O(s)$ and $H_2O(l)$, respectively, and that the heat of fusion is 1440 cal deg^{-1} mole^{-1}.

Ans. $\Delta S = \Delta S$ (heating $H_2O(s)$ from $-10°$ to the normal freezing point)
    $+ \Delta S$ (melting at $0°$)
    $+ \Delta S$ (heating $H_2O(l)$ from the normal freezing point to $10°$)
$= 9 \ln (273/263) + (1440/273) + 18 \ln (283/273) = 0.33 + 5.27 + 0.65 = 6.25$ eu.

Note The three contributions must be calculated separately. It is useless to attempt to find $\int_{263}^{283} C_P \, dT/T$ directly, for the heat absorbed involved both sensible and latent heats, C_P being infinite for the latter.

For pure substances undergoing a change in *both* temperature and pressure (without a phase change) the calculation may be made in two steps. For example, in finding ΔS for the gas in Gas $(T_1, P_1) \longrightarrow$ Gas (T_2, P_2), one may imagine the change to have taken place in two stages: an isothermal change in pressure followed by an isobaric change in temperature. Thus one first finds ΔS_{gas} for Gas $(T_1, P_1) \longrightarrow$ Gas (T_1, P_2), then finds ΔS_{gas} for Gas $(T_1, P_2) \longrightarrow$ Gas (T_2, P_2), and then adds the two. The total change in the entropy of an ideal gas (C_P and C_V independent of temperature) is thus:

$$\Delta S_{ideal\ gas} = nR\ \ln\ (P_1/P_2) + n\overline{C}_P\ \ln\ (T_2/T_1) \tag{2-4}$$

or

$$\Delta S_{ideal\ gas} = nR\ \ln\ (V_2/V_1) + n\overline{C}_V\ \ln\ (T_2/T_1) \tag{2-5}$$

depending on whether pressures or volumes are given.

Example 2-8 Find the entropy change which 5 moles of oxygen undergoes in changing from $27°$ and 1 atm to $127°$ and 5 atm, taking $\overline{C}_P$ to be 6.95 cal deg^{-1} mole^{-1}.

Ans. $\Delta S_{gas} = 5(1.99)\ \ln\ (1/5) + 5(6.95)\ \ln\ (400/300) = -16.0 + 10.0 = -6.0$ eu.

Note The increase in entropy from the temperature rise was more than offset by the decrease in entropy from the pressure rise.

Example 2-9 Two 3-liter bulbs are connected through a stopcock. One contains 0.5 moles of ideal gas at $27°$ and the other is evacuated. Find the increase in entropy of the gas which occurs on opening the stopcock.

Ans. The initial volume is 3 liters, the final volume is 6 liters. There is no change in temperature because the gas is ideal (cf. Joule experiment, Chap. 1) $\Delta S = nR\ \ln\ (V_2/V_1) = 0.5(2)(300)\ \ln\ (6/3) = 0.69$ eu.

Note An erroneous argument is to say that since no heat was absorbed or evolved $q = 0$, so $q_{rev} = 0$ and therefore $\Delta S = q/T = 0/T = 0$. The fallacy in this reasoning is that even though $q = 0$ the change was an irreversible one so $q \neq q_{rev}$. It is thus not true that $q_{rev} = 0$. Actually $q_{rev} = nRT\ \ln\ (V_2/V_1) = 207$ cal.

For all *reversible*, adiabatic changes, since $q = q_{rev} = 0$, ΔS will be zero too, for the substance undergoing the change. It will also be zero for the surroundings. Observe that if any two of the following three conditions obtain, the third must also obtain: $q = 0$, process is reversible, $\Delta S_{system} = 0$.

Example 2-10 Twenty moles of $H_2O(l)$ at $50°$ and 1 atm are compressed adiabatically and reversibly to a pressure of 5000 atm. What is the entropy change?

Ans. $\Delta S_{H_2O} = 0$.

For *irreversible* adiabatic changes, however, $\Delta S_{substance}$ is not zero, even though ΔS of any adjacent heat reservoir is zero. One must then fall back on the methods already described, and illustrated below, recalling that for a given change ΔS will not depend on how the change was carried out anyway.

Example 2-11 If 2 moles of ideal gas ($\overline{C}_V = 3.000$ cal $\deg^{-1}$ mole^{-1}) at 300°K and 20 atm are expanded adiabatically against a pressure of 10 atm, what entropy change does the gas suffer?

Ans. Using the methods of Chap. 1 (Example 22) we find that $P_1 = 20$ atm, $V_1 = 2.46$ liters, $T_1 = 300°K$, $P_2 = 10$ atm, $V_2 = 3.94$ liters and $T_2 = 240°K$. Therefore using Eq. (2-4), $\Delta S_{gas} = 2(1.987) \ln (20/10) + 2(3.000 + 1.987) \ln (240/300) = 0.53$ eu.

One other situation in which ΔS may be desired is that in which heat flows directly from a reservoir at T_2 into one at $T_1 (T_2 > T_1)$, where the reservoirs are so large that their temperatures do not change from the loss or gain of heat. If $|q|$ cal are transferred in this way—this is, of course, an irreversible process—we may, in order to find q_{rev}, imagine that the heat transfer occurs with the help of an ideal gas. The latter absorbs the $|q|$ cal reversibly and isothermally from the T_2 reservoir, thereby expanding. The gas is now isolated thermally and allowed to expand reversibly and adiabatically until its temperature drops to T_1. Finally it is brought into contact with the T_1 reservoir and compressed isothermally and reversibly until $|q|$ cal have passed into the T_1 reservoir. The entropy increase of the T_2 reservoir is $-|q|/T_2$, and that of the T_1 reservoir is $|q|/T_1$, so ΔS for the reservoirs as a whole is $-|q|/T_2 + |q|/T_1$. (Incidentally, the entropy change of the gas is $|q|/T_2 - |q|/T_1$.)

Example 2-12 When 1000 cal of heat are conducted from a reservoir at 700°K to one at 300°K what is the change in the entropy of the reservoir system?

Ans. $\Delta S_{reservoirs} = -(1000/700) + (1000/300) = 1.90$ eu.

Example 2-13 Two identical bricks, one at 700°K and the other at 300°K, each weighing 2000 g, are placed in contact. Find ΔS_{bricks} if the heat capacity of brick is 0.20 cal $\deg^{-1}$ g^{-1}.

Ans. Final temperature of both bricks = 500°K. C_P for each brick = (2000)(0.20) = 400 cal $\deg^{-1}$. Therefore $\Delta S_{bricks} = 400 \ln (500/700) + 400 \ln (500/300) = 70$ eu.

GENERAL DEPENDENCE OF ENTROPY ON PRESSURE AND TEMPERATURE

It has been shown following Example 2-5 that, for reversible changes in temperature at constant pressure, $dS = C_P dT/T$, and that, for reversible changes in temperature at constant volume, $dS = C_V dT/T$. These may be written:

$$(\partial S/\partial T)_P = C_P/T \tag{2-6}$$

and

$$(\partial S/\partial T)_V = C_V/T \tag{2-7}$$

To complete the picture the following relations are here included. They are two of the four "Maxwell relations" which will be derived and discussed later:

$$(\partial S/\partial V)_T = (\partial P/\partial T)_V \qquad (2\text{-}8)$$

and

$$(\partial S/\partial P)_T = -(\partial V/\partial T)_P \qquad (2\text{-}9)$$

The right-hand side of Eq. (2-9) is so small for liquids and solids that their entropy varies only slightly with pressure. By combining Eqs. (2-6) to (2-9) with $PV = nRT$, Eqs. (2-4) and (2-5) may be readily obtained for ideal gases.

ENTROPY CHANGES IN CHEMICAL REACTIONS

When chemical reactions occur ΔS for the system is still given by $\int D q_{rev}/T$, of course, and this becomes q_{rev}/T as usual when the reactants and products are all at the same temperature T.

Example 2-14 Find ΔS_{system} for $H_2\,(g, 25°, 1\,atm) + Cl_2\,(g, 25°, 1\,atm) \longrightarrow 2\,HCl\,(g, 25°, 1\,atm)$, if q_{rev} is 1412 cal.

Ans. $\Delta S_{system} = 1412/298 = 4.74$ eu.

Note Just how q_{rev} is actually determined will be described in a later chapter.

ENTROPY CHANGE AS A CRITERION OF IRREVERSIBILITY

Any reversible heat transfers must by definition occur between bodies which are at temperatures that differ infinitesimally. Thus when a system absorbs heat reversibly from, or gives up heat reversibly to, its environment the latter must gain or lose the same amount of entropy as the system has lost or gained. Hence we may say that, in a *reversible* process, $\Delta S_{total} = 0$. The word "total" is most important, since neither ΔS_{system} nor ΔS_{surr} will, in general, be zero.

We now ask: Is there an analogous quality of *irreversible* processes? We shall see later that the criterion sought is $\Delta S_{total} > 0$ for an isolated system undergoing any irreversible process. This is known as the **Clausius inequality**. But first let us look at some of the previous worked examples in this chapter and endeavor to apply the Clausius inequality to them. To do so we will now have to consider not only what happens to the system (substances) but also what happens to the immediate surroundings, *for the two together comprise the isolated system* in question. This in turn will require us to know not only what change is being considered but *specifically what process is to be used.*

In Example 2-4 we may imagine that the whole isolated system consisted of one mole of the substance water (the system proper) and the immediate surroundings, which acquired the heat evolved and which did the work of compressing the vapor to liquid. *If* these surroundings were also at 100°, and *if* $P = p_{ex} = 1$ atm *throughout* the change, then 9710 cal of heat would have been acquired by the surroundings, and so $\Delta S_{surr} = 9710/373$ eu. Since ΔS_{H_2O} was $-9710/373$, the value of ΔS_{total} was zero.

In Example 2-5, we were not told how the expansion occurred, i.e. whether it was reversible or irreversible, and, if irreversible, what the conditions were, so we can make no calculation of ΔS_{surr}. *If* the expansion had been reversible we would have found that $\Delta S_{surr} = -4.14$ eu so that $\Delta S_{total} = 0$. *If*, however, the expansion had been against a constant external pressure of, e.g., 1 atm, the change would have occurred irreversibly. In the latter case, since $V_1 = 3(0.082)(300)/2 = 36.9$ liters and $V_2 = 73.8$ liters, $w = 1(73.8 - 36.9) = 36.9$ liter-atm $= 893$ cal $= q$. This quantity of heat would have to be provided by the surroundings. *If* the surroundings were at 27° they would suffer an entropy *loss* of $893/300 = 2.98$ eu. We thus have $\Delta S_{gas} = 4.14$ eu, $\Delta S_{surr} = -2.98$ eu and $\Delta S_{total} = 1.16$ eu. The Clausius inequality is therefore satisfied. Notice that the surroundings, supposedly large, and supposedly losing the 893 cal without change in temperature, are taken to *lose* this heat reversibly even though the gas did not *acquire* it reversibly. This supposition must be made for lack of further information if we are to apply the Clausius inequality criterion in a problem of this type. In Examples 2-6, 2-7 and 2-8, we could not find ΔS_{surr} or ΔS_{total} without more information about the temperature of the environment.

In Example 2-9, since the environment was completely unaffected, its entropy remained unchanged. We have, therefore, $\Delta S_{gas} = 0.69$ eu, $\Delta S_{surr} = 0$, $\Delta S_{total} = 0.69$ eu, which is greater than zero, as anticipated.

In Example 2-10 $\Delta S_{H_2O} = \Delta S_{surr} = \Delta S_{total} = 0$, as in all reversible adiabatic changes, but in Example 2-11 $\Delta S_{total} = 0.53 + 0 = 0.53$ eu, which is positive as it should be, since the process was irreversible. In Examples 2-12 and 2-13 no environment was involved so $\Delta S_{system} = \Delta S_{total} > 0$.

Finally, in Example 2-14, supposing the surroundings to be at 25°, assuming $P = p_{ex} = $ constant throughout the change, and given that the standard heat of formation of HCl(g) is $\Delta H_{298}^{\circ} = -22.063$ kcal mole^{-1}, $\Delta S_{surr} = 44,126/298 = 0.148$ eu and $\Delta S_{system} = 4.74$ eu, so $\Delta S_{total} = 0.148 + .74 = 4.89$ eu, again bearing out the Clausius inequality.

We now proceed to prove that for isolated systems the Clausius inequality, shown to be true in the above examples, is always true, provided that the Kelvin-Planck statement of the second law is accepted.

Consider an isolated system consisting of a homogeneous substance at a uniform temperature and pressure (state A) which has undergone a spontaneous change to a different but uniform temperature and pressure (state B). With a little ingenuity it is always possible to imagine a series of completely reversible processes by which state A can be restored, and in which all nonadiabatic steps are isothermal and at a single temperature. During the restoration the condition of isolation is dropped, so work may be done on or by the system. The same is true for the isothermal step or steps in which heat transfer is permitted into or out of the system. It is evident that any change in entropy suffered by the system during its return to state A must have occurred during the isothermal step(s). Since the system executes a complete cycle its net energy change is zero, so $q_{cycle} = w_{cycle}$. Therefore either q_{cycle} and w_{cycle} are both >0 or both $= 0$ or both <0. Now both cannot be >0, however, for this means that work has been produced in a cyclic process from a single reservoir—the one used in the isothermal steps—and the Kelvin-Planck statement says this is impossible. Both cannot be zero because, if $q_{cycle} = 0$, q in the isothermal step(s) of the restoration process must be zero, for all the other steps are adiabatic, including the original change in the isolated system. If q in the isothermal step(s) is zero there must be no change in entropy in going from B to A. This means that $S_A = S_B$, and if that is true the original change, A to B, must be reversible, since it is adiabatic. This is contrary to our original assumption that the change A $\longrightarrow$ B is spontaneous. We must conclude that both q_{cycle} and w_{cycle} are <0. Since the heat transfer in the isothermal step(s) is reversible at a single temperature the entropy of the system has decreased in the return from B to A. Thus $S_A < S_B$ or, for the original irreversible change from A to B, the entropy of the isolated system has increased.

If, as is likely in practice, the isolated system is not at a single temperature and pressure, and not homogeneous (it may well consist of working substances and heat reservoir) the return processes from B to A may be imagined to be performed on the several portions *separately*. Now, however, the *same* heat reservoir is used for all the portions, and all the heat transfers in which the reservoir is involved are combined. The total q for the isothermal steps must, again, be <0, and the argument of the previous paragraph may be followed from here.

We thus conclude that $\Delta S_{E,V} > 0$ for all irreversible processes, the subscripts conveying the restriction to an isolated system. This is often written $dS_{E,V} > 0$, since the law is true for infinitesimal changes too. It is also expressed as:

$$dS_{E,V} \geq 0 \tag{2-10}$$

meaning that S_{total} increases in irreversible and remains constant in reversible processes occurring in isolated systems. Clearly, entropy is not conserved in nature even though energy is. Regarding the universe as an isolated system we may say, with Clausius, "The entropy of the universe tends towards a maximum." Any isolated system, having come to equilibrium, can suffer no further entropy change (by itself, that is—otherwise it would not be isolated), so we may also say that at true equilibrium the entropy of an isolated system *is* a maximum.

The increase in entropy of the system and that part of the environment which is affected by an irreversible process (the two together comprising the isolated system), is also known as the **irreversible entropy** or the

internal entropy production because it is entropy created within the isolated system. A heat quantity, q', such that $\Delta S_{total} = q'/T$ for a spontaneous isothermal change at temperature T, is sometimes called the **uncompensated heat**. It should be noted, parenthetically, that the term "total entropy" as used by some authors has not always the same connotation it has here.

Example 2-15 An isolated system consists initially (state A) of supercooled liquid water at $-10°$ and 1 atm in contact with a block of iron. The water freezes spontaneously to ice and the heat evolved warms the resulting ice and the iron to $-8°$ at 1 atm (state B). Devise a scheme whereby the original state A can be restored reversibly to show that $S_B > S_A$.

Ans. (Ref. schematic: Figs. 2-6 and 2-7.)   Choose a reservoir at any arbitrary temperature, say $-1°$.   Separate the H_2O from the Fe (both are at $-8°$ and 1 atm).

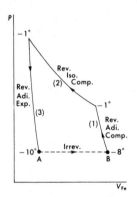

Fig. 2-6. Restoration of Fe.

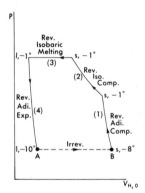

Fig. 2-7. Restoration of H_2O.

Take the Fe through the following changes: (1) Subject it to reversible adiabatic compression until its temperature has risen to $-1°$. (2) Compress it isothermally and reversibly in contact with the reservoir at $-1°$ until its entropy is that of Fe at $-10°$. Heat (q_{Fe}) will be transferred from the Fe to the reservoir. (3) Expand the Fe adiabatically and reversibly until its temperature drops to $-10°$ and its pressure to 1 atm.

Take the ice through the following changes: (1) Subject it to reversible adiabatic compression until its temperature has risen to $-1°$. (2) Compress it isothermally and reversibly in contact with the reservoir at $-1°$ until its pressure is that at which ice and liquid water are in equilibrium at $-1°$. Heat will be transferred from the ice to the reservoir. (3) With the ice and reservoir still in contact, allow heat to pass reversibly at constant pressure into the ice until it is completely molten. (4) Subject the resulting water to reversible adiabatic expansion until it is restored to $-10°$ and 1 atm. Let q_{H_2O} be the algebraic sum of the heat transfers in (2) and (3).

Place the H_2O and Fe in contact again. We have thus restored the original state A, and the only heat transfers have been q_{Fe} and q_{H_2O} at $-1°$. Following the arguments given earlier in this section the sum of q_{Fe} and q_{H_2O} must be < 0 if the second law is to apply, and so for the combined return processes the final entropy must be less than the initial. Therefore $S_B > S_A$.

One of the basic questions that is asked of thermodynamics by the chemist, viz. how can one predict whether a given change is possible under given circumstances, can thus be answered by application of the Clausius inequality.

It is sometimes suggested that a change which, under given environmental conditions, takes place irreversibly and therefore "by itself," be described as a spontaneous change, and that the adjective "spontaneous" be used *only* to describe such a change and *not* to describe the process by which it occurs. Since, however, one cannot determine whether a given change will occur "by itself" *without* describing the environmental conditions (either explicitly or by inference), confining the word "spontaneous" to *changes* and not applying it to the *process* draws a distinction where none exists.

There are at least two serious drawbacks in the practical application of the Clausius inequality as a criterion of irreversibility. (1) No matter how easy it may be to find ΔS_{system}, the value of ΔS_{surr} is often difficult and cumbersome, or even impossible, to calculate. The very designation of the boundaries of the environment may be in question. (2) If the value of ΔS_{total} indicates that the change is possible, thermodynamics gives no information as to how quickly it will take place. The first difficulty is avoided by developing other more convenient criteria—this will be considered in Chapter 4. The second difficulty cannot be surmounted by thermodynamics alone.

VARIATION OF ENTROPY CHANGE WITH TEMPERATURE

Just as the variation of entropy with temperature at constant pressure is given by Eq. (2-6), the variation of ΔS with temperature at constant pressure is expressed as:

$$(\partial \Delta S/\partial T)_P = \Delta C_P/T \qquad (2-11)$$

This is obtained from Eq. (2-6) just as Eq. (1-18) was obtained from Eq. (1-8). The left-hand side is the *rate of change of the change* of entropy with temperature at constant pressure. By similar reasoning we have the following:

$$(\partial \Delta S/\partial T)_V = \Delta C_V/T \qquad (2-12)$$

Example 2-16 Find ΔS for $H_2O(l, -10°, 1 \text{ atm}) \longrightarrow H_2O(s, -10°, 1 \text{ atm})$, given that C_P is 9 and 18 cal deg^{-1} mole^{-1} for $H_2O(s)$ and $H_2O(l)$, respectively, and that the heat of fusion at $0°$ and 1 atm is 1440 cal mole^{-1}.

Ans. $\Delta S^°_{273} = 1440/273 = -5.27$ eu and $\Delta C_P = 9 - 18 = -9$ cal deg^{-1}

mole^{-1}. Since $(\partial \Delta S / \partial T)_P = \Delta C_P / T$, $\displaystyle\int_{263}^{273} d\Delta S = \int_{263}^{273} \Delta C_P dT/T$ or

$$\Delta S_{273} - \Delta S_{263} = \int_{263}^{273} - 9 d \ln T \text{ or } -5.27 - \Delta S_{263} = -9 \ln (273/263) \text{ eu,}$$

so $\Delta S_{263} = -4.94$ eu (cf. Example 2-7).

PROOF THAT $w_{\text{irrev}} < w_{\text{rev}}$ FOR ISOTHERMAL PROCESSES

In Chapter 1 some examples were given to illustrate the principle that, for a given isothermal change, $w_{\text{irrev}} < w_{\text{rev}}$. We are now in a position to prove this from the second law.

Let A and B be any two states of the same system at the same temperature T. Suppose, first, that the change A to B is carried out reversibly and isothermally, and is followed by the change from B to A again, by the exact reverse of the forward reversible process. Letting the subscripts f and r denote the forward and reverse processes we have $\Delta E_f = q_{\text{rev}(f)} - w_{\text{rev}(f)}$ and $\Delta E_r = q_{\text{rev}(r)} - w_{\text{rev}(r)}$ by the first law. However, $\Delta E_f = -\Delta E_r$ and, because of the reversibility, $q_{\text{rev}(f)} = -q_{\text{rev}(r)}$ and $w_{\text{rev}(f)} = -w_{\text{rev}(r)}$.

If, instead, the change A to B be carried out irreversibly, followed by the change from B to A carried out reversibly, the work done by the system in the forward process is $w_{\text{irrev}(f)}$ and that in the return $w_{\text{rev}(r)}$ or $-w_{\text{rev}(f)}$. The heat absorbed by the system in the forward process is $q_{\text{irrev}(f)}$ and that in the return $q_{\text{rev}(r)}$ or $-q_{\text{rev}(f)}$. The net work done in the cycle is $w_{\text{irrev}(f)} - w_{\text{rev}(f)}$ and the net heat absorbed $q_{\text{irrev}(f)} - q_{\text{rev}(f)}$. Since ΔE for the complete cycle is zero, $w_{\text{irrev}(f)} - w_{\text{rev}(f)} = q_{\text{irrev}(f)} - q_{\text{rev}(f)}$. Now *if* we suppose that $w_{\text{irrev}(f)} > w_{\text{rev}(f)}$, then $w_{\text{irrev}(f)} - w_{\text{rev}(f)} > 0$, and so $q_{\text{irrev}(f)} - q_{\text{rev}(f)} > 0$. This means that a complete isothermal cyclic operation has been carried out in which a net amount of heat, $q_{\text{irrev}(f)} - q_{\text{rev}(f)}$, has been absorbed by the system at a single temperature, while at the same time an amount of work, $w_{\text{irrev}(f)} - w_{\text{rev}(f)}$, has been done. This contravenes the Kelvin-Planck statement of the second law. The original supposition, $w_{\text{irrev}(f)} > w_{\text{rev}(f)}$, is therefore false. Since $w_{\text{irrev}(f)}$ cannot equal $w_{\text{rev}(f)}$ (contradiction in terms), $w_{\text{irrev}(f)}$ must be less than $w_{\text{rev}(f)}$. We have thus proved that

$$w_{\text{irrev}} < w_{\text{rev}} \quad (T \text{ constant}) \tag{2-13}$$

so that w is a maximum for a given isothermal change when that change is carried out reversibly. Conceivably there might be more than one reversible isothermal process by which the given change could be conducted. However, these would all have to do the same amount of work,

w_{rev}—if not it could be shown by the same kind of argument as just given that the second law had been contravened. For *isothermal* changes, then w_{rev} or w_{max} is independent of the path or process and is, in fact, a function of state. This will be brought out in a different way in Chapter 4.

Finally, since for a given isothermal change, ΔE is independent of the path, and since $w_{irrev} < w_{rev}$ for such a change, the following is true:

$$q_{irrev} < q_{rev} \quad (T \text{ constant}) \tag{2-14}$$

HEAT PUMPS AND REFRIGERATORS

When a device for converting heat into work (a heat engine) is reversed, it converts work into heat and becomes a **heat pump**, i.e., a device upon which work is done and which, as a result, pumps heat from a reservoir at one temperature into another reservoir at a higher temperature. The need for the expenditure of work is evident from the Clausius statement of the second law. If, as before, the q's are positive for heat absorbed by the system and w is positive for work done by the system, $(q_2 + q_1)/q_2$ still equals $(T_2 - T_1)/T_2$, but now q_2 is negative, q_1 positive and $w = q_2 + q_1$ is negative. Simple manipulation of this relation leads to:

$$-\frac{w}{q_1} = \frac{\text{work done on the system}}{\text{heat absorbed from } T_1 \text{ reservoir}} = \frac{T_2 - T_1}{T_1} \tag{2-15}$$

which is valid only for a completely reversible pump. Any actual heat pump will require more work to be done on the system in order to remove the same amount of heat from the T_1 reservoir.

Heat pumps may be used (1) to remove heat from an already cooler reservoir and so behave as refrigerators or (2) to pump heat into an already warmer reservoir and so behave as heating agents.

(1) As refrigerators the action is analogous to that of the household electric refrigerator which pumps heat from the already cooler interior of the refrigerator to the already warmer room.

Example 2-17 (a) What is the minimum amount of work needed to remove 5000 cal of heat from the interior of a refrigerator at 0° if the room temperature is 30°? (b) How much heat is discharged into the room?

Ans. (a) Since $-w/5000 = (303 - 273)/273$, $-w = 549$ cal, so at least 549 cal of work are required.
(b) Since $w = q_1 + q_2$, $-549 = 5000 + q_2$, or $q_2 = -5549$ cal, so 5549 cal of heat must have been discharged into the room.

(2) As heating agents heat pumps should be, at least theoretically, highly efficient. This is seen by recalling that $-w = -q_2 - q_1$ or $-q_2 = -w + q_1$. More energy is available for heating than is needed to drive the device, since $-q_2$, $-w$ and q_1 are all positive quantities. Thus a given quantity of externally available energy will deliver more heat at T_2 by using it to run a heat pump than by converting it directly into heat.

Example 2-18 Compare the quantities of heat delivered to a room at 300°K by (a) direct conversion of 1000 joules of electrical energy and (b) the use of 1000 joules of electrical energy to run a reversible heat pump with the outdoors as a low-temperature reservoir at 240°K.

Ans. (a) Direct conversion will give 1000 joules or 239.0 cal of heat to the room.

(b) Used to run a heat pump, T_2 and T_1 being at 300°K and 240°K, respectively, and the pump being reversible, we have $-1000/-q_2 = (300 - 240)/300$ or $-q_2 = 5000$ joule $= 1195$ cal.

Note The extra heat delivered in (b) comes from the outdoors.

UNATTAINABILITY OF ABSOLUTE ZERO

Eq. (2-15) determines the minimum work needed to remove a given amount of heat from a low-temperature region and discharge it into a region at higher temperature. Now as cooling proceeds T_1 decreases, $T_2 - T_1$ remains a positive number, and q_1 also remains positive if any cooling is to be accomplished. The value of $-w$ must therefore become larger and larger as T_1 becomes smaller and smaller. As T_1 approaches absolute zero $-w$ approaches infinity, so that an infinite amount of work will be needed to bring T_1 down to zero, even using a *reversible* pump! It is thus impossible to cool any region down to absolute zero.

ABSOLUTE AND THERMODYNAMIC TEMPERATURE SCALES

It has been shown in the Introduction that ideal gas behavior can be used as a basis for a temperature scale which is independent of the thermometric substance. There is, however, another temperature scale that is independent of the thermometric substance, viz. the **thermodynamic** or **Kelvin scale**. This and the absolute gas scale are identical, though, so °A and °K are identical. Since the symbol °K is more prevalent it is used throughout this book.

   To show the meaning of the thermodynamic scale of temperature we proceed as follows. Let us (following Lord Kelvin) invent a temperature scale according to which either one of the reservoirs in a Carnot engine is directly proportional to the quantity of heat given to or removed from it, other things being held constant. ("Other things being held constant" means holding constant the temperature of the other reservoir and the quantity of heat given to or removed from it.) Let θ indicate the temperature on this scale. In other words, we define θ such that $\theta_{1 \text{ or } 2} \propto |q_{1 \text{ or } 2}|$ (where the subscripts refer to the lower and higher reservoir temperatures), the other θ and $|q|$ being held constant. Since, then, $\theta \propto |q|$, $\theta_1/|q_1| = \theta_2/|q_2|$, or $|q_1|/|q_2| = \theta_1/\theta_2$, or $1 - (|q_1|/|q_2|) = 1 - (\theta_1/\theta_2)$, or $(|q_2| - |q_1|)/|q_2| = (\theta_2 - \theta_1)/\theta_2$. Now $|q_2| - |q_1| = w_{\text{cycle}}$, and $|q_2| = q_2$, since q_2 is positive for heat engines. Therefore $w_{\text{cycle}}/q_2 = (\theta_2 - \theta_1)\theta_2$. We have shown, however, that $w_{\text{cycle}}/q_2 = (T_2 - T_1)/T_2$, where the T's are, strictly, the reservoir temperatures on the ideal gas scale. Therefore

$(\theta_2 - \theta_1)/\theta_2 = (T_2 - T_1)/T_2$. This will be true if $\theta \propto T$. Thus the thermodynamic temperature, defined as above, gives a scale that is proportional to the ideal gas scale. For convenience the proportionality constant is made equal to unity so that $\theta = T$, and the readings on the two scales become identical. We see, then, that $|q|$ is the "thermometric property" on the Kelvin scale.

PROBLEMS

1. The thermodynamic efficiency of a certain heat engine is 0.47 when the boiler is at 300° and the sink at 0°.
   (a) Is the engine reversible or not?
   (b) How much work is done for every 4000 cal withdrawn from the boiler?
2. A brick weighing 2500 g, with a heat capacity of 500 cal deg^{-1} and a temperature of 200° is dropped into a large Dewar flask containing 900 g of ice at 0°.
   (a) If the heat of fusion of ice is 1440 cal mole^{-1} and the heat capacity of $H_2O(l)$ is 18.0 cal deg^{-1} mole^{-1} find the final temperature.
   (b) Calculate ΔS_{brick}, ΔS_{H_2O} and ΔS_{total}, and show that the Clausius inequality is illustrated.
3. The standard heat of formation of HI(g) at 25° is $\Delta H^{\circ}_{298} = 6.20$ kcal mole^{-1}. For $\frac{1}{2}H_2(g, 298°K, 1$ atm$) + \frac{1}{2}I_2(s, 298°K, 1$ atm$) \longrightarrow$ HI(g, 298°K, 1 atm), $q_{rev} = 5870$ cal. Will this change be permissible thermodynamically when the substances are in contact with a large reservoir at 25° and when P and p_{ex} are kept equal to 1 atm?
4. In Example 2-8 it was shown that, for $5O_2(g, 300°K, 1$ atm$) \longrightarrow 5O_2(g, 400°K, 5$ atm$)$, the value of $\Delta S = -6.0$ eu, taking $\overline{C}_p$ for this gas to be 6.95 cal deg^{-1} mole^{-1}.
   (a) Find ΔH for this change.
   (b) Suppose that this change had occurred by sudden exposure to a constant external pressure of 5 atm and a very large heat reservoir at 400°K. Find q, ΔS_{surr} and ΔS_{total}.
   (c) Is the result in (b) consistent with the Clausius inequality?
5. (a) In connection with the irreversible adiabatic change described in Example 2-11 devise a means of returning to the initial state from the final state using only one isothermal step. (Hint: only two steps are needed for the return path if the isothermal step is at either 240°K or 300°K.)
   (b) Determine the values of P and V at the beginning and end of this isothermal step.
   (c) Calculate q during the isothermal step.
   (d) Find ΔS for the entire process of restoration and compare with the answer to Example 2-11.
   (e) Why *must* q be < 0 for the isothermal step?
6. One mole of ideal monatomic gas, $C_V = 3.00$ cal deg^{-1} mole^{-1}, at 6 atm and 27°, is suddenly placed in contact with a large reservoir at

17° and expanded against a pressure of 2 atm. The temperature of the gas drops to 17°.

(a) Find q and w for the gas.

(b) Find ΔE_{gas}, ΔH_{gas}, ΔS_{gas}, ΔS_{surr} and ΔS_{total}.

(c) Is the above change irreversible? Why?

7. The normal boiling point of benzene is 80° and the heat of vaporization at this temperature is 7353 cal mole^{-1}. For $C_6H_6(l)$ and $C_6H_6(g)$, C_p is 36.2 and 20.3 cal deg^{-1} mole^{-1}, respectively.

(a) Find ΔS for $C_6H_6(l, 70°, 1\ atm) \longrightarrow C_6H_6(g, 70°, 1\ atm)$.

(b) Find ΔS for $C_6H_6(l, 70°, 1\ atm) \longrightarrow C_6H_6(g, 90°, 1\ atm)$.

3

The third law of thermodynamics—
absolute entropy

In the previous chapter our concern with entropy has been with entropy *changes*, not with the absolute value of the entropy (absolute entropy). This is also true for internal energy and enthalpy. We might have attempted to determine the absolute internal energies or enthalpies of the initial and final states, subtracting one from the other to find ΔE or ΔH, but to find absolute values we need some state with a zero value and the assignment of zero energy is always an arbitrary matter. It is true, nevertheless, that the enthalpies of the elements are often assigned values of zero at 1 atm and 25°. While this is convenient, it is still arbitrary.

Inability to determine absolute energies and enthalpies is not a serious handicap, but the situation is somewhat different for entropies. The evaluation of ΔS for the system at a given temperature is not always possible by the methods of the preceding chapter. Since $\Delta S = q_{rev}/T$, we are faced with determining q_{rev}. The direct calorimetric measurement of q_{rev} is usually an impossible task, particularly for a chemical reaction. However, the third law of thermodynamics permits us to find the entropies of the reactants and of the products; we can then find ΔS by subtracting one from the other.

THE THIRD LAW OF THERMODYNAMICS

In order to know what the absolute entropy, or simply the entropy, of a substance is, we must, as already indicated, have a state of that substance which has known entropy. As entropy decreases with temperature $((\partial S/\partial T)_P = C_P/T$, C_P and T both being positive), a drop in temperature would cause it to approach zero, considering it to be positive at the original temperature. We shall attempt to show later in this chapter, by a statistical approach, that it is convenient to assign positive values to entropy, and so any value of zero for entropy would have to occur at lower temperatures. A considerable amount of experiment work at low temperatures, conducted at the turn of this century on the electromotive force of galvanic cells, led to the observation that, for reactions involving condensed systems, both ΔS and ΔC_P approach zero as the temperature is lowered.* This in turn led to a proposal which, for practical purposes, may be stated as follows: *The entropy of all pure, perfectly crystalline solids is zero at the absolute zero of temperature.* This statement, viz.

$$S_0 \text{ (s, pure, perfectly crystalline)} = 0 \qquad (3\text{-}1)$$

is known as the **third law of thermodynamics**, although the use of the word "law" in this connection has been questioned. The adjectives "pure" and "perfectly crystalline" are important in the statement, for the entropy of an *impure* crystalline solid at $0°K$ and the entropy of a pure *amorphous* solid at $0°K$ are not zero. The words "pure" and "perfectly crystalline" indicate not only chemical purity but the absence of crystal defects, including (frequently unavoidable) heterogeneities in the orientation of the molecules of the crystal lattice. It should be noticed that no mention of pressure is made in the third law. This is because the value of zero for entropy at $0°K$ is assigned at *all* pressures. Finally, a pure, perfectly crystalline solid need not be thermodynamically stable at $0°K$ in order that its entropy be zero.

Example 3-1 Between 0 and $60°K$ the heat capacity of Ag(s) is given approximately by the following expression: $\overline{C}_P$ (cal mole^{-1} deg^{-1}) $\pm 0.1 = -0.023T + 2.5(10^{-3})T^2 - 1.9(10^{-5})T^3$. (a) About how much more entropy has a mole of Ag(s) at $60°K$ than at $0°K$? (b) If, according to the third law, $S_{Ag(s)}$ is assigned a value of zero at $0°K$ what is its value at $60°K$?

Ans. (a) Since $(\partial S/\partial T)_P = C_P/T$, the increase in entropy resulting from the temperature rise is $\Delta \overline{S} = \overline{S}_{60} - \overline{S}_0 = \int_0^{60} \overline{C}_P dT = \int_0^{60} [(-0.23T + 0.0025T^2 - 0.000019T^3)/T] dT = 1.8$ eu mole^{-1} (cf. Examples 1-16 and 2-6).

(b) Since $\Delta \overline{S} = \overline{S}_{60} - \overline{S}_0 = 1.8$ eu mole^{-1} and $\overline{S}_0 = 0$, $\overline{S}_{60} = 1.8$ eu mole^{-1}.

---

*Known as the **Nernst heat theorem.**

Having agreed to call the entropy of pure solids zero at $0°K$, we are now in a position to evaluate absolute entropies. This idea has been illustrated in the preceding example. Since, in warming a pure solid from $0°$ to $T°K$ at constant pressure, $\Delta S = \int_0^T [C_P(s)/T]dT = \int_0^T C_P(s)\,d\ln T =$

$2.303 \int_0^T C_P(s)\,d\log T = S_T - S_0$, and since $S_0 = 0$, $\Delta S = S_T$. The integral may be evaluated by finding the area under the curve of $C_P(s)$ vs. $\log T$ between $T = 0$ and $T = T$, and multiplying it by 2.303, or by finding the area under the curve of $C_P(s)/T$ vs. T between the same limits (cf. Fig. 3-1). The fact that the first of these two plots extends to $-\infty$ is of no concern because the area below $15°K$ is actually evaluated by special means (see below). Since C_P depends strongly upon T at low temperatures, we must not remove it from the integrand. The integral can also be determined analytically, as in Example 3-1. If the $C_P(s)$'s refer to 1 mole then S_T refers to 1 mole. Entropies determined in this way are sometimes called **third law entropies** or **thermal entropies**, to distinguish them from values determined by statistical means.

The all-important experimental quantity in finding third law entropies is obviously the heat capacity. This is determined down to as low a temperature as possible. A common procedure is to obtain experimental C_P's down to about $15°K$ and then to use the "Debye third power rule," according to which $C_P \propto T^3$ or $C_P = aT^3$, where "a" is a constant below $15°K$. The value of "a" need not be known—it disappears as follows: we express the integral $\int_0^T (\overline{C}_P/T)dT$ as the sum of two parts, viz.

$$\int_0^{15} \frac{\overline{C}_P}{T}\,dT + \int_{15}^T \frac{\overline{C}_P}{T}\,dT = \overline{S}_{15} + \int_{15}^T \frac{\overline{C}_P}{T}\,dT.$$

However, we also have:

$$\overline{S}_{15} = \int_0^{15} \frac{aT^3}{T}\,dT = \int_0^{15} aT^2\,dT = \frac{aT^3}{3}\Big|_0^{15} = \frac{\overline{C}_P \text{ at } 15°K}{3}$$

Thus we obtain:

$$\overline{S}_T = \frac{\overline{C}_P \text{ at } 15°K}{3} + \int_{15}^T \frac{\overline{C}_P}{T}\,dT,$$

where the last integral is evaluated as already described.

It may be mentioned that the Debye rule can often be improved upon by the use of an additional term, giving $C_P = aT^3 + bT$ or $C_P/T = aT^2 + b$.

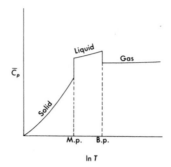

Fig. 3-1. Typical Heat Capacity—
Temperature Plot for Purposes of
Evaluating Absolute Entropy.

A plot of C_P/T vs. T^2 down to the lowest experimental values of C_P
then permits linear extrapolation to absolute zero and the prediction of
more reliable values of C_P at temperatures below those of direct measurement.

The above description is valid only for a pure, perfectly crystalline
solid. The restriction is implied that C_P does not show discontinuities
such as would arise if the solid underwent a transition at some temperature between 0 and $T°K$. For example, a transition from one crystalline
form to another would give $C_P = \infty$ at that temperature and so vitiate the
simple treatment above. As measurements of C_P are made at gradually
increasing temperatures most solids will eventually melt or even vaporize,
and C_P would again pass through infinity. It is still desirable, however,
to determine the absolute entropies of liquids and gases. We shall now
see how the above procedure is extended for this purpose.

Suppose, e.g., we wish to find the entropy of $Cl_2(g)$ at 298°K and 1
atm. At that pressure the melting point is 171°K and the boiling point
239°K. We imagine that $Cl_2(s)$ at 0°K and 1 atm is heated at constant
pressure until the temperature is 298°K, in the course of which the solid
melts at 171°K and vaporizes at 239°K, the entropy increasing meanwhile
from zero upwards. This entropy increase (ΔS) will thus be the required
entropy of $Cl_2(g)$. The value of ΔS will be given by the sum of the following entropy gains (temperatures are in °K): ΔS for heating $Cl_2(s)$ from
0 to 171°, ΔS for fusion at 171°, ΔS for heating $Cl_2(l)$ from 171 to 239°,
ΔS for vaporization at 239° and ΔS for heating $Cl_2(g)$ from 239 to 298°.
The heat of fusion of $Cl_2(s)$ is 1531 cal mole^{-1} at 171° and the heat of
vaporization is 4878 cal mole^{-1} at 239°, so the entropy gains in fusion
and vaporization are 1531/171 and 4878/239 eu mole^{-1}, respectively.
The total ΔS is given, therefore, by:

$$\int_0^{171} \frac{\overline{C}_P(s)}{T}\,dT + \frac{1531}{171} + \int_{171}^{239} \frac{\overline{C}_P(l)}{T}\,dT + \frac{4878}{239} + \int_{239}^{298} \frac{\overline{C}_P(g)}{T}\,dT$$

The first integral could be found with the help of the Debye rule, as already shown. These five terms turn out to have the following values, respectively: 16.9, 8.9, 5.2, 20.4, 1.8 eu mole^{-1}. The sum, 53.2 eu, is thus the absolute entropy of 1 mole of $Cl_2(g)$ at 298°K and 1 atm ($\overline{S}_{298}$). Notice that the major contribution occurs in the vaporization process (cf. Trouton's rule). It may be remarked that what is called the **standard entropy** of a gas at a given temperature is the value its entropy would have at 1 atm if it behaved as an ideal gas. Since $Cl_2(g)$ is not quite ideal the value 53.2 must be corrected slightly, by about +0.1 eu, to give the "standard entropy" of $Cl_2(g)$ at 298°K, $\overline{S}^{\circ}_{298}$, viz. 53.3 eu mole^{-1}. If $Cl_2(s)$ had undergone a polymorphic change, say from Form I to Form II, at some temperature, T_t, below its melting point, the first integral would have had to be replaced by

$$\int_0^{T_t} \frac{\overline{C}_P(\text{s, I})}{T}\, dT + \frac{\Delta \overline{H}_t}{T_t} + \int_{T_t}^{171} \frac{\overline{C}_P(\text{s, II})}{T}\, dT,$$

where $\Delta \overline{H}_t$ is the heat of the transition. Clearly, if we had wished for the entropy of liquid Cl_2 at 1 atm and some temperature T, we would then have used the following, assuming no polymorphism:

$$\overline{S}_T = \int_0^{171} \frac{\overline{C}_P(\text{s})}{T}\, dT + \frac{\Delta \overline{H}_f}{T} + \int_{171}^{T} \frac{C_P(\text{l})}{T}\, dT$$

Figure 3-1 shows a schematic plot of typical $\overline{C}_P$ vs. ln T relations for a substance which is successively solid, liquid and gaseous with rise in temperature at constant pressure. The integrals required for the evaluation of $\overline{S}$ are the areas under these curves within the appropriate limits. To these must be added any entropies of transition, as already indicated.

Now that we have shown how absolute entropies are found we may illustrate an obvious use of them.

Example 3-2 Find ΔS°_{298} for $Ti(s) + 2Cl_2(g) \longrightarrow TiCl_4(l)$ if the standard entropies at 25° of $Ti(s)$, $Cl_2(g)$ and $TiCl_4(l)$ are 7.2, 53.3 and 60.4 eu mole^{-1}, respectively.

Ans. $\Delta S^{\circ}_{298} = 60.4 - [7.2 + (2)(53.3)] = -53.4$ eu.

Note This is ΔS for the system only.

METASTABLE SOLIDS

The third law applies to metastable as well as to stable solids. We may illustrate by reference to sulfur, of which the rhombic form is stable from 0 to 369°K and the monoclinic stable from 369° to the melting point. The latter form, metastable below 369°, can, however, be cooled to near absolute zero without transforming to the rhombic form. In this metastable condition its heat capacity can be measured, and thus its entropy, at

369°, e.g., can be found from the expression

$$\int_0^{369} [\overline{C}_P(\text{s, monoclinic})/T]\,dT$$

since the third law applies to it in spite of its metastability. On the other hand, the same monoclinic state at 369° can be reached by warming the rhombic form from 0 to 369° and then permitting it to transform to the monoclinic at the latter temperature. Its entropy can thus also be calculated as follows:

$$\int_0^{369} [\overline{C}_P(\text{s, rhombic})/T]\,dT + \Delta \overline{H}_t/369$$

where $\Delta \overline{H}_t$ is the heat of transition. These two alternative expressions for $\overline{S}_{369}(\text{s, monoclinic})$ should be equal, i.e.,

$$\int_0^{369} \frac{\overline{C}_P(\text{s, monoclinic})}{T}\,dT = \int_0^{369} \frac{\overline{C}_P(\text{s, rhombic})}{T}\,dT + \frac{\Delta \overline{H}_t}{369}$$

The left-hand side has the value 9.04 and the right-hand side 8.83 + 0.26 = 9.09 eu mole^{-1}. Experimental confirmations such as this are common, and inspire further confidence in the third law.

COROLLARIES OF THE THIRD LAW

There are certain interesting corollaries of the third law. For example, since the entropy of a solid is zero at 0°K regardless of the pressure the entropy must be independent of pressure at that temperature, so $(\partial S/\partial P)_{T=0} = 0$. Since the volume depends only on pressure at 0°K, $(\partial S/\partial V)_{T=0} = 0$ too. Then, in view of Eqs. (2-8) and (2-9) mentioned in Chapter 2, but not yet derived, $-(\partial V/\partial T)_P$ and $(\partial P/\partial T)_V$ must also both be zero at 0°K. It follows that α, the coefficient of expansion, $(1/V)(\partial V/\partial P)_T$, is zero at that temperature.

There are still more corollaries. Since S for all pure solids becomes zero in the limit at 0°K, so must ΔS for reactions in all-solid systems. Furthermore, since $S_T = \int_0^T (C_P/T)\,dT$ is to remain finite as T approaches zero, C_P must also approach zero, and therefore so must ΔC_P for all-solid reactions. It follows that $(\partial \Delta H/\partial T)_P$ approaches zero. Observe, however, that ΔH does not. Finally, by analogous arguments, C_V, ΔC_V and $(\partial \Delta E/\partial T)_V$ all approach zero too, but ΔE does not.

Example 3-3 In connection with the change Sn(gray) $\longrightarrow$ Sn(white) consider the data of Table 3-1 and show that (a) ΔS and ΔC_P and (b) $(\partial \Delta S/\partial T)_P$ approach zero as T approaches 0°K.

TABLE 3-1

Temperature, °K	Sn(gray)		Sn(white)	
	$\bar{S}$ eu mole^{-1}	$\bar{C}_P$ cal deg^{-1} mole^{-1}	$\bar{S}$ eu mole^{-1}	$\bar{C}_P$ cal deg^{-1} mole^{-1}
10	0.12	0.36	0.14	0.45
20	0.29	0.84	0.36	1.1
50	1.9	2.7	2.7	3.7

Ans. (a) At 10° $\Delta S = 0.14 - 0.12 = 0.02$ and $\Delta C_P = 0.45 - 0.36 = 0.09$. At 20°, similarly, $\Delta S = 0.07$ and $\Delta C_P = 0.3$. At 50° $\Delta S = 0.8$ and $\Delta C_P = 1.0$. By inspection both ΔS and ΔC_P approach zero as 0° is approached. (b) Between 10 and 20° the average $(\partial \Delta S/\partial T)_P$ is $(0.07 - 0.02)/(20 - 10) = 0.005$. Between 20 and 50° the average $(\partial \Delta S/\partial T_P$ is $(0.8 - 0.07)/(50 - 20) = 0.02$. By inspection $(\partial \Delta S/\partial T)_P$ also approaches zero as 0° is approached.

STATISTICAL NATURE OF ENTROPY

Classical thermodynamics, the prime subject of this book, has been greatly illuminated in the last 50 years by the development of statistical thermodynamics—the application of statistical mechanics to thermodynamic concepts. The still more recent development of quantum mechanics has permitted a much further growth of the statistical approach, so that the two aspects, classical and statistical, are now quite complementary. The former deals with the experimental behavior of matter in bulk, and is completely phenomenological; the latter uses the properties of individual molecules obtained mostly by spectroscopic means to predict the statistical behavior of large numbers of them. To learn how a few spectroscopic measurements can give the same results as the classical thermal measurements is an exciting discovery, but we shall here refer to statistical thermodynamics only insofar as it has a bearing on the third law.

It will be recalled that an isolated system suffers an entropy increase if it is not already in its most stable state. If such a change is represented by A ⟶ B, we may confidently assume that B is a more probable state than A, and so realize that there should be some connection between entropy and probability. We recognize further that, in the light of everyday experience, a disordered state in an isolated system is a more probable one than an ordered state. Systems undergoing spontaneous changes often become more disordered. The final state of the isolated system is one of greater probability, greater entropy, than the initial state. Thus we are led to recognize entropy as a measure of probability. This is not to say, however, that entropy equals probability numerically, but that when entropy increases then so does probability. To relate the two we need a quantitative definition of probability. For our present purpose we shall define the **probability**, W, of a given state, as the number of ways of realizing that state. For example, in throwing a pair of dice, $W = 3$ for a throw of 4, since 4 can be thrown in three ways: $3 + 1$, $2 + 2$, $1 + 3$. Similarly $W = 6$ for a throw of 7, since 7 can be thrown in six ways: $6 + 1$, $5 + 2$, $4 + 3$, $3 + 4$, $2 + 5$, $1 + 6$. Thus a throw of 7 is twice as probable as a throw of 4. (Probability as used here is not the same as, but is proportional to, probability as used in mathematics, in which it is defined as the ratio of the number of favorable events to the total number of possible different events.) The student should be warned, however, that "the number of ways of realizing a given state" can be ambiguous, as will be illustrated later.

Let us review some elementary aspects of permutation theory, and ask the question, in how many ways can n_o distinguishable objects be distributed in n_c (distinguishable) cells, no more than one object to a cell, assuming that $n_c \geq n_o$? The first of the n_o objects can be placed in n_c possible locations, leaving $n_c - 1$ possible locations for the second object for *each* of the n_c choices for the first. There are thus $n_o(n_c - 1)$ ways of distributing the first two objects. For each of these ways there are $n_c - 2$ ways of distributing the third object, so there are $n_c(n_c - 1)(n_c - 2)$ ways of distributing the first three objects. Continuing in this way we conclude that the number of ways of distributing all n_o objects is $n_c(n_c - 1)(n_c - 2)(n_c - 3)\ldots(n_c - n_o + 1)$. If, however, the objects are indistinguishable, i.e. identical in appearance, etc., the number of distinguishable distributions will be fewer by a factor of $1/n_o!$, viz.

$$\frac{n_c(n_c - 1)(n_c - 2)(n_c - 3)\ldots(n_c - n_o + 1)}{n_o!}$$

For example, the distribution of 3 distinguishable objects, a, b, and c, in 4 boxes can be done in $4(3)(2) = 24$ ways, viz.

but, if the objects are indistinguishable (a = b = c) there are only $4(3)(2)/3(2)(1) = 4$ ways, viz.

Clearly, the matter of distinguishability is very important.

Let us now apply this idea to an ideal gas in a given state, where the volume of the gas as a whole may be imagined to consist of n_c cells, each just large enough to accommodate one molecule, and with n_0 of these cells occupied by n_0 molecules, one to a cell. As a gas is mostly empty space, $n_c \gg n_0$. Since the molecules are all alike they are indistinguishable: the number of ways of placing them in the cells will be, as before, $[n_c(n_c - 1)(n_c - 2)\dots(n_c - n_0 + 1)]/n_0!$. Here, however, since n_c is so very much larger than n_0, each of the factors in the numerator has virtually the same value. As there are n_0 factors, the numerator is effectively $n_c{}^{n_0}$, and the whole expression may be written $n_c{}^{n_0}/n_0!$ without appreciable error. Assuming that all the cells are equally accessible to each molecule this expression gives the probability, W, of the gas. (It must be added that this illustration of W is greatly oversimplified. Specifying the state of a gas specifies a fixed distribution of molecular energies, and we have ignored the differences of energies of the individual molecules. A more exact meaning for W, such as is necessary for a fuller comprehension of statistical thermodynamics, would have to include considerations of such differences. For the present purpose, however, we may imagine that the n_0 molecules which we are distributing are all average molecules. We may also observe that our choice of an ideal gas means that there is no potential energy—energy of a molecule by virtue of its position—to complicate the issue.)

Consider now an ideal gas expanding from a smaller volume V to a greater one, the total final volume being V'. There should be no temperature change as the gas is ideal. The probability of the gas in the initial volume V, which we shall call W, is $n_c{}^{n_0}/n_0!$, where n_0 is the number of molecules and n_c the number of cells in the volume V. Similarly the probability W' of the gas in volume V' is $n_c'{}^{n_0}/n_0!$. It follows that $W'/W = n_c'{}^{n_0}/n_c{}^{n_0} = (n_c'/n_c)^{n_0}$. The number of cells, however, is directly proportional to the volume, so $n_c'/n_c = V'/V$. Therefore $W'/W = (V'/V)^{n_0}$. Now the entropy increase suffered by n moles of gas in the (isothermal) expansion is, from Chapter 2, $\Delta S = nR \ln (V'/V)$. Since $n = n_0/N$, N being the Avogadro number, we have $\Delta S = (n_0/N) R \ln (V'/V) = n_0 k \ln (V'/V) = k \ln (V'/V)^{n_0}$, where k, the Boltzmann constant, is R/N. We thus have $\Delta S = k \ln (V'/V)^{n_0} = k \ln (W'/W)$, which is a quantitative relation between entropy and probability.

We now examine the above isothermal expansion of n moles or n_0 molecules of an ideal gas from an initial volume V to a (total) final volume V' from a different point of view. (The increase in volume is thus $V' - V$.) Let us visualize the state in which the volume V' is occupied by the n_0 molecules. Now the chance of finding any one of these molecules in the V portion of the whole volume V' is V/V'. If, e.g., $V' = 2V$ the chance is one-half. The chance of finding all n_0 molecules in the V portion is $(V/V')^{n_0}$, since probabilities are multiplicative. On the other hand, the chance of finding all n_0 molecules in the volume V' is unity (a dead certainty) since they must all be somewhere in that volume. Thus the ratio of the probability, W', of finding the gas in volume V', to the probability of finding it in volume V is $1 \div (V/V')^{n_0}$ or $(V'/V)^{n_0}$, so $W'/W =$

$(V'/V)^{n_o}$. The entropy increase is, however, $\Delta S = nR \ln (V'/V)$ which equals $k \ln (W'/W)$ as in the previous example. We have therefore reached the same conclusion as before, but have used a somewhat different meaning for probability.

These two approaches have been given to illustrate that W can have various meanings. Failure to recognize this can result in much difficulty. To say that the probability of a system is the number of ways in which it can be realized depends on what we mean by "ways." W', the probability of the gas in the final volume V', was $n_c'^{n_o}/n_o!$ in the first approach, a colossal number, whereas it was regarded as unity in the second approach. Nevertheless, for both, the ratio W'/W was the same and correctly equal to $(V'/V)^{n_o}$.

The relation $\Delta S = k \ln (W'/W)$ can be true only if $S = k \ln W$ + constant. Planck carried this an important step further by postulating the "constant" to be zero provided that W was given the correct meaning (described later). We shall use the symbol Ω (omega) for this "correct" W and call it the **thermodynamic probability**. The resulting expression,

$$S = k \ln \Omega \qquad (3\text{-}2)$$

is known as the **Boltzmann-Planck relation** and is one of the most fundamental of all scientific relationships. It may be observed that it is consistent with the fact that entropies are additive (for mechanical mixtures only, or for mixing quantities of identical substances in identical states) but probabilities are multiplicative: if two systems with entropies S_1 and S_2 are mixed the resulting entropy, $S_1 + S_2$, is $k \ln \Omega_1 + k \ln \Omega_2 = k \ln (\Omega_1 \Omega_2)$, so $\Omega_1 \Omega_2$ is the probability of the mixture.

A thorough discussion of thermodynamic probability, Ω cannot be presented here: it will suffice to indicate its meaning by some simple examples. We begin by considering the number of ways in which n distinguishable balls can be distributed in distinguishable boxes. (The balls, e.g., are all colored differently, and the boxes are all numbered.) All the boxes are supposed equally accessible to each ball. If we specify that there shall be n_1 balls in the first box, n_2 balls in the second, n_3 in the third, and so on, ($n = \Sigma \, n_i$ where i is the box number) then the number of different ways of making such a distribution is $n!/n_1!n_2!n_3! \ldots$, or $n!/\Pi n_i!$. Notice that this is the number of ways of making this particular distribution, not the number of distributions. Thus if we ask for the number of ways in which six balls can be distributed in four boxes so that the first box has two balls, the second has three, the third one and the fourth none, the answer is $6!/2! \, 3! \, 1! \, 0! = 60$ ways. (Note that $0! = 1$.)

If we now turn our consideration from the distribution of balls among boxes to the distribution of molecules among energy levels, we may say that there are 60 ways of assigning six distinguishable molecules to four energy levels such that in these levels there are respectively two, three, one and no molecules. Once again it is supposed that all the energy

levels are equally accessible to each molecule. But there is now an additional matter to consider, and that is the total energy of all the molecules—in other words, we are not only restricted by the number of molecules available for distribution, and by the energy levels available to the
molecules, but also by the total energy they have. To illustrate, let us
suppose that we have a hypothetical system of seven molecules distributed among four energy levels, which we shall designate as ground,
first excited, second excited and third excited states, respectively, these
levels having energies $\varepsilon_0 = 0$, $\varepsilon_1 = 1$, $\varepsilon_2 = 2$ and $\varepsilon_3 = 3$ ergs, respectively. Furthermore, let us suppose that the total energy is 3 ergs. If we
specify that there shall be five molecules in the ground state ($n_0 = 5$),
one molecule in the first excited state ($n_1 = 1$), one molecule in the second excited state ($n_2 = 1$), and none in the third excited state ($n_3 = 0$), we
note, first, that we have complied with the requirement that the total number of molecules is 7 ($= \Sigma n_i = 5 + 1 + 1 + 0$) and, secondly, that the total energy, E, is 3 ergs [$= \Sigma n_i \varepsilon_i = (5)(0) + (1)(1) + (1)(2) + (0)(3)$]. This
is a particular distribution:

$$n_0 = 5, \quad n_1 = 1, \quad n_2 = 1, \quad n_3 = 0. \tag{1}$$

It can be realized in $7!/5! \ 1! \ 1! \ 0! = 42$ ways. There are, however, two
other distributions which still comply with the requirements that $n = \Sigma n_i = 7$, $E = \Sigma n_i \varepsilon_i = 3$ ergs, viz.

$$n_0 = 6, \quad n_1 = 0, \quad n_2 = 0, \quad n_3 = 1 \quad \text{(realizable in 7 ways)} \tag{2}$$

$$n_0 = 4, \quad n_1 = 3, \quad n_2 = 0, \quad n_3 = 0 \quad \text{(realizable in 35 ways)} \tag{3}$$

There are thus three possible distributions, (1), (2) and (3), meeting all
the requirements. The thermodynamic probability, Ω, of this system,
which is the total number of ways of having $n = 7$ and $E = 3$ ergs, when
$\varepsilon_0 = 0$, $\varepsilon_1 = 1$, $\varepsilon_2 = 2$ and $\varepsilon_3 = 3$ ergs, is therefore $42 + 7 + 35 = 84$. Of
the three ways of distribution (1) can be realized in the greatest number
of ways and so is the most probable distribution, and the one expected to
be found in an actual system under these circumstances. Of the 84 ways
of realizing the system, 42 of them are ways of realizing the most probable distribution. From the Boltzmann-Planck relation the entropy of the
system would be given by

$$k \ln \Omega = 1.38(10^{-16}) \ln 84 = 6.1(10^{-16}) \text{ erg deg}^{-1}$$
$$= 1.46(10^{-23}) \text{ cal deg}^{-1} \text{ or eu}$$

Example 3-4 Using the symbols of the previous illustration determine
the most probable distribution and Ω for a system of eight molecules, with
a total energy of 4 ergs, where the available energy levels have 0, 1, 2,
3, 4, 5 ergs, respectively.

Ans.

Distribution	$\varepsilon_0 = 0$ n_0	$\varepsilon_1 = 1$ n_1	$\varepsilon_2 = 2$ n_2	$\varepsilon_3 = 3$ n_3	$\varepsilon_4 = 4$ n_4	$\varepsilon_5 = 5$ n_5	No. of ways
(1)	7	0	0	0	1	0	8
(2)	6	1	0	1	0	0	56
(3)	6	0	2	0	0	0	28
(4)	5	2	1	0	0	0	168[a]
(5)	4	4	0	0	0	0	70
							$\Omega = 330$

[a]The most probable distribution

Example 3-5 Repeat Example 3-4 for a total energy of 5 ergs. Has the increased availability of energy increased or decreased the probability of the system? the entropy?

Ans.

Distribution	$\varepsilon_0 = 0$ n_0	$\varepsilon_1 = 1$ n_1	$\varepsilon_2 = 2$ n_2	$\varepsilon_3 = 3$ n_3	$\varepsilon_4 = 4$ n_4	$\varepsilon_5 = 5$ n_5	No. of ways
(1)	7	0	0	0	0	1	8
(2)	6	1	0	0	1	0	56
(3)	6	0	1	1	0	0	56
(4)	5	2	0	1	0	0	168
(5)	5	1	2	0	0	0	168
(6)	4	3	1	0	0	0	280[a]
(7)	3	5	0	0	0	0	56
							$\Omega = 792$

[a]The most probable distribution

Increasing the available energy from 4 to 5 ergs has increased the probability of the system and therefore the entropy.

The systems described in the above illustration are, of course, hypothetical. In real systems one is dealing with a very large number of molecules, a very large number of available energy levels and (usually) an uneven spacing of the energy levels, rather than the uniform spacing (1 erg) of the illustration. There are also other complications such as the occurrence of **degeneracy** (several states with the same energy), which will not be considered. Quantum mechanics has provided much of the necessary information regarding the values of the various energy levels. Translational, rotational, vibrational, electronic and potential energies of interaction between molecules must all be considered in evaluating Ω.

STATISTICAL NATURE OF THE THIRD LAW

Our discussion of the statistical nature of entropy showed that the tendency of an isolated system to increase in entropy until equilibrium is reached corresponds to the attainment of the most probable state—the one for which Ω is a maximum under the given conditions. The second law of thermodynamics, as stated in the Clausius inequality, thus has a statistical basis through the Boltzmann-Planck relation $S = k \ln \Omega$. The third law, however, tells us that S for a pure, perfectly crystalline solid is zero at $0°K$. For this to be so, Ω for such a solid must be unity at that temperature. We are now in a position to see why this should be so.

In a perfect crystal at $0°K$ the structural units (molecules, atoms, ions) are in as perfectly ordered an arrangement as possible. Except for the unremovable zero-point energy of oscillation, there is no vibrational energy to disturb the orderliness, and there is no rotational or electronic energy. Every atom is in place. There are no defects. The number of ways in which such a state can be realized is one. (Although the molecules, atoms or ions are identical they are not considered indistinguishable since each one occupies a distinct site in the lattice, and interchange between pairs of sites is inadmissible.)

VISUAL COMPARISON OF ENTROPIES

The idea of entropy as a measure of probability permits certain generalizations to be made, particularly for ideal gases. Other things being equal, the molar entropy increases markedly with increase in volume, temperature, molecular weight and moment(s) of inertia. It also increases with the number of vibrational modes and decreases with increasing symmetry, rigidity and frequency of vibrational modes. In general, gases have more entropy than liquids, and liquids more entropy than solids. The entropy of vaporization of liquids is about 20 eu mole^{-1} at 1 atm (Trouton's rule). The entropy of fusion is considerably less than this. Molecular simplicity favors increase in entropy.

With these facts in mind one can often make satisfactory predictions as to which of two materials has the greater entropy. The following are given as illustrations (temperatures are taken to be about $298°K$ and pressures 1 atm):

(1) Xenon has a larger molar entropy than neon for it has the greater molecular weight. No other factors need be considered, since only translational energy is present.

(2) CO has slightly greater entropy than N_2. The molecular weights and moments of inertia are about the same but N_2 has more symmetry. There is usually little contribution from vibrational energy for diatomic gases at room temperature, except for the halogens.

(3) A gram atom of monatomic hydrogen has more entropy than half a mole of diatomic hydrogen (but less than that of a whole mole of diatomic hydrogen), the monatomic form being the simpler structure.

(4) n-Butane(g) has more entropy than isobutane(g)—the former has less symmetry and is a more "floppy" molecule (has greater probability).

(5) An equimolar mixture of $PCl_3(g)$ and $Cl_2(g)$ has more entropy than a mole of $PCl_5(g)$, the former being a "simpler form" of PCl_5.

(6) An equimolar mixture of CaO(s) and CO_2(g) has more entropy than a mole of calcite, $CaCO_3$(s), the former being a "simpler form" of $CaCO_3$.

Example 3-6 The entropy of 1 mole of Cl_2(g) at 298°K and 1 atm is 53.2 eu, and that of 2 g atoms of Cl(g) at 298°K and 2 atm is 76.2 eu. If the change Cl_2(g) $\longrightarrow$ 2Cl(g) were to take place under these conditions the volume would remain constant and the entropy of the system would increase by 76.2 − 53.2 = 23.0 eu. Why does Cl_2(g) at 298°K and 1 atm not dissociate spontaneously in an isolated system? (Assume ΔE to be 57 kcal at all temperatures.)

Ans. For the system to be isolated there must be no heat transfer to or from the surroundings, in addition to the stipulation of constant volume. Any dissociation of Cl_2(g) would require energy to break the Cl—Cl bonds, and this would have to come from the system itself, the temperature of which would therefore drop. In order to make a proper evaluation of the spontaneity in an isolated system one would therefore have to compare the entropy of Cl_2(g) at 298°K and 1 atm with the entropy of 2Cl(g) at whatever final temperature (and pressure) might result from the energy absorption. An absorption of 57,000 cal would cause such a drop in temperature that the entropy of the 2Cl would be lower than that of the Cl_2. The given change is thus forbidden in an isolated system.

PROBLEMS

1. For a certain substance A, $\overline{C}_p$ for the solid form is 0.195 cal deg^{-1} $mole^{-1}$ at 15°K. From this temperature to the normal melting point, 200°K, it varies with temperature (T°K) according to $\overline{C}_p(s) = 0.0085T + 0.00030T^2$ cal deg^{-1} $mole^{-1}$. For the liquid $\overline{C}_p(l) = 14.50 + 0.0043T$, and for the gas at 1 atm $\overline{C}_p(g) = 12.00$ cal deg^{-1} $mole^{-1}$. The heat of fusion is 1.800 kcal $mole^{-1}$. The heat of vaporization is 7.05 kcal $mole^{-1}$ at the normal boiling point, 300°K. Find the entropy of A(g) at 350°K and 0.5 atm, assuming it to be ideal.

2. (a) Find ΔS°_{298} and ΔS°_0 for Na(s) + KCl(s) $\longrightarrow$ K(s) + NaCl(s) if the standard entropies of Na(s), K(s), NaCl(s) and KCl(s) at 25° are 12.2, 15.2, 17.3 and 19.8 eu $mole^{-1}$, respectively.
   (b) Find q_{rev} at 298°K and 1 atm.
   (c) What, if anything, can be said about the spontaneity of this reaction at 298°K from the data given? Give reasons.

3. (a) Find the relation between α, the coefficient of expansion $[(1/V)(\partial V/\partial T)_P]$, β, the compressibility $[-(1/V)(\partial V/\partial P)_T]$ and the thermal pressure coefficient $[(\partial P/\partial T)_V]$.
   (b) Show that the third law tells us nothing about the limiting value of β for pure solids as temperature approaches 0°K.

4. Consider the mixing of N_A molecules of ideal gas A with N_B molecules of ideal gas B at a constant temperature. The pressure of each of the

original gases is the same as the total pressure of the final mixture. Following the kind of argument advanced on pp. 65 we may picture this as follows:

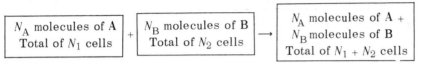

(a) Find the probabilities, W_A and W_B, of the unmixed gases and the probability, W_{AB}, of the mixture. Then determine ΔS for the mixing process from $\Delta S = k \ln W_{final} - k \ln W_{initial}$.

(b) Show that $\Delta S = -R(X_A \ln X_A + X_B \ln X_B)$ per mole of mixture formed, where X_A and X_B are the mole fractions of A and B in it.

5. Arrange the following in the expected order of increasing entropy at 298°K and 1 atm: *p*-xylene(g), ethylbenzene(g), *o*-xylene(g), ethylbenzene(l).

4

Work content and free energy— Maxwell relations

In this chapter we introduce the remaining thermodynamic functions and, with them, criteria of irreversibility which are more readily applied than the Clausius inequality. As a preliminary to doing so we first combine the first and second laws into a single statement.

The first law, $q = \Delta E + w$, becomes $Dq = dE + Dw$ for infinitesimal changes, and $Dq_{rev} = dE + Dw$ when they are reversible. The definition of entropy, $dS = Dq_{rev}/T$ or $Dq_{rev} = TdS$, may be combined with this to give:

$$TdS = dE + Dw \qquad (4\text{-}1)$$

for *reversible* changes at temperature T. The work Dw is really Dw_{max}.

Suppose, on the other hand, that the same change in the system be carried out *irreversibly* at the same temperature T. As proved in Chapter 2 for isothermal changes, Dw is now less than it was for the reversible process, although T, dE, and dS are the same. It follows that $TdS > dE + Dw$. The above two results are commonly indicated by:

$$TdS \geq dE + Dw \qquad (4\text{-}2)$$

where the equality refers to a reversible and the inequality to an irreversible process. Eq. (4-2) has been called the **fundamental equation of ther-**

modynamics because it embodies all that is important in the first and second laws.

For reversible processes at constant temperature, in which only *P-V* work is done, Eq. (4-1) becomes $TdS = dE + p_{ex}dV = dE + PdV$, or:

$$dE = TdS - PdV \qquad (4\text{-}3)$$

However, since $H = E + PV$, $dH = dE + PdV + VdP$, and combining this with Eq. (4-3) yields:

$$dH = TdS + VdP \qquad (4\text{-}4)$$

These relations will be referred to later.

We now observe that, for a system undergoing no entropy change $(dS = 0)$ and doing no work on the rest of the universe $(Dw = 0)$, Eq. (4-2) becomes $0 \geq dE$ or, more specifically:

$$dE_{S,V} \leq 0 \qquad (4\text{-}5)$$

This tells us that, entropy and volume being constant, energy strives for a minimum—another criterion of spontaneity, but one of little use to a chemist because the entropy is rarely constant in the changes with which he is dealing.

WORK CONTENT

To arrive at a more useful criterion we must first introduce two new thermodynamic functions. The first of these is the **work content**, or **maximum work function**, or **Helmholtz free energy**, denoted here and generally by the letter "*A*" (for "Arbeit," the German word for "work") and defined by

$$A = E - TS \qquad (4\text{-}6)$$

Since E and TS are dependent only on state, A must be a state function. Let us examine the implications of this definition. For any change, $\Delta A = \Delta E - \Delta(TS)$. For changes at constant temperature:

$$\Delta A = \Delta E - T\Delta S \qquad (4\text{-}7)$$

or

$$dA = dE - TdS \qquad \text{or} \qquad TdS = dE - dA. \qquad (4\text{-}8)$$

Combining this with Eq. (4-2) gives $dE - dA \geq dE + Dw$, or $-dA \geq Dw$. Therefore, for reversible changes, where the equality applies, $-dA = Dw$ or, since w is now w_{max}:

$$-dA = Dw_{max} \qquad \text{and} \qquad -\Delta A = w_{max} \text{ (constant } T) \qquad (4\text{-}9)$$

We thus arrive at the operational meaning of *A*: *that property of a system the decrease in which, for a given change at constant temperature, is a measure of the maximum work that could be done by the system for the given change.* We see now why it is called the maximum work function. Like all other thermodynamic functions ΔA is independent of the path or process used. Although, for isothermal changes, it may be evaluated by calculating $-w_{max}$ it is often more convenient to use Eq. (4-7), or Eq. (4-15) which is yet to be discussed, depending on available information.

By examining $A = E - TS$ or $E = A + TS$ we realize that the internal energy is the sum of two contributions, A and TS, A being that part of the energy which is available for doing work and TS that part which is not. We may call TS the "isothermally unavailable energy" and S the "isothermally unavailable energy per degree." Since the absolute value of E cannot be determined, neither can that of A.

Example 4-1 Find ΔA for O_2(g, 27°, 2 atm) $\longrightarrow O_2$(g, 27°, 1 atm), assuming that the gas is ideal.

Ans. Since the change is isothermal $-\Delta A = w_{max}$. But $w_{max} = nRT \ln (P_1/P_2) = 1(1.987)(300) \ln (2/1) = 414$ cal. Therefore $\Delta A = -414$ cal.

Note This is the value of ΔA regardless of the process used to carry out the given change.

Example 4-2 For the combustion of benzene, C_6H_6(l) $+ 7\frac{1}{2}O_2$(g) $\longrightarrow$ $6CO_2$(g) $+ 3H_2O$(l); $\Delta H^\circ_{298.2} = -780,980$ cal. If 1 mole of benzene(l) and $7\frac{1}{2}$ moles of O_2(g) at 25° and 1 atm react completely in a bomb of fixed volume to give 6 moles of CO_2(g) and 3 moles of H_2O(l) at 25° find $\Delta A_{298.2}$ for the change. The standard entropies of C_6H_6(l), O_2(g), CO_2(g) and H_2O(l) are 41.30, 49.00, 51.06 and 16.72 eu mole^{-1}, respectively, at 298.2°K.

Ans. $\Delta A = \Delta E - T\Delta S$ is applicable to this change for it is isothermal. We must determine ΔE and $T\Delta S$. Now $\Delta H = \Delta E + \Delta n_{gases}RT$, so $-780,980 = \Delta E_{298.2} - (3/2)(1.987)(298.2)$, giving $\Delta E_{298.2} = -780,090$ cal. In finding ΔS we must recognize that the pressure of the products is different from that of the reactants: the CO_2(g) and H_2O(l) are not under a pressure of 1 atm. Now the entropy of liquids is relatively unaffected by changes in pressure, so we take that of the H_2O(l) to be 16.72 eu mole^{-1} even at the new pressure. However the entropy of the CO_2(g) will be affected. Since its pressure is $6/7.5 = 0.8$ rather than 1 atm, its molar entropy will be $51.06 + R \ln (1.0/0.8)$ (cf. Eq. (2-4)) or $51.06 + 0.44 = 51.50$ eu mole^{-1}. This gives ΔS(for the reaction, substances only) = $[6(51.50) + 3(16.72)] - [1(41.30) + 7.5(49.00)] = -49.64$ eu. Therefore $\Delta A = -780,090 - (298.2)(-49.64) = -765,290$ cal.

Note Although $w_{max} = 765,290$ cal, $w = 0$.

Example 4-3 One mole of neon, for which $\overline{C}_V$ is 2.980 cal deg^{-1} mole^{-1}, is heated at constant volume from 298 to 398°K. If its standard entropy at 298°K is 34.95 eu mole^{-1} find ΔE, ΔS and ΔA.

Ans. $\Delta E = C_V \Delta T = 2.980(100) = 298$ cal. $\Delta S = n\overline{C}_V \ln (T_2/T_1) = 1(2.980) \ln (398/298) = 0.863$ eu $= \overline{S}_{398} - 34.95$, so $\overline{S}_{398} = 35.81$ eu mole^{-1}. Therefore $\Delta A = \Delta E - \Delta(TS) = 298 - [398(35.81) - 298(34.95)] = -3540$ cal.

In the discussion leading to Eq. (4-9) we saw that, for isothermal changes, $-dA \geq Dw$. If we specify further that no work whatsoever be done during this spontaneous change—this would also require that the volume of the system remain constant—then we have:

$$dA_{V, T} \leq 0 \qquad (4\text{-}10)$$

(The specification of constant volume in this way is taken conventionally to mean that no work whatsoever is done, even though one could, it is true, by a suitable arrangement, perform electrical work without change in volume.) This tells us that, in any irreversible process at constant volume and constant temperature, in which no work is done, A must decrease. If the change is reversible A remains constant. It is the work content of the system that is being referred to here, and not that of the environment, so the application of this criterion does not require us to involve the surroundings in our calculations. We see here an improvement over the criterion $dS_{E, V} > 0$ of Chapter 2. Nevertheless the restriction of constant volume in Eq. (4-10) is a severe one: in many reactions the volume does change, even though the temperature does not. The value of ΔA for the combustion of benzene in Example 4-2 was < 0 and, since the reaction was at constant volume, we can say immediately that the change was a spontaneous one. On the other hand, in Example 4-3, although the volume was constant and $\Delta A < 0$, we know nothing of the spontaneity of the change, for the temperature did not remain constant.

Example 4-4 Suppose the change in Example 4-3 occurred as the result of placing the container of neon in thermal contact with a large heat reservoir at 398°K. Show that the change is now known to be spontaneous.

Ans. $\Delta S_{gas} = 0.863$ eu as before; ΔS_{surr} = heat absorbed by surroundings/398 = $-298/398$ = -0.749 eu. Therefore $\Delta S_{total} = 0.869 - 0.749 = 0.120$ eu, which is > 0, and so the change is a spontaneous one.

Before leaving the discussion of work content one other relation involving A may be derived: since $A = E - TS$, $dA = dE - TdS - SdT$. For reversible processes involving only P-V work we may combine this with Eq. (4-3) to give:

$$dA = -PdV - SdT \qquad (4\text{-}11)$$

FREE ENERGY

The last thermodynamic function to be introduced is the **free energy**, or **Gibbs free energy**, or **Gibbs function**, or **free enthalpy**, denoted here by G (for "Gibbs"). (The symbol F, for "free," is also in common use, but most current texts use G.) When referring to one mole of pure substance it is called the molar free energy or chemical potential and given the symbol $\overline{G}$ or μ. These terms are also applied, with some modification, to substances in solution. (We shall postpone use of the term "chemical potential" and the symbol μ until solutions are considered in Chapter 6.)

The free energy is defined by:

$$G = H - TS \tag{4-12}$$

Since H and TS are functions of state, so is G, and therefore ΔG is independent of path. For any change $\Delta G = \Delta H - \Delta(TS)$, and for changes at constant temperature T, the following relation applies:

$$\Delta G = \Delta H - T\Delta S \qquad \text{or} \qquad dG = dH - TdS \tag{4-13}$$

Now from Eq. (4-12), since $H = E + PV$, we obtain:

$$G = E + PV - TS = A + PV \tag{4-14}$$

For changes at constant pressure $dG = dA + PdV$, or $-dA = -dG + PdV$, or we have:

$$\Delta A = \Delta G - P\Delta V \quad (P = \text{constant}) \tag{4-15}$$

If T is also constant, $-dA = Dw_{\max}$ so, when $P = p_{\text{ex}}$, $Dw_{\max} = -dG + p_{\text{ex}}dV$ or we have the following expression:

$$w_{\max} = -\Delta G + p_{\text{ex}}\Delta V \quad (P = p_{\text{ex}} = \text{constant}, T = \text{constant}) \tag{4-16}$$

Thus for isothermal changes at constant pressure, with $P = p_{\text{ex}}$, $-dG$ is that portion of the maximum work which is not P-V work. We have then the following operational meaning of free energy: it is *that property of a system the decrease in which is a measure of the maximum work, excluding P-V work, which can be accomplished in a given change at constant temperature and pressure when $P = p_{\text{ex}}$.* For this reason the free energy decrease, $-\Delta G$, is known as the **net work** or the **maximum useful work** of the change. (The last mentioned is a misleading term, however, for it suggests that P-V work is useless. The operation of the internal combustion engine, in which work of expansion plays such an important role is hardly useless!) The term "affinity" is also occasionally applied to $-\Delta G$, for reasons which will be apparent later.

The relations between E, H, A and G, embodied in Eqs. (1-6), (4-6), (4-12), and (4-14) may be represented schematically by Fig. 4-1, which is useful as a mnemonic (et. C. C. Coffin, *J. Chem. Educ.*, **23**, 584 (1946)).

Example 4-5 Find ΔG for $O_2(g, 27°, 2 \text{ atm}) \longrightarrow O_2(g, 27°, 1 \text{ atm})$.

Ans. $\Delta G = \Delta H - T\Delta S$, since the temperature is constant. But $\Delta H = 0$ and $\Delta S = R \ln(V_2/V_1) = 1.99 \ln 2 = 1.38$ eu. Therefore $\Delta G = 0 - (300)(1.38) = -414$ cal.

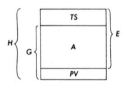

Fig. 4-1

Note Alternatively we could have solved the problem as follows: $\Delta A = \Delta G + \Delta(PV)$ or $\Delta G = \Delta A - \Delta(PV) = -w_{max} - \Delta(PV)$ since T is constant. However, $\Delta(PV) = 0$ for isothermal changes in ideal gases, and $w_{max} = nRT \ln (V_2/V_1) = 1(1.99)(300) \ln 2 = 414$ cal. Therefore $\Delta G = -414 - 0 = -414$ cal as before. (We shall encounter still another method later in this chapter using Eq. (4-28).)

Example 4-6 For $C_6H_6(l) + 7\frac{1}{2}O_2(g) \longrightarrow 6CO_2(g) + 3H_2O(l)$ find $\Delta G^{\circ}_{298.2}$ and q_{rev} at $298.2°K$, using the data given in Example 4-2.

Ans. $\Delta G = \Delta H - T\Delta S$, since the temperature is constant. But $\Delta H^{\circ}_{298.2} = -780,980$ cal and $\Delta S = [6(51.06) + 3(16.72)] - [41.30 + 7\frac{1}{2}(49.00)] = -52.28$ eu. Therefore $\Delta G^{\circ}_{298.2} = -780,980 - (298.2)(-52.28) = -765,390$ cal. $q_{rev} = T\Delta S = (298.2)(-52.28) = -15,590$ cal.

Example 4-7 Compute ΔG for the change $H_2(g, 298°K, 1 \text{ atm}) \longrightarrow H_2(g, 323°K, 2 \text{ atm})$, given that $H_2(g)$ is ideal, that its $\overline{C}_P$ is constant at 6.90 cal deg^{-1} mole^{-1} over this temperature range, and that $\overline{S}_{298}$ for $H_2(g)$ is 31.21 eu mole^{-1}.

Ans. Since $\Delta G = \Delta H - \Delta(TS)$ we need to know the absolute entropy of both the initial and final states. As this is given for the initial state it is convenient to find it for the final state by first finding ΔS. Now by Eq. (2-4) $\Delta S = 1.987 \ln (1/2) + 6.90 \ln (323/298) = -0.820$ eu. Therefore $\overline{S}$ for $H_2(g, 323°K, 2 \text{ atm}) = 31.21 - 0.82 = 30.39$ eu. Furthermore $\Delta H = C_P \Delta T = 6.90(25) = 172$ cal. Hence $\Delta G = \Delta H - \Delta(TS) = 172 - [323(30.39) - 298(31.21)] = -348$ cal.

For isobaric changes Eq. (4-15) permits the direct calculation of ΔA from ΔG, or ΔG from ΔA. Since only gases contribute appreciably to ΔV we may write $P\Delta V \sim \Delta n_{gases}RT$ (cf. derivation of Eq. (1-17)) to give $\Delta A = \Delta G - \Delta n_{gases}RT$.

Example 4-8 Given that $\Delta G^{\circ}_{298.2} = -765.39$ kcal for:

$$C_6H_6(l) + 7\frac{1}{2}O_2(g) \longrightarrow 6CO_2(g) + 3H_2O(l)$$

find $\Delta A^{\circ}_{298.2}$.

Ans. The free energy decrease is 765.39 kcal when all substances are at 1 atm. This is therefore an isobaric process and so Eq. (4-15) applies. Substitution in $\Delta A = \Delta G - \Delta n_{gases}RT$ gives $\Delta A^{\circ}_{298.2} = -765,390 - (-3/2)(1.987)(298.2) = -764,500$ cal.

Note ΔG must be in calories if R is in calories. Compare this example with Example 4-2.

The last and most useful criterion of spontaneity may now be obtained readily as follows. Differentiation of Eq. (4-14) gives $dG = dE + PdV + VdP - TdS - SdT$, or $TdS = dE + PdV + VdP - SdT - dG$. However, when only P-V work is done, Eq. (4-2) can be written:

$$TdS \geq dE + p_{ex}dV \qquad \text{(only } P\text{-}V \text{ work)} \qquad (4\text{-}17)$$

and, if $P = p_{ex}$ this becomes:

$$TdS \geq dE + PdV \qquad \text{(only } P\text{-}V \text{ work, } P = p_{ex}) \qquad (4\text{-}18)$$

We thus have

$$dE + PdV + VdP - SdT - dG \geq dE + PdV$$

or

$$VdP - SdT \geq dG$$

or

$$dG \leq VdP - SdT \qquad \text{(only } P\text{-}V \text{ work, } P = p_{ex}) \qquad (4\text{-}19)$$

For reversible processes, therefore, we have:

$$dG = VdP - SdT \qquad \text{(only } P\text{-}V \text{ work, } P = p_{ex}) \qquad (4\text{-}20)$$

for irreversible processes,

$$dG < VdP - SdT \qquad \text{(only } P\text{-}V \text{ work, } P = p_{ex}) \qquad (4\text{-}21)$$

and, for all processes at constant temperature and constant pressure,

$$dG_{P,T} \leq 0 \qquad \text{(only } P\text{-}V \text{ work, } P = p_{ex}) \qquad (4\text{-}22)$$

This highly important relation tells us that, in irreversible processes at constant pressure and temperature, in which only P-V work is done, and in which $P = p_{ex}$, the free energy strives for a minimum, whereas in a reversible process under the same conditions the free energy remains constant for an infinitesimal change. When finite quantities are involved Eq. (4-22) becomes:

$$\Delta G_{P,T} \leq 0 \qquad \text{(only } P\text{-}V \text{ work, } P = p_{ex}) \qquad (4\text{-}23)$$

Before illustrating this relation we observe that both it and Eq. (4-10) involve directly only the thermodynamic functions of the system and not those of the surroundings. This is why these criteria are more convenient than Eq. (2-10) which involves the entropy of the system *and* the surroundings. Furthermore Eq. (4-22) is, in turn, more convenient than Eq. (4-10), for changes at constant pressure are more common than changes at constant volume. It is true that the temperature usually changes during the course of the reaction but we are here interested primarily in comparing the stabilities of the reactants and products at the same temperature (usually about 25°) and at the same pressure (about 1 atm). We see now why $-\Delta G$ is a measure of "affinity," for its sign and magnitude indicate the relative stabilities of the initial and final states. We also see why G is termed chemical potential: a spontaneous change in the direction of lower free energy corresponds to a drop from a system at higher chemical potential to one of lower.

One other point should be mentioned. The fact that the surroundings do not appear explicitly in Eqs. (4-10) and (4-22) must not mislead one into thinking that he can disregard the environment. Rather, the environment has entered the result disguised: the conditions of constant volume and temperature for Eq. (4-10) and of constant pressure and temperature for Eq. (4-22), as well as the restriction of w to P-V work and the equality of P and p_{ex}, are really restrictions imposed on the surroundings.

Example 4-9 Apply the free energy criterion (Eq. (4-22)), where possible, to Examples 4-5, 4-6, and 4-7, and draw conclusions as to the spontaneity or lack of it of the changes indicated.

Ans. The free energy criterion, $\Delta G_{P,T} < 0$, cannot be applied to the changes of Example 4-5 or 4-7, for in neither were both P and T constant. In Example 4-6, however, we may say that the mixture $6CO_2(g)$ and $3H_2O(l)$ at $25°$ and 1 atm is more stable than the mixture $C_6H_6(l)$ and $7\frac{1}{2}O_2(g)$ at $25°$ and 1 atm, and that the former mixture should be formed from the latter under conditions where no work other than P-V work is done, the temperature and pressure remaining constant.

Example 4-10 (a) Given that for $2C(\text{graphite}) + H_2(g) \longrightarrow C_2H_2(g)$, $\Delta H°_{298.2} = 54.194$ kcal, $\Delta S°_{298.2} = 14.064$ eu and for $6C(\text{graphite}) + 3H_2(g) \longrightarrow C_6H_6(l)$, $\Delta H°_{298.2} = 11.718$ kcal, $\Delta S°_{298.2} = -60.50$ eu, find $\Delta G°_{298.2}$ for $3C_2H_2(g) \longrightarrow C_6H_6(l)$.
(b) Which of the following is the least and which the most stable at $298.2°K$ and 1 atm: (i) a mixture of 6 g atoms of $C(\text{graphite})$ and 3 moles of $H_2(g)$, (ii) 3 moles of $C_2H_2(g)$, (iii) 1 mole of $C_6H_6(l)$?

Ans. (a) For $2C(\text{graphite}) + H_2(g) \longrightarrow C_2H_2(g)$, $\Delta G°_{298.2} = 54,194 - (298.2)(14.064) = 50,000$ cal. For $6C(\text{graphite}) + 3H_2(g) \longrightarrow C_6H_6(l)$, $\Delta G°_{298.2} = 11,718 - (298.2)(-60.50) = 29,759$ cal. Multiplying the first of these equations by 3 gives $6C(\text{graphite}) + 3H_2(g) \longrightarrow 3C_2H_2(g)$, $\Delta G°_{298.2} = 150,000$ cal. Subtracting this from the other one gives $3C_2H_2(g) \longrightarrow C_6H_6(l)$, $\Delta G°_{298.2} = -120,241$ cal.
(b) We see that $C_6H_6(l)$ is more stable than $3C_2H_2(g)$ under these conditions. But $6C(\text{graphite}) + 3H_2(g)$ is more stable than $C_6H_6(l)$. $3C_2H_2(g)$ is thus the least stable of the three and the mixture $6C(\text{graphite}) + 3H_2(g)$ is the most stable.

Note The above stabilities are thermodynamic ones but do not tell us how readily acetylene transforms into benzene or benzene into its elements. Nevertheless thermodynamics predicts the possibility of converting acetylene into benzene at room temperature should some way be found to increase the reaction rate, e.g., by a suitable catalyst. It also predicts the impossibility of benzene decomposing into acetylene.

COUPLED REACTIONS

It often happens that the spontaneous formation of a certain product from a certain reactant is forbidden thermodynamically but that the change can be made to become spontaneous by coupling it with another spontaneous change. For example, suppose we wish to make $CuSO_4(aq)$ from $Cu(s)$ and $H_2SO_4(aq)$. We know that the following change is forbidden at $25°$:

$$Cu(s) + H_2SO_4(aq) \longrightarrow CuSO_4(aq) + H_2(g)$$

since $\Delta G_{298}^{\circ} = +15.5$ kcal. However, by coupling this change to:

$$2H_2(g) + O_2(g) \longrightarrow 2H_2O(l)$$

for which $\Delta G_{298}^{\circ} = -113.4$ kcal, in such a way as to eliminate hydrogen, i.e., by doubling the first equation and adding it to the second, we obtain:

$$2Cu(s) + 2H_2SO_4(aq) + O_2(g) \longrightarrow 2CuSO_4(aq)$$

$$+ 2H_2O(l), \quad \Delta G_{298}^{\circ} = -82.4 \text{ kcal.}$$

This tells us that, in the presence of $O_2(g)$, Cu will dissolve in dilute H_2SO_4 to give $CuSO_4(aq)$. The obvious requirement is that the second change have a more negative ΔG than the forbidden change has positive, so that the sum of the two ΔG's is negative. It is evident that while in this way we accomplish the objective of making $CuSO_4(aq)$ from Cu(s) and $H_2SO_4(aq)$ we do so at the expense of $O_2(g)$.

ΔG IN RELATION TO ΔH AND ΔS

The relation $\Delta G = \Delta H - T\Delta S$ (Eq. (4-13)) for isothermal changes is worthy of closer examination. We may first observe that, by expressing it as $-\Delta G/T = -\Delta H/T + \Delta S$, we can relate the free energy criterion, $\Delta G_{P,T} \leq 0$, to the entropy criterion, $\Delta S_{E,V} \geq 0$. Now ΔS in Eq. (4-13) is the entropy increase in the *system* and $-\Delta H$ is $-q$, if we are discussing a change in which only P-V work is permitted and in which $P = p_{ex} = $ constant. We may therefore rewrite $-\Delta G/T = -\Delta H/T + \Delta S$ as $-\Delta G/T = -q/T + \Delta S$. The first term on the right is the same as ΔS_{surr} in these circumstances (cf. Chapter 2), so the whole right-hand side represents ΔS_{total} under these conditions. We may say then that $-\Delta G/T = \Delta S_{total}$, so that the criterion $\Delta S_{total} \geq 0$, is equivalent to $\Delta G/T \leq 0$ at constant P and T, or $\Delta G_{P,T} \leq 0$, since $T > 0$. The above argument may be taken as an alternative proof of the free energy criterion.

The full significance of $\Delta G = \Delta H - T\Delta S$ should be appreciated. For changes at constant P and T the spontaneity, or sign of ΔG, will depend on the absolute values of ΔH and ΔS. Now ΔH represents an energy change—it includes any change in internal energy and any work done by or on the surroundings; ΔS is the change in "probability." Other things being equal energy strives for a minimum; other things being equal entropy strives for a maximum. If, for a given change, $\Delta H < 0$ and $\Delta S > 0$, both strivings are being satisfied—this will make $\Delta G < 0$. If $\Delta H > 0$ and $\Delta S < 0$ both strivings are being resisted—this will make $\Delta G > 0$. If ΔH and ΔS have the *same* sign then the sign of ΔG will depend on the relative numerical values of ΔH and $T\Delta S$. Quite commonly $|\Delta H| > |T\Delta S|$ so that the sign of ΔH will determine the sign of ΔG. Less frequently $|\Delta H| < |T\Delta S|$—this will occur when $|\Delta H|$ is small and/or T is large. The fact that $|\Delta H|$ frequently *is* larger than $|T\Delta S|$ is what led to the early erroneous idea that the heat of reaction was a measure of affinity.

Example 4-11 Using the data given, determine which of the changes presented below are obviously spontaneous or forbidden according to the signs and magnitudes of ΔH and ΔS. Determine by calculation which of the remaining are spontaneous or forbidden.

(i) $\frac{1}{2}H_2(g) + \frac{1}{2}I_2(s) \longrightarrow HI(g)$, at $298\,°K$ and 1 atm,
   $\Delta H^\circ_{298} = 6,200$ cal, $\Delta S^\circ_{298} = 19.7$ eu.

(ii) $C_6H_6(l) + 7\frac{1}{2}O_2(g) \longrightarrow 6CO_2(g) + 3H_2O(l)$, at $298\,°K$ and 1 atm,
   $\Delta H^\circ_{298} = -780,980$ cal, $\Delta S^\circ_{298} = -52.28$ eu.

(iii) $C_6H_6(l) \longrightarrow 3C_2H_2(g)$, at $298\,°K$ and 1 atm,
   $\Delta H^\circ_{298} = 150,864$ cal, $\Delta S^\circ_{298} = 102.69$ eu.

(iv) $C(graphite) + \frac{1}{2}O_2(g) \longrightarrow CO(g)$ at $298\,°K$ and 1 atm,
   $\Delta H^\circ_{298} = -26,420$ cal, $\Delta S^\circ_{298} = 21.44$ eu.

(v) $CO(g) + H_2O(g) \longrightarrow CO_2(g) + H_2(g)$
   $\Delta H^\circ_{298.2} = -9,838$ cal, $\Delta S^\circ_{298.2} = -10.135$ eu.

(vi) $CO(g) + H_2O(g) \longrightarrow CO_2(g) + H_2(g)$
   $\Delta H^\circ_{1200} = -7,870$ cal, $\Delta S^\circ_{1200} = -7.075$ eu.

Ans. (iv) is obviously spontaneous for $\Delta H < 0$ and $\Delta S > 0$.
(ii) is spontaneous too. Even though ΔH and ΔS have the same sign ΔH is so large that the sign of ΔH is the sign of ΔG.
(iii) is forbidden. Again ΔH and ΔS have the same sign but ΔH is large and so its sign determines the sign of ΔG.
(i) $\Delta G = 6200 - (298)(19.7) = 330$ cal, so the change is forbidden. The smallness of ΔH makes this less obvious by inspection.
(v) $\Delta G = -9838 - (298.2)(-10.135) = -6816$ cal, so the change is spontaneous.
(vi) $\Delta G = -7870 - (1200)(-7.075) = 620$ cal, so the change is forbidden. The large value of T has increased the importance of the $T\Delta S$ term over what it was in (v).

METHODS OF FINDING ΔG

ΔG may be calculated from other suitably chosen ΔG's exactly as was done for ΔH in Chapter 1. The described states of the substances may be hypothetical, e.g., $H_2O(g, 298\,°K, 1$ atm). The **standard free energy of formation** of a substance, ΔG°_f, often with a subscript indicating the temperature in °K, is the value of ΔG when one mole of that substance is formed from its elements in their stable states at the same temperature, the compound and elements all being at a pressure of 1 atm. Once again we note that, where gases are involved, the superscript zero implies not only a pressure of 1 atm but also ideal gas behavior. The manner of correcting G at 1 atm to G° will be shown in Chapter 5. In Example 4-11, $\Delta G^\circ_{298} = 330$ cal is the standard free energy of formation of $HI(g)$ at $25°$. Standard free energies of formation are obviously zero for the elements themselves in their stable states. (In this connection note that ΔG°_f for

$I_2(g)$ at 25° is *not* zero, for the stable state of iodine at 25° and 1 atm is $I_2(s)$.) As shown for ΔH, the value of ΔG in any given isothermal change is:

$$\Delta G = \sum_{\text{products}} \Delta G_f - \sum_{\text{reactants}} \Delta G_f$$

Free energy equations may be added, subtracted, etc., as is done with thermochemical equations.

Example 4-12 Find $\Delta G^{\circ}_{298.2}$ for eq. (ii) of Example 4-11 if the standard free energies of formation of $C_6H_6(l)$, $CO_2(g)$ and $H_2O(l)$ are 29.756, −94.260 and −56.690 kcal mole^{-1}, respectively, at 25°.

Ans. $\Delta G^{\circ}_{298.2} = 6(-94.260) + 3(-56.690) - 1(29.756) + 7\frac{1}{2}(0) = -765.386$ kcal.

Note $C_6H_6(l)$ is one of the comparatively few substances for which $\Delta G^{\circ}_f > 0$ at room temperature.

In addition to finding ΔG's from tabulations of ΔG_f's they may be found from tabulations of the **free energy function** to be described later in this chapter.

The above illustration of finding ΔG is not a direct experimental method: it presupposes the availability of values of ΔG_f. The same applies to finding ΔG from $\Delta H - T\Delta S$ using tabulated values of ΔH_f and S for the various substances in the equation. Experimentally, however, there are three principal methods of finding ΔG directly: (1) from direct experimental measurements of ΔH and S, (2) from measurements of equilibrium constant and (3) from measurements of emf, when applicable. Methods (2) and (3) will be described in later chapters. Method (1) is a "purely thermal method," for not only is ΔH measured calorimetrically but each S is found by the third law method which requires heat capacity experiments again with a calorimeter. The calculation of ΔG from ΔH and absolute entropies has been illustrated in Example 4-6.

THE MAXWELL RELATIONS

Let us re-examine Eqs. (4-3), (4-4), (4-11), and (4-20), viz.

$$dE = -PdV + TdS \qquad (4\text{-}3)$$

$$dH = TdS + VdP \qquad (4\text{-}4)$$

$$dA = -SdT - PdV \qquad (4\text{-}11)$$

$$dG = VdP - SdT \qquad (4\text{-}20)$$

for systems in equilibrium with their environment (which includes the condition $P = p_{ex}$), undergoing reversible changes, and excluding all forms of work except P-V work. Their validity is also confined to closed systems—as indeed do all the relations discussed so far in this book. They lead in turn to numerous other relations. For example Eq. (4-3) tells us that $(\partial E/\partial V)_S = -P$, $(\partial E/\partial S)_V = T$ and $(\partial S/\partial V)_E = P/T$. We note that, since P and T are both > 0, entropy increases with energy at constant volume and increases with volume at constant energy. We have had occasion to observe this in Eq. (2-5) for the change in entropy of an ideal gas undergoing a change in both temperature and volume, and again in Example 3-5.

Now dE, dH, dA, and dG are all exact differentials, so we may apply the **property of reciprocity** (or the **Euler criterion**) to show immediately:

$$(\partial - \dot{P}/\partial S)_V = (\partial T/\partial V)_S \quad \text{or} \quad (\partial S/\partial P)_V = -(\partial V/\partial T)_S \quad (4\text{-}24)$$

$$(\partial T/\partial P)_s = (\partial V/\partial S)_P \quad \text{or} \quad (\partial S/\partial V)_P = (\partial P/\partial T)_S \quad (4\text{-}25)$$

$$(\partial - S/\partial V)_T = (\partial - P/\partial T)_V \quad \text{or} \quad (\partial S/\partial V)_T = (\partial P/\partial T)_V \quad (4\text{-}26)$$

$$(\partial V/\partial T)_P = (\partial - S/\partial P)_T \quad \text{or} \quad (\partial S/\partial P)_T = -(\partial V/\partial T)_P, \quad (4\text{-}27)$$

giving us still another set of relationships. Eqs. (4-24) through (4-27) are known as the **Maxwell relations**. Eq. (4-26), also known as the **Clapeyron equation**, and Eq. (4-27) will be seen to be identical to Eqs. (2-8) and (2-9) introduced earlier without proof.

It must be realized that the four expressions for the total differentials of E, H, A, and G and those relations obtainable directly therefrom, although restricted to reversible changes, are not only of academic importance. Integration of Eq. (4-26), e.g., to give $\int_{S_1}^{S_2} dS = \int_{V_1}^{V_2} (\partial P/\partial T)_V dV$ yields a value of ΔS for a given isothermal volume change which is independent of how that change is carried out.

We now illustrate how the Maxwell relations may be used by an example based on Eq. (4-27).

Example 4-13 The coefficient of expansion of $CCl_4(l)$ is 0.00124 deg^{-1}, and its molar volume is 97.1 cm^3 mole^{-1} at 25° and 1 atm. (a) By how much does the molar entropy of $CCl_4(l)$ change for an increase in pressure of 20 atm at 25°? (b) If the entropy is 51.25 eu mole^{-1} at 25° and 1 atm what is the entropy at 25° and 20 atm?

Ans. (a) $(1/\overline{V})(\partial \overline{V}/\partial T)_P = 0.00124$ deg^{-1} and $\overline{V} = 97.1$ cm^3 mole^{-1}, so $(\partial V/\partial T)_P = 0.00124(97.1) = 0.120$ cm^3 deg^{-1} mole^{-1}. But this equals $-(\partial S/\partial P)_T$ by Eq. (4-27), so $dS = -0.120$ dP (where dS is in cm^3 atm deg^{-1} mole^{-1} if P is in atmospheres). Assuming that $(\partial \overline{V}/\partial T)_P$ is independent of pressure over the range 1 to 20 atm we may integrate this as follows:

$$\int_1^{20} dS = \Delta S = -0.120(20 - 1) = -2.28 \text{ cm}^3 \text{ atm deg}^{-1} \text{ mole}^{-1}$$

or $-2.28(0.0242) = -0.055$ eu mole^{-1}.
(b) $\overline{S}_{298}$ at 20 atm $= 51.25 - 0.06 = 51.19$ eu mole^{-1}.

Note This slight dependence of entropy on pressure for liquids (and for solids too) is to be contrasted with the considerable dependence for gases. Observe the need for consistency in the use of units. The value of ΔS found in (a) is independent of whether the pressure increase occurred reversibly or not, i.e., independent of the path, even though the Maxwell relation used applies only to reversible changes.

It will be seen that Eqs. (4-26) and (4-27), when applied to ideal gases, give $(\partial S/\partial V)_T = nR/V$ and $(\partial S/\partial P)_T = -nR/P$, respectively, corresponding to Eqs. (2-4) and (2-5) for $T_1 = T_2$.

ENTROPY CORRECTION FOR REAL GASES

It is often desirable to correct the value of absolute entropy as measured by the third law, or thermal, method to the value it would have if the gas were ideal, i.e., to the **standard entropy**. This is because when entropies are calculated by statistical thermodynamics the gas is considered to be ideal.

If $\overline{S}^{\circ}_{id}$ and $\overline{S}^{\circ}_{act}$ are the ideal and thermal molar entropies at 1 atm, respectively, then $\overline{S}^{\circ}_{id} - \overline{S}^{\circ}_{act}$ will be the desired correction. To find this we imagine 1 mole of the gas to be taken, at constant temperature, from the actual to the ideal state via a very attenuated state at pressure $P*$, $P*$ being nearly zero, as follows:

Gas (actual, 1 atm) $\overset{(1)}{\longrightarrow}$ Gas (actual, $P*$ atm) $\overset{(2)}{\longrightarrow}$ Gas (ideal, $P*$ atm) $\overset{(3)}{\longrightarrow}$

Gas ideal, 1 atm)

Let the entropy increase in each step be indicated by ΔS with the appropriate subscript. From Eq. (4-27) we obtain:

$$\Delta S_{(1)} = \int_1^{P*} -(\partial \overline{V}/\partial T)_P \, dP = \int_{P*}^1 (\partial \overline{V}/\partial T)_P \, dP;$$

for ideal gases $(\partial \overline{V}/\partial T)_P = R/P$ so we have:

$$\Delta S_{(3)} = \int_{P*}^1 -(R/P) \, dP$$

At nearly zero pressure all gases are ideal so the initial and final states of step (2) are identical and $\Delta S_{(2)} = 0$. Therefore we have:

$$\Delta S_{(1)} + \Delta S_{(2)} + \Delta S_{(3)} = \int_{P*}^1 [(\partial \overline{V}/\partial T)_P - R/P] \, dP = \overline{S}^{\circ}_{id} - \overline{S}^{\circ}_{act}.$$

The integral, evaluated by finding the area under the curve of $(\partial \overline{V}/\partial T)_P - R/P$ vs. P between $P = 0$ and $P = P$, is the desired correction, and this is added to the actual or thermal value to give the ideal or standard value. There are, however, alternative ways of expressing the integral which are more suitable for purposes of computation.

VARIATION OF FREE ENERGY AND OF FREE ENERGY CHANGE WITH PRESSURE*

The importance to the chemist of the free energy property warrants an examination of its dependence on pressure and temperature and the dependence of the free energy *change* on pressure and temperature. In seeking these relations we turn to Eq. (4-20), which gives us:

$$(\partial G/\partial P)_T = V \qquad (4\text{-}28)$$

For molar quantities this becomes $(\partial \overline{G}/\partial P)_T = \overline{V}$. Thus the change in free energy of a substance which results from changing the pressure on it from P_1 to P_2 at constant temperature can be determined from the following:

$$\Delta G = \int_{P_1}^{P_2} V \, dP$$

Observe that since V is always > 0 free energy always increases with pressure (or decreases with volume) at constant temperature. For liquids and solids it may be noted that $\overline{V}$ is comparatively small. It is also only slightly pressure dependent, so that the integral becomes $\overline{V}(P_2 - P_1)$ per mole, and G varies only slightly with pressure. For gases this is not so.

Example 4-14 By how much does the free energy of 1 mole of $H_2O(l)$ increase at 25° when the pressure on it is increased from 1 to 10 atm? The density of $H_2O(l)$, molecular weight = 18.0, is 1.00 g cm^{-3}.

Ans. $\overline{V}_{298} = 18.0$ cm^3 $mole^{-1}$, so $\Delta G = 18.0(10 - 1) = 162$ cm^3 atm $mole^{-1} = 3.92$ cal $mole^{-1}$.

For gases $\overline{V}$ is comparatively large and is noticeably pressure dependent. For ideal gases we have $dG = V dP = (nRT/P) dP$, so $\Delta G = nRT \ln (P_2/P_1)$ for an isothermal change of pressure from P_1 to P_2.

Example 4-15 By how much does the free energy of 1 mole of $H_2O(g)$ increase at 200°C when the pressure is increased from 1 to 10 atm? (Assume ideal gas behavior.)

Ans. $\Delta G = nRT \ln (10/1) = 1(1.99)(473)(2.303) \log 10 = 2210$ cal.

Note Cf. Examples 4-5 and 4-14.

We have seen above how G varies with P, but how does ΔG vary with P? A given change, forbidden at one pressure, might well become spontaneous at another, so it would be useful to be able to calculate what that pressure would be. The desired relationship is found immediately by differentiating $\Delta G = \sum\limits_{\text{products}} G - \sum\limits_{\text{reactants}} G$ with respect to pressure at

---

*For a graphical representation of the relationships between G and P, and between G and T, see N. O. Smith, *J. Chem. Educ.*, **28**, 462 (1951).

constant temperature and replacing each resulting $(\partial G/\partial P)_T$ term by V according to Eq. (4-28). This gives immediately

$$(\partial \Delta G/\partial P)_T = \Delta V \qquad (4\text{-}29)$$

where $\Delta V = \displaystyle\sum_{\text{products}} V - \sum_{\text{reactants}} V.$ (Cf. the discussion preceding Eq. (1-18).) This provides us with the rate of change of the free energy change with pressure at constant temperature. For changes involving only solids and liquids ΔV is small and so ΔG changes only slightly with pressure. For changes involving gases the effect can be very considerable unless ΔV happens to be small as a result of the initial and final states having nearly equal volumes.

Example 4-16 For $CO(g) + H_2O(g) \longrightarrow CO_2(g) + H_2(g)$, $\Delta G^{\circ}_{298} = -6820$ cal. Find ΔG_{298} at 5 atm assuming ideal behavior.

Ans. Since reactants and products both occupy the same volume at the same pressure and temperature, $\Delta V = 0$. Therefore ΔG shows no change with P. Since $\Delta G_{298} = -6820$ cal at 1 atm, $\Delta G_{298} = -6820$ cal at 5 atm, too.

Example 4-17 If the vapor pressure of $H_2O(l)$ at 354.9°K is 380 mm find $\Delta G^{\circ}_{354.9}$ for $H_2O(l) \longrightarrow H_2O(g)$.

Ans. At 354.9°K and 380 mm, $H_2O(l)$ is in equilibrium with $H_2O(g)$, so, for $H_2O(l,\ 354.9°K,\ 380\ \text{mm}) \longrightarrow H_2O(g,\ 354.9°K,\ 380\ \text{mm})$, $\Delta G = 0$. To find ΔG at a pressure of 1 atm we need to know $\Delta V = \overline{V}_{H_2O(g)} - \overline{V}_{H_2O(l)}$. Since $\overline{V}_{H_2O(l)} \ll \overline{V}_{H_2O(g)}$ we may write $\Delta V \sim \overline{V}_{H_2O(g)}$, so $d\Delta G = \overline{V}_{H_2O(g)}\,dP$. Taking the vapor to be ideal we have $\overline{V}_{H_2O(g)} = RT/P$, so

$$\int d\Delta G = \Delta G \text{ at 760 mm} - \Delta G \text{ at 380 mm} = \int_{380}^{760} (RT/P)\,dP$$

or

$$\Delta G \text{ at 760 mm} - 0 = RT \ln (760/380)$$

or

$$\Delta G \text{ at 760 mm} = 0 + RT \ln (2) = 488.9 \text{ cal}$$

Note Water vapor is unstable with respect to the liquid form at 354.9°K and 1 atm.

Example 4-18 For $Na_2SO_4 \cdot 10H_2O(s) \longrightarrow Na_2SO_4(s) + 10H_2O(g)$, $\Delta G^{\circ}_{298.2} = 21.79$ kcal. At what pressure will $\Delta G_{298.2} = 0$?

Ans. As in the preceding example we may ignore all condensed phases and consider that any volume change is due to the gases, in this case $H_2O(g)$. Thus $\Delta V \sim V_{H_2O(g)} = 10RT/P$. Integrating $d\Delta G = (10RT/P)\,dP$

between $P = P'$ and $P = 1$ atm where P' is the required pressure, gives $0 - 21.790 = 10 RT \ln (P'/1)$ or $P' = 0.02530$ atm $= 19.23$ mm. Therefore $\Delta G = 0$ at a pressure of 19.23 mm.

Note At pressures less than 19.23 mm (at 25°C) the above change will therefore be spontaneous. At a pressure of 19.23 mm $Na_2SO_4 \cdot 10H_2O(s)$, $Na_2SO_4(s)$ and $H_2O(g)$ are all in equilibrium at 25°C. This illustrates how the spontaneity of a change may be altered by a change of pressure.

VARIATION OF FREE ENERGY AND OF FREE ENERGY CHANGE WITH TEMPERATURE*

Free energy is sensitive to temperature changes for all states of aggregation, not just for gases, so the effect is even more important than the pressure effect just considered. We again return to Eq. (4-20) and see the following:

$$(\partial G/\partial T)_P = -S \qquad (4\text{-}30)$$

Since S is always > 0 (except for solids at 0°K), G decreases with rise in T, and since S is usually larger for gases than for liquids or solids the rate of decrease is in general greater for gases. Eq. (4-30) can be cast into a variety of forms for different purposes. Since $G = H - TS$ or $-S = (G - H)/T$ we have:

$$(\partial G/\partial T)_P = (G - H)/T \qquad (4\text{-}31)$$

Moreover, observing that $[\partial(G/T)/\partial T]_P = [T(\partial G/\partial T)_P - G(\partial T/\partial T)_P]/T^2 = [T(\partial G/\partial T)_P - G]/T^2$, we may introduce Eq. (4-30) to give $[\partial(G/T)/\partial T]_P = [T(-S) - G]/T^2 = -(TS + G)/T^2 = -H/T^2$. We thus have another version of Eq. (4-30), viz.

$$[\partial(G/T)/\partial T]_P = -H/T^2 \qquad (4\text{-}32)$$

which is often more convenient than Eqs. (4-30) or (4-31). Since S, G and H are all temperature dependent, it is necessary to know this dependence in order to integrate these equations, unless the temperature change is quite small.

Example 4-19 The standard entropy of Ar(g) as a function of temperature is given by $\bar{S}°$ (eu mole^{-1}) $= 8.68 + 11.44 \log T$°K. Find the change in free energy suffered by 1 mole of Ar(g) when its temperature is changed from 298°K to 348°K at a constant pressure of 1 atm.

Ans. $\displaystyle\int_{298}^{348} dG = \int_{298}^{348} -\bar{S}° dT = -\int_{298}^{348} (8.68 + 11.44 \log T) dT$, or $\Delta G =$

$-8.68(348 - 298) - 11.44 [(348 \log 348 - 348/2.303) - (298 \log 298 - 298/2.303)] = -1870$ cal mole^{-1}.

*See footnote to preceding section.

By a method entirely analogous to that used for finding Eq. (4-29) from (4-28) one can easily show the following from Eq. (4-30):

$$(\partial \Delta G / \partial T)_P = - \Delta S \qquad (4.33)$$

By analogy with Eqs. (4-31) and (4-32) we have:

$$(\partial \Delta G / \partial T)_P = (\Delta G - \Delta H)/T \qquad (4-34)$$

and

$$[\partial (\Delta G/T)/\partial T]_P = - \Delta H/T^2 \qquad (4-35)$$

Eqs. (4-30, 31, 32, 33, 34 and 35) are all referred to as the **Gibbs-Helm-holtz relation**. The last three of these provide ways of finding ΔG at one temperature from ΔG at another, when ΔS, $\Delta G - \Delta H$, or ΔH, respectively, are known as functions of T. Of these three, ΔH is the most readily expressed in terms of T, so Eq. (4-35) is the most convenient for integration. In this connection it may be recalled that a common form of the function is $\Delta H_T = \Delta H_I + \Delta a T + (\Delta b/2)T^2 + (\Delta c/3)T^3 + \ldots$. This will be illustrated in Example 4-21. Further reference to the integration of the Gibbs-Helmholtz relation will be made in Chapter 7.

Example 4-20 For iso-$C_4H_{10}(g) \longrightarrow n$-$C_4H_{10}(g)$, $\Delta G^{\circ}_{298.2} = 0.542$ kcal, so the change is forbidden at 298.2°K and 1 atm. $\Delta S^{\circ}_{298.2}$ is 3.68 eu. If we wish to attempt this reaction at a temperature where the change is spontaneous should we try higher or lower temperatures?

Ans. Since $(\partial \Delta G^{\circ}/\partial T)_P = - \Delta S^{\circ}$, and since $\Delta S^{\circ} > 0$, the value of ΔG° must decrease with increase in temperature. A decrease in ΔG° would be in the right direction for it should eventually lead to negative values. Higher temperatures should therefore be tried.

Example 4-21 For $H_2O(l) \longrightarrow H_2O(g)$, $\Delta G^{\circ}_{298.2} = 2.0545$ kcal and $\Delta H^{\circ}(cal) = 13,644 - 10.84\,T + 1.187(10^{-3})T^2 + 0.89(10^{-7})T^3$. Find $\Delta G^{\circ}_{380.0}$.

Ans.

$$\int_{298.2}^{380.0} d(\Delta G^{\circ}/T)$$

$$= - \int_{298.2}^{380.0} \frac{13,644 - 10.84T + 1.187(10^{-3})T^2 + 0.89(10^{-7})T^3}{T^2} \, dT$$

or

$$\Delta G^{\circ}_{380.0}/380.0 - 2,054.5/298.2 = 13,644(1/380.0 - 1/298.2)$$

$$+ 10.84(2.303) \log (380.0/298.2) - 1.187(10^{-3})(380.0 - 298.2)$$

$$- [0.89(10^{-7})/2](380.0^2 - 298.2^2)$$

This gives $\Delta G^{\circ}_{380.0} = -135$ cal.

Example 4-22 For the change $2Ag(s) + Hg_2Br_2(s) \longrightarrow 2AgBr(s) + 2Hg(l)$, $\Delta G^\circ_{298} = -3.138$ kcal and the temperature coefficient of this change, $(\partial \Delta G^\circ_{298}/\partial T)_P$, is -14.39 cal deg^{-1}. Find ΔH°_{298}.

Ans. Using Eq. (4-34) we have $-14.39 = (-3138 - \Delta H^\circ_{298})/298$, the solution of which is $\Delta H^\circ_{298} = 1150$ cal.

Note Measurements of $(\partial \Delta G/\partial T)_P$ provide in this way a means of determining ΔH without resorting to calorimetry, especially for reactions which can be harnessed to give electrical energy. This will be referred to later.

THE FREE ENERGY FUNCTION AND ITS USE IN CALCULATIONS

It is common to find free energy data tabulated in terms of the **free energy function** rather than free energy of formation. This function is defined as $(\overline{G}^\circ_T - \overline{H}^\circ_{ref. T})/T$, where, as usual, the superscript zero means standard state (1 atm) at the temperature indicated by the subscript, and "ref. T" is usually $0°K$, but frequently $298°K$. This particular form is chosen for several reasons: (1) it is readily obtained for gases by the methods of statistical thermodynamics and for all states of aggregation using heat capacity data, (2) its value shows only a small change with temperature and so makes for more accurate interpolations, (3) the smallness of the range of its values makes for neater printing of tables.

We illustrate first its calculation from heat capacity data. Suppose, by a thorough study of the heat capacity of $N_2(g)$, we have determined that, in the range 300 to $1500°K$, $\overline{C}_p$ (cal deg^{-1} $mole^{-1}$) $= 6.4492 + 1.4125(10^{-3}) T - 0.807(10^{-7}) T^2$, and that $\overline{S}^\circ_{298.2}$ has been found to be 45.767 eu $mole^{-1}$, by third law methods. From these data we wish to find, e.g. $(\overline{G}^\circ_{1500} - \overline{H}^\circ_{298.2})/1500$. Now $(\overline{G}^\circ_T - \overline{H}^\circ_{298.2})/T = [(\overline{G}^\circ_T - \overline{H}^\circ_T) + (\overline{H}^\circ_T - \overline{H}^\circ_{298.2})]/T = -\overline{S}^\circ_T + (\overline{H}^\circ_T - \overline{H}^\circ_{298.2})/T$. We first find $\overline{S}^\circ_{1500}$: using Eq. (2-6) we write:

$$\overline{S}^\circ_{1500} - \overline{S}^\circ_{298.2}$$

$$= \int_{298.2}^{1500} \frac{6.4492 + 1.4125(10^{-3})T - 0.807(10^{-7})T^2}{T} dT = 12.03 \text{ eu mole}^{-1}.$$

Therefore $\overline{S}^\circ_{1500} = 45.767 + 12.03 = 57.80$ eu $mole^{-1}$. We evaluate $\overline{H}^\circ_{1500} - \overline{H}^\circ_{298.2}$ by integration of Eq. (1-8) as follows:

$$\overline{H}^\circ_{1500} - \overline{H}^\circ_{298.2} =$$

$$= \int_{298.2}^{1500} [6.4492 + 1.4125(10^{-3})T - 0.807(10^{-7})T^2] dT = 9187 \text{ cal mole}^{-1}$$

This gives $(\overline{H}^\circ_{1500} - \overline{H}^\circ_{298.2})/1500 = 6.12$ cal deg^{-1}. Therefore the free energy function, $(\overline{G}^\circ_{1500} - \overline{H}^\circ_{298.2})/1500 = -57.80 + 6.12 = -51.68$ cal $mole^{-1}$ deg^{-1}.

When the reference temperature is $0°K$ a similar computation is made.

Let us now illustrate how tabulations of the free energy function may be used to determine $\Delta G°$ and other quantities for a given change. Such tabulations, besides listing $(\overline{G}^°_T - \overline{H}^°_{298})/T$ and/or $(\overline{G}^°_T - \overline{H}^°_0)/T$, often include values of $\Delta H^°_0$, $\Delta H^°_{298}$ (the standard heats of formation at $0°$ and $298°K$), and even $\overline{H}^°_{298} - \overline{H}^°_0$. Actually the negative of the free energy function is given to avoid repetition of minus signs. Typical data are presented in Table 4-1.

Table 4-1[a]

Substance	$-(\overline{G}^°_T - \overline{H}^°_0)/T$, cal deg^{-1} mole^{-1}				$\overline{H}^°_{298} - \overline{H}^°_0$ kcal mole^{-1}	$\Delta H^°_0$ kcal mole^{-1}
	298.2°K	500°K	1000°K	1500°K		
C (graphite)	0.53	1.16	2.78	4.19	0.251	0
$Cl_2(g)$	45.93	49.85	55.43	58.85	2.194	0
$H_2(g)$	24.42	27.95	32.74	35.59	2.024	0
$N_2(g)$	38.82	42.42	47.31	50.28	2.072	0
$O_2(g)$	42.06	45.68	50.70	53.81	2.07	0
$CO(g)$	40.25	43.86	48.77	51.78	2.073	-27.202
$CO_2(g)$	43.56	47.67	54.11	58.48	2.238	-93.969
$COCl_2(g)$	57.50	63.33	72.79	79.13	3.075	-52.06
$CH_4(g)$	36.46	40.75	47.65	52.84	2.397	-15.99
$HCl(g)$	37.72	41.31	46.16	49.08	2.065	-22.019
$H_2O(g)$	37.17	41.29	47.01	50.60	2.368	-57.107
$NH_3(g)$	37.99	42.28	48.63	53.03	2.37	-9.37

[a]Quoted from *Thermodynamics* by G. N. Lewis and M. Randall, revised by K. S. Pitzer and L. Brewer. Copyright 1961 by the McGraw-Hill Book Company, Inc. Used by permission of McGraw-Hill Book Company.

Such tables give considerable information as will now be shown.

(1) Values of the free energy function referred to $0°K$ can be changed to values referred to $298°K$. Since $-(\overline{G}^°_T - \overline{H}^°_{298})/T = (\overline{H}^°_{298} - \overline{H}^°_0)/T + -(\overline{G}^°_T - \overline{H}^°_0)/T$, we can find $-(\overline{G}^°_{1000} - \overline{H}^°_{298})/1000$ from $-(\overline{G}^°_{1000} - \overline{H}^°_0)/1000$. For $N_2(g)$, e.g., $-(\overline{G}^°_{1000} - \overline{H}^°_{298})/1000 = 2072/1000 + 47.31 = 49.38$ cal deg^{-1} mole^{-1}.

(2) Since $-(\overline{G}^°_{298} - \overline{H}^°_{298})/298 = \overline{S}^°_{298}$, the negative of the free energy function at $298°K$, referred to $298°K$, is the standard entropy at $298°K$. Thus $\overline{S}^°_{298}$ for $N_2(g) = 2072/298 + 38.82 = 45.77$ eu mole^{-1}. We can therefore readily find standard entropies at $298°K$ for all substances listed and, from these, $\Delta S^°_{298}$ values for changes involving them.

(3) Since, from Eq. (1-16), $\Delta H^°_0 = \Delta(\Delta H^°_f$ at $0°K) = \Delta(\Delta H^°_0)$ we can find heats of reaction at $0°K$. For example, for:

$$\tfrac{1}{2}N_2(g) + \tfrac{3}{2}H_2(g) \longrightarrow NH_3(g)$$

$$\Delta H^°_0 = (-9.37) - \left[\tfrac{1}{2}(0) + \tfrac{3}{2}(0)\right] = -9.37 \text{ kcal.}$$

(4) Since, for a given change $\Delta H^\circ_{298} = \Delta(\overline{H}^\circ_{298} - \overline{H}^\circ_0) + \Delta(\Delta H^\circ_0)$, we can find heats of reaction at 298°K. For example, for the formation of $NH_3(g)$ immediately above,

$$\Delta H^\circ_{298} = \left[2.37 - \left(\tfrac{1}{2} \times 2.072 + \tfrac{3}{2} \times 2.024\right)\right] + \left[(-9.27) - \left(\tfrac{1}{2} \times 0 + \tfrac{3}{2} \times 0\right)\right]$$
$$= -11.07 \text{ kcal}$$

(5) Most important of all we can find ΔG°_T values for any temperature for any changes involving the substances listed. This is because the following relations may be applied:

$$T\left[\frac{\Delta(\Delta H^\circ_0)}{T} - \Delta\frac{-(\overline{G}^\circ_T - \overline{H}^\circ_0)}{T}\right] = T\left[\frac{\Delta(\Delta H^\circ_0)}{T} + \frac{\Delta G^\circ_T}{T} - \frac{\Delta H^\circ_0}{T}\right]$$
$$= \Delta(\Delta H^\circ_0) + \Delta G^\circ_T - \Delta H^\circ_0 = \Delta G^\circ_T$$

or

$$\Delta G^\circ_T = T\left[\frac{\Delta(\Delta H^\circ_0)}{T} - \Delta\frac{-(\overline{G}^\circ_T - \overline{H}^\circ_0)}{T}\right] \tag{4-36}$$

Let us use this relationship to find, e.g., ΔG°_{1200} for

$$\tfrac{1}{2}N_2(g) + \tfrac{3}{2}H_2(g) \longrightarrow NH_3(g)$$

We require the free energy functions for each of the three substances at 1200°K. Linear interpolation of the data in Table 4-1 gives values of $-(\overline{G}^\circ_{1200} - \overline{H}^\circ_0)/1200$ equal to 48.50, 33.88 and 50.39 cal deg^{-1} mole^{-1} for $N_2(g)$, $H_2(g)$ and $NH_3(g)$, respectively. Furthermore $\Delta(\Delta H^\circ_0) = -9.37$ kcal as shown previously. Therefore $\Delta G^\circ_{1200} = 1200\left[-9370/1200 - \left(50.39 - \tfrac{1}{2} \times 48.50 - \tfrac{3}{2} \times 33.88\right)\right] = -9370 + 29,620 = 20250$ cal $= 20.25$ kcal. Notice the conversion of $\Delta(\Delta H^\circ_0)$ to calories.

It is worth emphasizing that all the values of ΔG, calculated as shown for the given chemical changes, refer to the changes in the thermodynamic functions accompanying the *complete* conversion of reactants into products. The possibility of a *partial* conversion will be considered in Chapter 7.

VARIATION OF WORK CONTENT WITH VOLUME

We may now examine the dependence of A on P and T. For this purpose we turn to Eq. (4-11) and observe the following:

$$(\partial A/\partial V)_T = -P \tag{4-37}$$

This gives the volume dependence of A (at constant temperature) but not the pressure dependence. In effect, however there is little difference, since for a pure homogeneous substance pressure is determined by volume at a given temperature.

Example 4-23 Find ΔA for the compression of 2 moles of ideal gas at 300°K from a pressure of 10 atm to 20 atm.

Ans. $\Delta A = -nRT \ln (V_2/V_1) = -nRT \ln (P_1/P_2) = nRT \ln (P_2/P_1) = 2(1.99)$ (300)(2.303) log (20/10) = 827 cal.

Note This is merely another way of looking at calculations of w_{max} as illustrated in Examples 1-8 and 1-10.

VARIATION OF WORK CONTENT AND OF CHANGE IN WORK CONTENT WITH TEMPERATURE

Eq. (4-11) leads not only to Eq. (4-37) but to

$$(\partial A/\partial T)_V = -S \qquad (4\text{-}38)$$

which tells us how A varies with temperature at constant volume. Observe the close similarity to Eq. (4-30). Clearly, A must decrease with temperature if volume remains constant, for S is a positive quantity. Use of $E = A - TS$ readily leads to alternative expressions for Eq. (4-38), analogous to Eqs. (4-31) and (4-32), viz.

$$(\partial A/\partial T)_V = (A - E)/T \qquad (4\text{-}39)$$

and

$$[\partial(A/T)/\partial T]_V = -E/T^2 \qquad (4\text{-}40)$$

Example 4-24 For He(g), $\bar{S}^\circ_{298} = 30.13$ eu mole^{-1} and $\bar{C}_V = 3.02$ cal deg^{-1} mole^{-1}. By how much does the work content of 3 moles of He, initially at 298°K and 1 atm, change in being heated at constant volume to 398°K?

Ans. By Eq. (4-38) ΔA for this temperature change is given by $\displaystyle\int_{298}^{398} -SdT$,

but S depends on T. To find this dependence we recall Eq. (2-7), viz. $dS_V = (C_V/T) dT_V = [3(3.02)/T] dT = 9.06 \, d\ln T$ or $S = 9.06 \ln T + \text{constant}$. To find the value of this integration constant we substitute the known value of S°_{298} viz. 3(30.13), to give 3(30.13) = 9.06 ln 298 + constant, or constant = 38.78, and so $S_V = 9.06 \ln T + 38.78$.

Therefore $\Delta A = \displaystyle\int_{298}^{398} -(9.06 \ln T + 38.78) dT = -9180$ cal, or the work content decreases by 9.18 kcal.

Of greater importance to the chemist is the manner in which ΔA changes with T, for we recall that $\Delta A < 0$ for spontaneous changes at constant volume. By a process analogous to that used for finding Eqs. (4-33), (4-34) and (4-35) from Eq. (4-30) we can, from Eq. (4-38), readily show the following:

$$(\partial\Delta A/\partial T)_V = -\Delta S \qquad (4\text{-}41)$$

$$(\partial\Delta A/\partial T)_V = (\Delta A - \Delta E)/T \qquad (4\text{-}42)$$

and

$$\partial[(\Delta A/T)/\partial T]_V = -\Delta E/T^2 \qquad (4\text{-}43)$$

With these it is possible to determine the spontaneity of a given constant volume change at one temperature from that at another temperature.

Example 4-25 A mole of ZnO(s) and a mole of CO_2(g) are sealed in a vessel of fixed volume at 298°K such that the pressure within it is 1 atm. Under these conditions $ZnCO_3$(s) is slowly formed and, for this change, ZnO(s) + CO_2(g) → $ZnCO_3$(s), $\Delta A = -3.91$ kcal and $\Delta E = -16.4$ kcal. The change is thus a spontaneous one for $\Delta A < 0$. Assuming ΔE to be independent of temperature find whether the change is still spontaneous at 500°K.

Ans. By Eq. (4-43) $d(\Delta A/T) = -(\Delta E/T^2) dT$. Integrating between the temperatures 298° and 500°K, assuming ΔE to be independent of T, gives

$$\Delta A_{500}/500 - \Delta A_{298}/298 = \Delta E(1/500 - 1/298)$$

or

$$\Delta A_{500}/500 - (-3910/298) = -16,400(1/500 - 1/298)$$

or

$$\Delta A_{500} = 4550 \text{ cal}$$

Since $\Delta A_{500} > 0$, the change is forbidden at the higher temperature.

THERMODYNAMIC EQUATION OF STATE

If the "fundamental equation of thermodynamics," Eq. (4-3), is divided through by ∂V for (reversible) changes at constant temperature we have $T(\partial S/\partial V)_T = (\partial E/\partial V)_T + P$. Combination of this with the Clapeyron relation, Eq. (4-26), yields:

$$P = T(\partial P/\partial T)_V - (\partial E/\partial V)_T \tag{4-44}$$

known as a **thermodynamic equation of state**: it is thermodynamic because it involves a thermodynamic energy function, E, and it is an equation of state because it relates P, V and T. The term $(\partial P/\partial T)_V$ is called the **thermal pressure**, so we have (Pressure of system) = (Thermal pressure) – (Internal pressure). For ideal gases, since $P = nRT/V$, $(\partial P/\partial T)_V = nR/V$, and the thermal pressure is $T(nR/V) = TnR \div (nRT/P) = P$. The internal pressure must therefore be zero. Thus the result of the Joule experiment is predictable from the ideal gas law and the first two laws of thermodynamics. It is clear that the thermal pressure is the pressure that the system would exert in the absence of the forces of intermolecular attraction, and that the internal pressure acts in the opposite direction to reduce the effect of the thermal pressure down to what is actually exerted on the walls of the containing vessel. For a van der Waals gas, since $P = nRT/(V - nb) - n^2a/V^2$, $(\partial P/\partial T)_V = nR/(V - nb)$ and $T(\partial P/\partial T)_V = nRT/(V - nb)$. The internal pressure is thus $-T(\partial P/\partial T)_V P = nRT/(V - nb) + n^2a/V^2 - nRT/(V - nb) = n^2a/V^2$ or $a/\overline{V}^2$.

Example 4-26 Assuming CO_2 to be a van der Waals gas with $a = 3.61$ liter^2 atm mole^{-2} and $b = 0.043$ liter mole^{-1} find the internal pressure of it at 250°K and 1 atm.

Ans. The internal pressure is $a/\overline{V}^2$ so we must first find $\overline{V}$. Now $(1 + 3.61/\overline{V}^2)(\overline{V} - 0.043) = 0.0821(250)$. Using the **method of successive approximations** we try $\overline{V} = \overline{V}_{ideal} = RT/P = 0.0821(250/1) = 20.52$ liters, so $(1 + 3.61/20.52^2)(\overline{V} - 0.043) = 20.52$, giving $\overline{V}$ to the next approximation as 20.38 liters. Now write $(1 + 3.61/20.38^2)(\overline{V} - 0.043) = 20.52$, giving $\overline{V}$ to the next approximation as 20.38 liters. As the last two solutions are the same no further steps are needed. Therefore the internal pressure is $3.61/20.38^2 = 0.0087$ atm.

By combining Eq. (4-4) with Eq. (4-27) we may, in a similar manner, obtain another **thermodynamic equation of state**, viz.

$$V = T(\partial V/\partial T)_P + (\partial H/\partial P)_T \qquad (4\text{-}45)$$

PROBLEMS

1. In the mnemonic of Fig. 4-1 do the relative *sizes* of the areas denoted by TS, A and PV have any meaning?

2. Find whether $Br_2(g)$ will oxidize $H_2S(g)$ to give $S(s)$ at 298°K and 1 atm if the standard free energies of formation of $H_2S(g)$, $Br_2(g)$ and $HBr(g)$ are -7.89, 0.75 and -12.72 kcal mole^{-1}, respectively, at that temperature.

3. (a) Would you expect the entropy of $I_2(s)$ to change appreciably with pressure? Why?
   (b) The standard entropy of $I_2(s)$ is 27.9 eu mole^{-1} at 298°K. Find its entropy at this temperature under a pressure of 100 atm if its (volume) coefficient of expansion is $2.64(10^{-4})$ deg^{-1}, its density is 4.94 g cm^{-3} and its molecular weight 254 g mole^{-1}.

4. According to the Berthelot equation of state:

$$(\partial \overline{V}/\partial T)_P = R/P + 27RT_c{}^3/32P_cT^3$$

   where P_C is the critical pressure and T_C the critical temperature (°K). Find $\overline{S}{}^\circ_{298}$ for $Cl_2(g)$ if its third law entropy at 25° and 1 atm is 53.23 eu mole^{-1}. The critical temperature and pressure of $Cl_2(g)$ are 417.2°K and 76.1 atm.

5. By how much does the free energy of 10 g of $H_2(g)$ change when it is compressed at 127° from a pressure of 1 atm to 10 atm? By how much does the work content change?

6. For $CaCO_3(s) \longrightarrow CaO(s) + CO_2(g)$, $\Delta G^\circ_{298} = 31.1$ kcal and $\Delta S^\circ_{298} = 38.4$ eu. Find (a) ΔG_{298} at 0.010 atm and (b) ΔG°_{308}, assuming that ΔS° is independent of temperature over this small temperature range.

7. The vapor pressure of $H_2O(l)$ at 81.7° is 0.500 atm. Find ΔG and ΔA for (a) $H_2O(l, 81.7°, 0.500$ atm$) \longrightarrow H_2O(g, 81.7°, 0.500$ atm$)$ and (b) $H_2O(l, 25.0°, 1.000$ atm$) \longrightarrow H_2O(g, 81.7°, 0.250$ atm$)$, given that the vapor is ideal, that the density of $H_2O(l)$ is 1.00 g cm^{-3}, that $\overline{C}_P(l)$ is 18.0 cal deg^{-1} mole^{-1} and that $\overline{S}{}^\circ_{298.2}$ for $H_2O(l)$ is 16.72 eu mole^{-1}.

8. For the reaction $H_2(g) + \frac{1}{2}O_2(g) \longrightarrow H_2O(l)$, $\Delta H^\circ_{298.15}$ is -68.317 kcal. The standard entropies $(\overline{S}^\circ_{298.15})$ of $H_2(g)$, $O_2(g)$ and $H_2O(l)$ are 31.211, 49.003 and 16.716 eu mole^{-1}, respectively.

   (a) What is the maximum "useful" work obtainable from this change?

   (b) What is the maximum work obtainable from this change?

   (c) Find $\Delta G^\circ_{299.15}$.

   (d) Find $\Delta G_{298.15}$ when all three substances are at a pressure of 2 atm.

9. From the information in Table 4-1 find (a) $\Delta S^\circ_{298.2}$, (b) $\Delta H^\circ_{298.2}$, (c) $\Delta G^\circ_{298.2}$ and (d) ΔG°_{800} for the change $COCl_2(g) \longrightarrow CO(g) + Cl_2(g)$. (e) Is there any reversal of spontaneity over the temperature range 298.2 to 800°K?

10. For $2HCl(g) + \frac{1}{2}O_2(g) \longrightarrow H_2O(g) + Cl_2(g)$, $\Delta G^\circ_{298} = -9.098$ kcal and $\Delta H^\circ_{298} = -13.672$ kcal. The heat capacities of these substances vary with temperature as follows:

    $\overline{C}^\circ_P$(cal deg^{-1} mole^{-1})

    for $HCl(g) = 6.7319 + 0.4325(10^{-3})\,T + 3.697(10^{-7})\,T^2$

    for $O_2(g) = 6.0954 + 3.2533(10^{-3})\,T - 10.171(10^{-7})\,T^2$

    for $H_2O(g) = 7.219 + 2.374(10^{-3})\,T + 2.67(10^{-7})\,T^2$

    for $Cl_2(g) = 7.5755 + 2.4244(10^{-3})\,T - 9.650(10^{-7})\,T^2$

    (a) Find ΔH° as a function of temperature.

    (b) Find ΔG°_{1000}.

    (c) Use the data of Table 4-1 to confirm your answer to (b).

11. Direct measurement of $(\partial P/\partial T)_V$ for $CS_2(l)$ at 20° and 1 atm showed it to be 12.67 atm deg^{-1}. Find the internal pressure of this liquid under these conditions.

5

Systems of pure substances in more than one phase—fugacity

This chapter describes the thermodynamics of systems of pure substances (elements or compounds) in which more than one state of aggregation or form of the substance may be present.

We have noted that V, E, H, S, A and G are state functions. For a system consisting of a given amount of a single homogeneous substance their values, whether referring to all of the substance present or per mole, are fixed if, and only if, the pressure and the temperature of the system are fixed. Such systems are said to be bivariant (two independent variables). When, however, we drop the restriction of homogeneity the situation is somewhat different. If the system is heterogeneous, there must be more than one phase present. A phase is a homogeneous portion of a system, homogeneous meaning that any one part of the phase is indistinguishable in properties from any other part. Although homogeneous, a phase need not be continuous: a mixture of crushed ice and water, e.g., consists of only two phases, ice and water, even though the ice phase is discontinuous, for all the ice particles have identical intensive properties. Similarly a mixture of water and water vapor consists of two phases; a mixture of ice, water and water vapor consists of three.

Now a system with more than one phase is defined when not only pressure and temperature are fixed but when the intensive properties of every phase are fixed.* It is found experimentally (and will be proved from the first and second laws in a later chapter) that when two phases of a pure substance are in equilibrium, such as solid and vapor, or two polymorphic solid forms, only the pressure *or* the temperature need be fixed in order to define the system. Such systems are said to be **univariant** (one independent variable). Thus, if water and water vapor are in equilibrium at 1 atm the temperature is automatically 100°—if the temperature is fixed at 100° the pressure is automatically 1 atm. The properties and therefore the state functions per mole of substance are then fixed for the water phase and fixed for the water vapor phase. However, the respective values in the two phases (except for the molar free energy, $\overline{G}$) are different. If three phases of a pure substance are in equilibrium the experimenter cannot select or fix either the pressure or the temperature. Such systems are said to be **invariant** (no independent variables). Again, $\overline{V}, \overline{E}, \overline{H}, \overline{S}, \overline{A}$ and $\overline{G}$ for each of the three phases are fixed and, except for $\overline{G}$, different for the ice, water and vapor.

PHASE DIAGRAMS

Graphical representations of the pressure-temperature-concentration relationships in a system are called **phase diagrams**. For systems of one substance there is no concentration variable if, as is customary, concentration is in mole or weight per cent or fraction, for every phase has the same concentration, viz. 100% of the substance. There are thus only two variables remaining: pressure and temperature. Since, for two-phase systems, the temperature determines the pressure, a line on a pressure-temperature plot suffices to represent the conditions under which the two phases can coexist. The most familiar of these lines is the **vapor pressure curve** for the coexistence of liquid and vapor. There is a similar curve for the sublimation pressure of a solid. Figure 5-1 shows these schematically as curves OA and OB, respectively. The vapor pressure curve ceases abruptly at A, the **critical point**. The point of intersection, O, must be the only temperature and pressure where solid, liquid and vapor coexist. Such a three-phase, invariant point is called a **triple point**. The line OC, called the **fusion curve**, gives the variation of the melting temperature with pressure and is nearly vertical. The 1-atm line cuts the OC line at the **normal melting point** and the vapor pressure curve of the liquid at the **normal boiling point**. Because OC is nearly vertical the temperature of the normal melting point is very close to that of the triple point. For some substances the pressure of the triple point is greater than 1 atm so the 1-atm line cuts only the sublimation curve OB giving rise to a **normal sublimation point**. The substance then has no normal melting point, e.g. carbon dioxide.

---

*In connection with phase equilibria and phase diagrams in general, the system is defined when the temperature, pressure and intensive properties of every phase are determined *regardless* of their quantities.

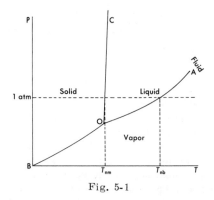

Fig. 5-1

If a system consisting of liquid in equilibrium with vapor at temperature T_{nb}, and therefore a pressure of 1 atm, be subjected to a greater pressure the vapor will condense and only liquid remain; if a system consisting of solid in equilibrium with liquid at temperature T_{nm} and therefore at 1 atm be subjected to a rise in temperature the solid will melt and, again, only liquid will remain. In this way we see that it is appropriate to label the area lying above OA and to the right of OC "liquid," representing the range of values of pressure and temperature under which the liquid has a stable existence. Similarly the other two areas are appropriately labeled "solid" and "vapor."

For the vast majority of substances OC has a positive slope. For water, however, depicted schematically in Fig. 5-2, the slope is negative. Observe that the normal melting point of ice in the *absence* of air is 0.0025°.

Many substances show **polymorphism** or the existence of more than one crystalline modification. When two such forms can have a stable coexistence they are said to be **enantiotropic**. Monoclinic and rhombic sulfur are in this category. Ice is also polymorphic but only at high pressures. A

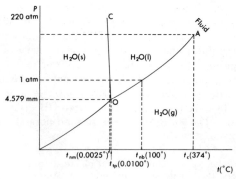

Fig. 5-2

system consisting of two enantiotropic solid forms in equilibrium is uni-variant like any other of the two-phase systems discussed, so can also be represented by a curve on a pressure-temperature plot—a transition curve which, like fusion curves, is steep. The existence of more than one solid form (S_1 and S_2) now makes possible more than one kind of triple point, e.g., S_1-S_2-Vapor, S_2-Liquid-Vapor, S_1-S_2-Liquid.

It is instructive to see how the thermodynamic functions for a given substance depend on the temperature. In Table 5-1 are assembled the values of $\overline{E}$, $\overline{H}$, $\overline{S}$, $\overline{A}$ and $\overline{G}$ for water at 1 atm over the range of temperature -200 to $+200°$ including, therefore, all three states of aggregation. In order to give numerical values to $\overline{E}$, $\overline{H}$, $\overline{A}$ and $\overline{G}$ an arbitrary value of zero has been assigned to the enthalpy of $H_2O(l)$ at $0°$. The principles underlying the calculation of all these quantities have already been described.

Table 5-1

State	Temp., °C	$P\overline{V}$, cal mole^{-1}	$\overline{E}$, cal mole^{-1}	$\overline{H}$, cal mole^{-1}	$\overline{S}$, eu mole^{-1}	$T\overline{S}$, cal mole^{-1}	$\overline{A}$, cal mole^{-1}	$\overline{G}$, cal mole^{-1}
(g)	200	935	11,445	12,380	48.84	23,110	$-11,660$	$-10,730$
(g)	150	835	11,115	11,950	47.87	20,260	$-9,150$	$-8,310$
(g)	100	730	10,786	11,516	46.79	17,460	$-6,674$	$-5,944$
(l)	100	0.455	1,802	1,802	20.76	7,746	$-5,944$	$-5,944$
(l)	50	0.441	900.4	900.8	18.16	5,868	$-4,968$	$-4,967$
(l)	0	0.436	-0.436	0	15.14	4,135	$-4,135$	$-4,135$
(s)	0	0.476	$-1,436$	$-1,436$	9.88	2,699	$-4,135$	$-4,135$
(s)	-100	0.47	$-2,155$	$-2,155$	6.7	1,160	$-3,315$	$-3,315$
(s)	-200	0.47	$-2,575$	$-2,575$	3.2	230	$-2,805$	$-2,805$

The required data are the heat capacity and density of all three states of aggregation at all temperatures and the heats of fusion and vaporization. The tabulated data, except $P\overline{V}$ and $T\overline{S}$, are plotted in Fig. 5-3, but it is to be noted that, with the scale used, the curves for $\overline{H}$ and $\overline{E}$ are indistinguishable for the solid and liquid forms. The same is true for $\overline{G}$ and $\overline{A}$. Observe that all the functions except $\overline{G}$ show discontinuities on fusion and vaporization. (The discontinuity in $\overline{A}$ at the melting point is not evident in the table because of an insufficient number of significant figures.) For $\overline{G}$ only the slope shows a discontinuity.

THE CLAUSIUS-CLAPEYRON RELATION

The slopes of the lines in phase diagrams such as Figs. 5-1 and 5-2 are given by the Clapeyron relation, already derived,

$$(\partial P/\partial T)_V = (\partial S/\partial V)_T \tag{4-26}$$

We note, first, that *for univariant systems* the constant volume restriction is unnecessary, for dP/dT is independent of volume for such systems: the vapor pressure of a system consisting of a pure liquid in equilibrium with

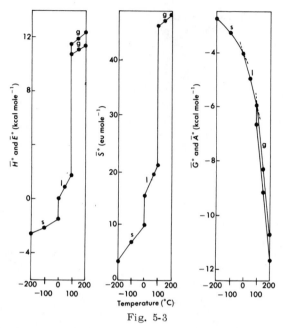

Fig. 5-3

its vapor, for instance, is fixed at a fixed temperature, regardless of the volume, and therefore dP/dT will be fixed at a fixed temperature too. Thus $(\partial P/\partial T)_V = dP/dT$. We note, secondly, that if such a univariant system be kept at constant temperature and its volume changed (with equilibrium still obtaining) the change in entropy will be proportional to the change in volume. An increase in volume, ΔV, will cause a certain amount of liquid to vaporize and give a certain entropy increase, ΔS. If we double the ΔV we will double the amount of liquid vaporized and double the ΔS. It is seen that ΔS is proportional to ΔV at fixed temperature, and so $(\partial S/\partial V)_T$ is identical to $(\Delta S/\Delta V)_T$. Consequently for univariant systems Eq. (4-26) can be rewritten:

$$dP/dT = \Delta S/\Delta V \qquad (5\text{-}1)$$

remembering that dP/dT, ΔS and ΔV all refer to the same temperature, dP/dT being the slope of the $P\text{-}T$ line for any univariant system and ΔS the entropy change corresponding to the volume change ΔV. The word "change" here refers to the conversion of one of the two coexisting phases to the other at the particular constant temperature. The amount of substance so converted is immaterial, for ΔS and ΔV are both proportional to the amount and so their ratio is independent of it. In using Eq. (5-1) due regard must be had for the units of the quantities.

Since for every substance $\overline{S}_{(g)} > \overline{S}_{(l)} > \overline{S}_{(s)}$, and for almost all substances $\overline{V}_{(g)} > \overline{V}_{(l)} > \overline{V}_{(g)}$ (water being the principal exception), dP/dT will always be positive for vaporization and sublimation curves, ΔS and

ΔV having the same sign. Fusion lines will almost always have positive slopes too, except for water (where ΔS is opposite in sign to ΔV).

Example 5-1 At the normal boiling point of water the slope of the vaporization curve is 27.15 mm deg^{-1}. The densities of the liquid and vapor at equilibrium at this temperature are 0.958 and $5.98(10^{-4})$ g cm^{-3}, respectively. Find ΔS for the vaporization of 1 mole of $H_2O(l)$ at its normal boiling point.

Ans. The molar volumes of (l) and (g) are $18.016/0.958 = 18.81$ and $18.016/5.98(10^{-4}) = 3.013(10^4)$ cm^3 mole^{-1}, respectively. For $H_2O(l) \longrightarrow H_2O(g)$, $\Delta V = 3.013(10^4) - 18.81 = 3.011(10^4)$ cm^3 mole^{-1} = 30.11 liter mole^{-1}. Furthermore $dP/dT = 27.15/760.0 = 0.03572$ atm deg^{-1}. Substitution in Eq. (5-1) gives $0.03572 = \Delta S/30.11$, where ΔS is in liter-atm deg^{-1}, or $\Delta S = 0.03572(30.11)(24.22) = 26.05$ eu mole^{-1}.

A further alteration in Eq. (4-26) is convenient. As we are here dealing with changes between phases *at equilibrium* ΔS may be replaced by $\Delta H/T$ to give:

$$dP/dT = \Delta H/T\Delta V \qquad (5\text{-}2)$$

This is the famous **Clausius-Clapeyron** relation (although this title is often applied to Eq. (5-3) below). As with Eqs. (4-26) and (5-1), it applies to all univariant systems. Clearly it permits the evaluation of the *equilibrium* heat of transition for any such phase changes at the temperature T. Thus from the slope of a vaporization curve and ΔV one can determine the heat of vaporization without measuring it directly. The data of Example 5-1, for instance, could have been used in Eq. (5-2) to give ΔH for the vaporization of $H_2O(l)$ at its normal boiling point, viz. $26.05(373.15) = 9721$ cal mole^{-1}. Or we may use the relation to predict quantitatively the effect of change of pressure on the temperature of equilibrium phase changes.

Example 5-2 (a) Rhombic and monoclinic sulfur (S_r and S_m) are in equilibrium at 1 atm and $95.4°$. When S_r becomes S_m under these conditions $\Delta V = 0.447$ cm^3 mole^{-1} and $\Delta H = 90$ cal mole^{-1}. The equilibrium is univariant, so that the transition temperature changes with the pressure. Find the rate of change, dP/dT, at $95.4°$ and 1 atm. (b) Assuming that ΔV and ΔH are independent of P and T over the range of conditions in question, estimate the transition temperature at a pressure of 1000 atm.

Ans. (a) From Eq. (5-2) $dP/dT = 90/(273.2 + 95.4)(0.447) = 0.546$ cal cm^{-3} deg^{-1} = $0.546/0.0242 = 22.6$ atm deg^{-1} (since 0.0242 cal cm^{-3} = 1 atm). Consequently $dT/dP = 1/22.6 = 0.0442$ deg atm^{-1}.
(b) If ΔV and ΔH are independent of P and T then dP/dT must be too, so the univariant *P-T* transition line is assumed to be straight and $dP/dT = \Delta P/\Delta T = 22.6$ atm deg^{-1}. For a change of pressure from 1 to 1000 atm $\Delta P = 999$ atm, so $\Delta T = 999/22.6 = 44.2°$K or $°$C. The transition temperature at 1000 atm is therefore $95.4 + 44.2 = 139.6°$C.

Example 5-3 J. H. Mathews (*J. Am. Chem. Soc.*, **48**, 562 (1926)) gives the following equation for the vapor pressure P (in mm) of $C_6H_6(l)$ as a function of temperature ($T°K$): $\log P = 7.2610 - 1402.46\,T^{-1} - 51387.5\,T^{-2}$. The molar volumes of the coexisting $C_6H_6(l)$ and $C_6H_6(g)$ at the normal boiling point (80.2°) were found to be 96 and 27,816 cm^3 $mole^{-1}$, respectively. Find ΔH for the equilibrium vaporization at 80.2°.

Ans. It is simpler to work with P in atm rather than mm, but we note that d $\log P$ (atm)/dT = d $\log P$ (mm)/dT, since $\log P$ (atm) = $\log P$ (mm) − log 760.0. Therefore differentiation of the analytical expression for $\log P$ yields d $\log P/dT = 1402.46\,T^{-2} + 2(51387.5\,T^{-3})$, regardless of the units of P! Now since d $\log P/dT = (1/2.303)$d $\ln P/dT = (1/2.303P)(dP/dT)$ we find, on substituting $P = 1$ atm and $T = 353.4°K$, that $dP/dT = 0.03122$ atm deg^{-1}. But $\Delta V = 27,816 - 96 = 27,720$ cm^3 $mole^{-1}$. Substitution in Eq. (5-2) then gives $0.03122 = \Delta H/353.4(27,720)$, or $\Delta H = 305.8$ cm^3 atm $mole^{-1} = 305.8(0.02422)$ or 7405 cal $mole^{-1}$.

Note Direct calorimetric measurement of this quantity gave a value of 7370 cal $mole^{-1}$, in satisfactory agreement.

THE "IDEALIZED" CLAUSIUS-CLAPEYRON RELATION

Eqs. (5-1) and (5-2) apply to all univariant systems as has been stated. If only pure substances are involved this means two-phase systems at equilibrium. Still another simplification is often made *when one of the two phases is a gas*, i.e., when we confine ourselves to sublimation and vaporization equilibria. Furthermore we restrict ΔH and ΔV to the *formation of one mole* of vapor, so we are speaking of either L $\longrightarrow$ G or S $\cdot\rightarrow$ V. We now replace ΔV in Eq. (5-2) by $\overline{V}_g$ since the volume of a given amount of substance is usually so much larger in the vapor state than in the liquid or solid states (cf. Example 5-1 where $\overline{V}_g = 3.013(10^4)$ and $\overline{V}_l = 18.81$ cm^3 mole H_2O^{-1}). This gives $dP/dT = \Delta H/T\overline{V}_g$. Next we assume that the vapor is ideal, permitting us to replace $\overline{V}_g$ by RT/P to give:

$$dP/dT = P\Delta H/RT^2 \quad \text{or} \quad d \ln P/dT = \Delta H/RT^2 \tag{5-3}$$

Finally we assume that ΔH is independent of T and integrate Eq. (5-3) as follows:

$$\int d \ln P = \int (\Delta H/RT^2)dT \quad \text{or} \quad \ln P = -(\Delta H/R)(1/T) + \text{constant} \tag{5-4}$$

Converting to common logarithms gives:

$$\log P = -(\Delta H/2.303R)(1/T) + \text{constant} \tag{5-5}$$

If P is in atm this constant is seen to be equal to $(\Delta H/2.303R)/T'$, where T' is the temperature at which P becomes 1 atm. A plot of $\log P$ vs. $1/T$ should give a straight line with a slope $-\Delta H/2.303R$ and, when P is in atm, an intercept on the $\log P$ axis of $(\Delta H/2.303R)/T' = \Delta S/2.303R$, where ΔS is the entropy change at 1 atm. Thus one can find ΔH from the slope of such a graph and the entropy of vaporization (or sublimation) from the intercept. The units of ΔH will depend on the units used for R.

There are several things to be emphasized about Eqs. (5-3), (5-4) and (5-5). In the first place ΔH refers to the *molar* heat of *vaporization* (or *sublimation*) under *equilibrium* conditions. Secondly these equations are valid only *if* (1) $\overline{V}_g \gg \overline{V}_l$ or $\overline{V}_s$, and *if* (2) the vapor is ideal. Thirdly, Eq. (5-5) is valid only *if* (3) ΔH is independent of T. Of these three conditions (1) may usually be assumed unless the vapor pressure is large (at least several atmospheres) but (2) and (3) are often not acceptable.

The approximate nature of Eqs. (5-3), (5-4) and (5-5), which we shall call the *idealized* Clausius-Clapeyron relations, can be illustrated with the accurate data for $C_6H_6(l)$ calculated by Mathews' analytical expression as stated in Example 5-3. These are shown in Table 5-2. A plot of

Table 5-2

$T(^\circ K)$	271.0	389.9	548.8	737.2
$(1/T)(10^4)$	30.93	30.00	29.13	28.38
$P(mm)$	270.0	389.6	549.2	737.1
$\log P$	2.4314	2.5906	2.7397	2.8675

$\log P$ vs. $1/T$ (not shown but similar to Figs. 5-4 and 5-5) appears to the naked eye to be quite straight. Its slope, $d \log P/d(1/T)$, may be obtained from the expression for $d \log P/dT$: since $d(1/T) = -dT/T^2$, $d \log P/d(1/T) = -(d \log P/dT)T^2 = -1402.46 - 2(51387.5 T^{-1})$. Putting $T = 353.4$ gives $d \log P/d(1/T) = -1693.3$ deg. This equals $-\Delta H/2.303R$ or $\Delta H = 7748$ cal mole^{-1} which is about 5% larger than the true value! Such an error is inherent in many computations of ΔH from the slope of $\log P$ vs. $1/T$ lines by this method. Ways of correcting for the error will be mentioned later in this chapter. If, however, V_g is known, one can proceed confidently as shown in Example 5-3 using Eq. (5-2), for one does not then have to rely on the applicability of the ideal gas law.

The errors just referred to are often overlooked in elementary work, and plots of $\log P$ vs. $1/T$ are required for data which are not given as analytical functions but as pairs of values of P and T. The lines are frequently straight, particularly if the temperature range is small. The student is often expected to assume linearity and to assume that ΔH is independent of T, in spite of the fact that ΔH for vaporization must decrease with rise in T, becoming zero at the critical temperature. Suppose, e.g., we are provided with vapor pressures for $(C_2H_5)_2O(l)$ at given temperatures, as shown in Table 5-3. In Fig. 5-4 $\log P$ is plotted against $1/T$. However, it is recommended that the student familiarize himself with the use of "semilog" paper in which the values of P, not $\log P$, are plotted, but on a logarithmic scale as in Fig. 5-5. The two graphs are identical but the use of semilog paper has eliminated the operation of taking logarithms.

Table 5-3

$T(°K)$	221.3	236.7	251.4	262.8
$P(mm)$	8.50	22.9	59.2	110.0
$(1/T)(10^4)$	45.18	42.25	39.77	38.05
$\log P(mm)$	0.93	1.360	1.772	2.041

Having plotted the data, the best straight line is then drawn through the points as shown, or calculated by a method such as that of least squares, and its slope determined. This is a source of difficulty for many students. There are several wrong ways to do it! One wrong way is to measure the angle the line makes with the $1/T$ axis and then to find its tangent. Another wrong way is to draw lines such as the dotted ones, measure the lengths of a and b with a ruler and then divide a by b. It is best to take two widely separated points on the line, such as A and B, and record their coordinates, ($\log P_2$, $1/T_2$) for A and ($\log P_1$, $1/T_1$) for B. The slope is then $(\log P_2 - \log P_1)/(1/T_2 - 1/T_1)$. (A common error, especially when using semilog paper, is to record the coordinates as (P_2, $1/T_2$) and (P_1, $1/T_1$), forgetting that it is not P that is plotted, but $\log P$.) Since $P_2 > P_1$ and $T_2 > T_1$ the slope will be negative and in $°K$. Equating it to $-\Delta H/2.303R$ gives ΔH immediately. In the present example point A is at $\log P = 2.079$ and $1/T = 37.80(10^{-4})$; B is at $\log P = 1.041$ and $1/T = 44.40(10^{-4})$. The slope is therefore $(2.079 - 1.041)/(37.80 - 44.40)(10^{-4}) = -1573 = -\Delta H/2.303R$, giving $\Delta H = 7200$ cal mole^{-1}.

There remains still another form of the idealized Clausius-Clapeyron relation to be mentioned. If Eq. (5-3) be integrated between pressures P_1 and P_2 at temperatures T_1 and T_2, assuming ΔH to be independent of T, we find:

$$\ln (P_2/P_1) = \frac{\Delta H}{R} \frac{(T_2 - T_1)}{T_1 T_2} \quad \text{or} \quad \log (P_2/P_1) = \frac{\Delta H}{2.303R} \frac{(T_2 - T_1)}{T_1 T_2} \quad (5\text{-}6)$$

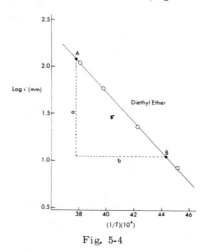

Fig. 5-4

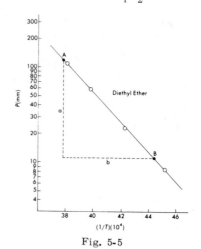

Fig. 5-5

which permits calculation of P at any temperature T if it is known at any other temperature, provided ΔH is known. Alternatively, if two points (P_1, T_1) and (P_2, T_2) are known Eq. (5-6) may be used to find ΔH. Clearly, this relation is no more accurate than the other idealized forms.

When values of log P are plotted against $1/T$ over a wide range of temperature it often happens that a line with a slight curvature results. *If we have reason to believe that* $\overline{V}_g \gg \overline{V}_l$ or $\overline{V}_s$ and that the vapor is ideal (e.g., when P is very small) we may proceed as follows: since $d(1/T) = -dT/T^2$ Eq. (5-3) can be written:

$$d \ln P/d(1/T) = -\Delta H/R \quad \text{or} \quad d \log P/d(1/T) = -\Delta H/2.303R \quad (5\text{-}7)$$

Since curvature means a change of slope with temperature the implication is that ΔH is temperature dependent. The slope at any given temperature can then be used to find ΔH at that temperature.

The impression may have been gained from the preceding that a linear log P vs. $1/T$ plot means that ΔH is independent of T and that the vapor is ideal. It must be emphasized that this is not so, for although the combination of a constant ΔH over a range of T with ideal behavior on the part of the vapor commonly give a linear plot, *the converse does not follow.* The data for $C_6H_6(l)$, e.g., give a practically linear plot and yet ΔH *does* vary with temperature and the vapor is *not* ideal: ΔH is 7400 and 7750 cal mole^{-1} at 80 and 50°, respectively; $\overline{V}_g$ at 80.2° is 27,816 cm^3 mole^{-1}, whereas the ideal value is 28,980. The same is true for many other liquids. How this can come about has been shown by O. L. I. Brown (*J. Chem. Educ.*, **28**, 428 (1951)) as follows: ΔV per mole $= \overline{V}_g - \overline{V}_l = \overline{V}_g[1 - (\overline{V}_l/\overline{V}_g)] = (zRT/P)[1 - (\overline{V}_l/\overline{V}_g)]$, where z is the compressibility factor of the vapor under the given conditions and is, of course, a function of P and T. Substituting this expression for ΔV in Eq. (5-2) gives $d \ln P/dT = \Delta H/zRT^2[1 - (\overline{V}_l/\overline{V}_g)]$. Replacing dT by $-T^2d(1/T)$ and $d \ln P$ by 2.303 d log P gives $d \log P/d(1/T) = -\Delta H/2.303zR[1 - (\overline{V}_l/\overline{V}_g)] = $ the slope of the line. Now z varies from unity at $P = 0$ to about 0.2 at the critical pressure. At the same time $1 - (\overline{V}_l/\overline{V}_g)$ varies from unity to zero, and ΔH drops from a sizeable quantity to zero. Thus with rise in T (approach to the critical point), both the numerator and denominator in the expression for d log $P/d(1/T)$ decrease. It is thus possible for the slope to remain effectively constant even though ΔH is changing considerably and the vapor is not ideal.

Finally, since vapor pressure curves are also boiling point curves expressions for dP/dT can be inverted to give dT/dP, which is the rate of change of boiling point with pressure. For liquids which obey Trouton's rule (ΔS for vaporization at the normal \ boiling point $= 21$) a simple, approximate expression for dT/dP at T_b, the normal boiling point, can be found from Eq. (5-2) by replacing $\Delta H/T_b$ by 21 eu mole^{-1} or 21/24.2 liter-atm deg^{-1} mole^{-1} and ΔV by $\overline{V}_g$ or $RT_b/P = 0.082T_b/1$ liter mole^{-1}. This yields, on inversion, $dT/dP = (0.082T_b)/(21/24.2) = 0.094T_b$ deg

$atm^{-1} = (0.094/760)T_b$ or $0.000124T_b$ deg mm^{-1}. For small changes this becomes:

$$\Delta T = 0.000124T_b \, [P(mm) - 760] \qquad (5.8)$$

which gives the difference between the normal boiling point and that under a pressure of P mm.

Example 5-4 Assuming that $C_6H_6(l)$ obeys Trouton's rule, and given that its normal boiling point is $80.2°$, find the boiling point under a pressure of 756 mm.

Ans. $\Delta T = 0.000124(353.4)(756 - 760) = -0.18°$. The boiling point at 756 mm is therefore $80.2 - 0.18 = 80.0°$.

FUGACITY

The equality of the free energies of two phases such as liquid and vapor in equilibrium can be viewed mechanistically: we may say that the escaping tendency of the vapor equals that of the liquid. The advantage of this viewpoint is that escaping tendency is a more tangible concept and common sense dictates that it be akin to a pressure and so measured in the same units as pressure. Similarly, in a saturated solution of a solid in a liquid, the escaping tendency of the dissolved solid equals that of the undissolved solid. (Here, however, the escaping tendency of the solid may not be directly demonstrable if it is an involatile solid, but this does not affect the argument.) The possibility of measuring escaping tendency directly as a pressure would appear to be a fruitful experimental approach to free energy.

In seeking to relate escaping tendency to free energy we may well think first in terms of an ideal gas. Eq. (4-28), applied to 1 mole, with $\overline{V}$ replaced by RT/P, gives $dG_T = RT \, d \ln P_T$ which on integration at constant temperature yields:

$$\overline{G} = RT \ln P + \text{constant} \qquad (5-9)$$

relating the pressure of an *ideal* gas to its free energy. The unknown absolute value of $\overline{G}$ is reflected in the unknown integration constant. For a real gas a similar function is desirable so that the real behavior will reduce to the ideal at small values of P. For this reason G. N. Lewis, who invented and developed the concept of escaping tendency, and called it **fugacity**, f, defined it for all substances, including those in solution, by:

$$\overline{G} = RT \ln f + B \qquad (5-10)$$

with the proviso that f approach the ideal pressure as the gas is made more and more ideal by reduction in its pressure. B is an unknown constant that depends only on the temperature and on the substance itself. For pure ideal gases f is identical with P, the pressure of the gas. (For ideal gas mixtures f is identical with partial pressure.) For an ideal gas, then, f is readily found by finding P. For non-ideal gases f will differ from P: sometimes greater, sometimes smaller. Fugacities of liquids or solids are found by equilibrating them with their vapors and finding the fugacities of the latter. The ratio f/P or, for gases in gas mixtures, f_i/p_i (where the subscript refers to the ith component and p is its partial pressure), is called the **activity coefficient** of the gas. We may think of f as a corrected P (or f_i as a corrected p_i). Observe that the ratios f/P approach unity as P is made indefinitely small. This state of infinite attenuation is sometimes called the **reference state** of the gas. Its activity coefficient is there unity.

Example 5-5 The vapor pressure of liquid mercury is 0.900 mm at 124°. What is the fugacity of Hg(l) at that temperature if its vapor is ideal?

Ans. If the equilibrium vapor is ideal its fugacity must be 0.900 mm or 0.00118 atm so the fugacity of the liquid must also be 0.00118 atm.

In determining f it is necessary to make a series of isothermal measurements which will extend to very small values of P, in order to provide the link between the numerical values of what is measured, viz. P, and what we wish to find, viz. f, for $\lim_{P \to 0} (f/P) = 1$. The method is as follows. We know from Eq. (4-28) that, for isothermal changes $d\overline{G} = \overline{V}dP$. We also know, by differentiating Eq. (5-10), that $d\overline{G} = RT \, d \ln f$. Therefore we have:

$$RT \, d \ln f = \overline{V}dP \qquad (5\text{-}11)$$

Let us define another quantity, b, as the difference between the molar volume of the gas at the given temperature, $\overline{V}$, and its volume if it were ideal, $\overline{V}_{id}$, i.e.:

$$b = \overline{V} - \overline{V}_{id} = \overline{V} - RT/P \qquad (5\text{-}12)$$

Usually $b < 0$, but high pressure and/or high temperature give $b > 0$. We note, parenthetically, that b corresponds to the **second virial coefficient** in the virial equation of state, $P\overline{V} = RT + \beta P + \gamma P^2 + \delta P^3 + \ldots$, when the pressure is so small as to make all but the first two terms on the right negligible. We can now write $\overline{V} = b + RT/P$ in Eq. (5-11) to give $RT \, d \ln f = (b + RT/P) dP$ or $d \ln (f/P) = (b/RT) dP$. Integrating from some very small pressure P^* to a pressure P gives:

$$\int_{P*}^{P} d \ln (f/P) = (1/RT) \int_{P*}^{P} b dP \qquad \text{or} \qquad \ln (f/P) - \ln (f*/P*)$$

$$= (1/RT) \int_{P*}^{P} b dP$$

At P^*, which is removed infinitesimally from zero, $f/P = 1$ so $\ln (f*/P*) = 0$. Furthermore, we may replace P^* by 0 in the lower limit of the other integral, so we have:

$$\ln (f/P) = (1/RT) \int_0^P b\,dP \tag{5-13}$$

This permits finding f corresponding to pressure P at temperature T. The integral can be determined by measuring the area under the curve in a plot of b vs. P, or by integration if b is known as a function of P. Clearly, the dependence of b on P is needed for either method.

Example 5-6 If a virial equation of state for $N_2(g)$ at $0°$ is $P\overline{V} = RT - 1.0512(10^{-2})P + 8.626(10^{-5})P^2 - 6.910(10^{-8})P^3 + 1.704(10^{-11})P^4$, where P is in atmospheres and $\overline{V}$ in liters per mole, find its fugacity at $0°$ and a pressure of 200 atm.

Ans. If the virial equation be divided through by P and the resulting expression for $\overline{V}$ be substituted in Eq. (5-12) for b we find $b = -1.0512(10^{-2}) + 8.626(10^{-5})P - 6.910(10^{-8})P^2 + 1.704(10^{-11})P^3$. Substitution of this in Eq. (5-13) gives, on integration, $\ln (f/200) = (-2.1024 + 1.7252 - 0.1842 + 0.0068)/22.414 = -0.02474$, or $f = 195$ atm.

Alternatively, b can be expressed in terms of z, the compressibility factor ($= P\overline{V}/RT$), by eliminating $\overline{V}$ from Eq. (5-12) and $\overline{V} = zRT/P$ to give $b = (RT/P)(z - 1)$. Insertion of this into Eq. (5-13) yields:

$$\ln (f/P) = \int_0^P (z - 1)\,d \ln P \tag{5-14}$$

which is used in the same way as Eq. (5-13).

When accurate values of b or z are not known f can be estimated in several ways. In one method advantage is taken of the fact that b is nearly independent of P at not-too-high pressures so, on integrating Eq. (5-13), we find:

$$\ln (f/P) = bP/RT \tag{5-15}$$

Taking antilogarithms gives $f/P = \exp(bP/RT)$ and expansion of the exponential (ignoring all but the first two terms of the expansion) yields $f/P \cong 1 + bP/RT = 1 + [\overline{V} - (RT/P)](P/RT) = \overline{V}P/RT = P/P_{id}$. This relation, viz.

$$f/P \cong P/P_{id} \tag{5-16}$$

is only an approximation, but a good one at low enough pressures and high enough temperatures.

Example 5-7 The density ρ of $NH_3(g)$ at $200°$ and 50.0 atm is 24.30 g liter^{-1}. Estimate its fugacity by means of Eq. (5-16). The molecular weight M is 17.03 g mole^{-1}.

Ans. For ideal gases $\rho = PM/RT$ so $P_{id} = (\rho/M)RT = (24.30/17.03)(0.0821)(473) = 55.4$ atm. From Eq. (5-16) $f \cong P^2/P_{id} = 50.0^2/55.4 = 45.1$ atm.

Note The correct value is 45.7 atm. Observe that f and P_{id} are similar but not identical in meaning: P_{id} is the pressure the same sample of gas would exert in the same volume at the same temperature if it were ideal; f is the quantity which is related to the free energy of the gas in the same way as P would be related to it if the gas were ideal.

Another approximate method utilizes generalized charts and the quantities **reduced pressure** (π) and **reduced temperature** (θ), where $\pi = P/P_c$ and $\theta = T/T_c$, P_c and T_c being the critical pressure and critical temperature, respectively. Since z is the *same* function of π and θ for all van der Waals gases, it is possible to estimate it, and therefore estimate f, from curves of z vs. π for various values of θ. Graphs of such data are called **generalized compressibility charts.** However, since f/P is also a universal function of π and θ for all van der Waals gases, as can be shown by examination of Eq. (5-14), it is possible to estimate f/P *directly* from the analogous **generalized fugacity charts** of which Fig. 5-6 is a sample. Other charts covering different ranges of π and θ are available. Each curve refers to a particular value of θ. To find the fugacity of $NH_3(g)$ at $723°K$ and 300 atm, e.g., we first determine that its critical temperature is $406°K$ and its critical pressure 111.5 atm. Under the given conditions, then, $\theta = 723/406 = 1.78$ and $\pi = 300/111.5 = 2.69$. We now find from Fig. 5-6, by interpolation, that for this pair of values $f/P \simeq 0.90$, so $f \simeq 0.90(300) = 270$ atm. Further reference to this method will be found in Chapter 10.

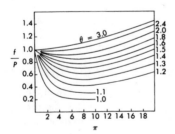

Fig. 5-6. (From Glasstone's *Thermodynamics*, Copyright 1947, D. Van Nostrand Company, Inc., Princeton, N. J.)

Still another approximate method of finding f from the critical constants is one which uses the Berthelot equation of state:

$$P\overline{V} = RT + (9RT_c P/128P_c)[1 - (6T_c^2/T^2)] \qquad (5\text{-}17)$$

The second term on the right equals bP, as shown earlier. Substitution of this value into Eq. (5-15) gives:

$$\ln(f/P) = (9T_c P/128P_c T)[1 - 6(T_c^2/T^2)] \qquad (5\text{-}18)$$

which provides approximate values of f at temperature T and pressure P when T_c and P_c are known.

Example 5-8 Find f for $NH_3(g)$ at $200°$ and 50.0 atm by means of Eq. (5-18) if its critical temperature and pressure are $406°K$ and 111.5 atm. Compare the result with that found in Example 5-7.

Ans. Eq. (5-18)   gives $\ln (f/50.0) = [9(406)(50.0)/128(111.5)(473)][1 - 6(406^2/473^2)]$, from which $f = 45.6$ atm. This result is nearer the correct value than that found by Eq. (5-16) in Example 5-7.

We illustrate how f may be used in calculating ΔG for a substance undergoing an isothermal change. If we write Eq. (5-10) for the initial and final states ($\overline{G}_1 = RT \ln f_1 + B$ and $\overline{G}_2 = RT \ln f_2 + B$) the free energy change per mole is given by the difference, viz.

$$\Delta G = RT \ln (f_2/f_1) \qquad (5-19)$$

the constant B being the same in both states for it refers to the same substance at the same temperature. Eq. (5-19) is valid for all states of aggregation. For ideal gases it reduces to $\Delta G = RT \ln (P_2/P_1)$ as in Chapter 4.

Example 5-9 When $N_2(g)$ is at $0°$ its fugacity is 1840 atm at a pressure of 1000 atm, and 195 atm at a pressure of 200 atm. Find ΔG_{273} for $2N_2(g, 1000 \text{ atm}) \longrightarrow 2N_2(g, 200 \text{ atm})$, and compare with the value for ideal behavior.

Ans. Substitution in Eq. (5-19) gives $\Delta G = 2RT \ln (195/1840) = 2(1.987) (273)(2.303) \log (195/1840) = -2435$ cal. If the gas had been ideal $\Delta G = 2RT \ln (200/1000) = -1745$ cal, a difference of nearly 30%.

STANDARD FREE ENERGY CHANGE FOR GASES

The symbol $\overline{G}°$ with reference to a gas stands for its molar free energy in the (hypothetical) ideal gas state at a pressure or fugacity of 1 atm (cf. $\overline{C}_P°$, $\overline{H}°$, $\overline{S}°$). In accurate work it is necessary to find the difference between $\overline{G}°$ and the free energy of the real gas at 1 atm, which we shall denote by $\overline{G}$. This difference is readily found by considering the following changes, all at temperature T:

$$\text{Real gas (1 atm, } f = f) \xrightarrow{\ (1)\ } \text{Ideal gas (1 atm, } f = 1)$$

$$\downarrow (2) \qquad\qquad\qquad \uparrow (4)$$

$$\text{Real gas } (P^* \text{ atm, } f = P^*) \xrightarrow{\ (3)\ } \text{Ideal gas } (P^* \text{ atm, } f = P^*)$$

P^* is some very small pressure. Now $\overline{G}° - \overline{G}$, the negative of the desired quantity, is given by ΔG in step (1) or the sum of the ΔG's in steps (2), (3) and (4). By Eq. (5-19) ΔG in (2) $= RT \ln (P^*/f)$. In (3) the initial and final states are identical, for all gases are ideal at low enough pressure, so $\Delta G = 0$. In (4) $\Delta G = RT \ln (1/P^*)$. Therefore ΔG in (1) $= RT \ln (P^*/f) +$ $RT \ln (1/P^*) = RT \ln (1/f) = \overline{G}^\circ - \overline{G}$, so we have:

$$\overline{G} - \overline{G}^\circ = RT \ln f \qquad (5\text{-}20)$$

where f is the fugacity of the gas at a pressure of 1 atm. Finding $\overline{G} - \overline{G}^\circ$ in this way for each gas in a given reaction permits converting ΔG's at 1 atm to ΔG°'s. In this way standard free energies of formation involving gases are found.

Example 5-10 If the fugacity of $CO(g)$ at -50° and 1 atm is 0.9980 atm what correction must be made to $\overline{G}$ for this gas at -50° and 1 atm to convert it to $\overline{G}^\circ$? Is this correction to be added or subtracted?

Ans. The correction is $\overline{G} - \overline{G}^\circ = RT \ln 0.9980 = -0.888$ cal, so 0.888 cal must be added to $\overline{G}$ to give $\overline{G}^\circ$.

VARIATION OF FUGACITY WITH PRESSURE AND TEMPERATURE

If we differentiate Eq. (5-10) with respect to pressure at constant temperature we find $(\partial \overline{G}/\partial P)_T = RT(\partial \ln f/\partial P)_T$. By Eq. (4-28) however, the left-hand side equals $\overline{V}$. We have, then,

$$(\partial \ln f/\partial P)_T = \overline{V}/RT \qquad (5\text{-}21)$$

from which f at one pressure can be found from f at another pressure by integration. For gases $\overline{V}$ must be known as a function of P. For liquids and solids $\overline{V}$ is approximately independent of pressure.

Example 5-11 The fugacity of $Hg(l)$ at 100° and 1.0 atm is 0.272 mm, its density 13.35 g cm^{-3}, and its molecular weight 200.6 g $mole^{-1}$. Find its fugacity at the same temperature under a pressure of 100.0 atm, assuming it to be incompressible.

Ans. $\overline{V} = 200.6/13.35 = 150.2$ cm^3 $mole^{-1}$, so $(\partial \ln f/\partial P)_T = 150.2/82.06(373.2) = 0.00490$ atm^{-1}. Integration gives $\log f$ at 100 atm -- $\log f$ at 1 atm $= 0.00490(100.0 - 1.0)/2.303 = 0.2106$ or f at 100 atm/f at 1 atm $= 1.624 = f$ at 100 atm/0.272, where f is in millimeters. Therefore f at 100 atm $= 1.624(0.272) = 0.442$ mm.

The variation of fugacity with temperature at constant pressure may be found by imagining the substance with whose fugacity we are concerned to be converted isothermally to the highly attenuated (and therefore ideal) gas state at some very small pressure P^* thus:

Substance $(T^\circ K, P$ atm, $f = f) \longrightarrow$ Ideal gas $(T^\circ K, P^*$ atm, $f = P^*)$

For this change $\Delta G = \overline{G}_{(P=P^*)} - \overline{G} = RT \ln (P^*/f)$ by Eq. (5-19). Dividing through by T and differentiating with respect to T at constant P gives:

$$[\partial(\overline{G}_{(P=P^*)}/T)/\partial T)]_{P^*} - [\partial(\overline{G}/T)/\partial T]_P = R[(\partial \ln P^*/\partial T)_{P^*} - (\partial \ln f/\partial T)_P]$$

Use of Eq. (4-32) now permits the left-hand side to be written as $-\overline{H}^*/T^2 - (-\overline{H}/T^2)$, where $\overline{H}^*$ is the molar enthalpy of the ideal gas (at any pressure, since enthalpy is then independent of pressure). Furthermore, $(\partial \ln P^*/\partial T)_{P*} = 0$. We have, then,

$$(\partial \ln f/\partial T)_P = (\overline{H}^* - \overline{H})/RT^2 \qquad (5\text{-}22)$$

which is the desired result. The quantity $\overline{H}^* - \overline{H}$ is the enthalpy change for converting a mole of substance to the ideal gas state (at any pressure) or to the actual gas state at zero pressure. It is known as the "**ideal heat of vaporization**" from the given state or, if the given state is also a gas, the "**Joule-Thomson heat.**"

Example 5-12 Find the per cent increase in the fugacity of $O_2(g)$ per degree rise in temperature in the neighborhood of 298°K and 200 atm if, under these conditions, the Joule-Thomson heat is 347 cal mole^{-1}.

Ans. $(\partial \ln f/\partial T)_P = 347/1.987(298^2) = \ln f_{T+1} - \ln f_T = \ln (f_{T+1}/f_T)$ or $f_{T+1}/f_T = 1.002$. The fugacity increases by about 0.2% per degree rise in temperature at 298°K and 200 atm.

HEAT OF VAPORIZATION—FURTHER CONSIDERATIONS

We have seen that, without a knowledge of the molar volume of the vapor in equilibrium with a liquid at a given temperature, it is not possible to find an accurate value for the heat of vaporization directly from the slope of the log P vs. $1/T$ line even though the line appears to be straight. This is because errors in the plot resulting from the variation of ΔH with T and the non-ideality of the vapor tend to cancel. If it is possible to find or estimate the fugacity of the vapor, however, ΔH can be found with considerable accuracy. The reader is referred to a paper by L. Brewer and A. W. Searcy (*J. Chem. Educ.*, **26**, 548 (1949)) for details.

VARIATION OF VAPOR PRESSURE WITH TOTAL PRESSURE

It is well known that the pressure of the vapor of a liquid in equilibrium with the liquid is fixed at a fixed temperature and is known as the vapor pressure. If, however, one introduces a foreign, insoluble gas into the vapor space, thereby increasing the total pressure in the system, the partial pressure of the vapor in the resulting vapor-gas mixture is also slightly increased, i.e., the vapor pressure of the liquid is increased. Although, in general, the effect is small, it can become quite appreciable if the added gas is at a sufficiently high pressure.

We shall suppose, for simplicity, that the resulting vapor-gas mixture is ideal. The increased total pressure on the liquid increases its fugacity according to Eq. (5-21), $(\partial \ln f/\partial P)_T = \overline{V}_1/RT$, where P is the total pressure and $\overline{V}_1$ the molar volume of the liquid. Now if the system is at equilibrium at all values of P the fugacity of the liquid will equal that of the vapor of the liquid in the vapor-gas mixture. Moreover, as we have assumed the mixture to be ideal the fugacity of the vapor will equal its partial pressure p. The above relation may then be written:

$$(\partial \ln p/dP)_T = \overline{V}_1/RT \tag{5-23}$$

which gives the variation of vapor pressure p with total pressure P. It must be emphasized that this is only true for insoluble gases which form ideal mixtures with the vapor of the liquid. Unfortunately, when P is large enough to have a sizeable effect on p these assumptions do not hold in the cases which have been studied experimentally!

Example 5-13 The vapor pressure of water at 30.0° is 31.82 mm. Predict its vapor pressure under nitrogen (assumed insoluble in water) at a pressure of 10.0 atm, supposing the water vapor-nitrogen mixture to be ideal. The density of $H_2O(l)$ is 0.996 g cm^{-3} under these conditions and its molecular weight 18.02 g $mole^{-1}$.

Ans. $\overline{V}_1 = 18.02/0.996 = 18.09$ cm^3 $mole^{-1}$. Substituting this in Eq. (5-23) and integrating gives:

$$\int_{p_1}^{p_2} d \ln p = \int_{P_1}^{P_2} [18.09/82.06(303.2)]\,dP$$

where $P_1 = 31.82/760.0 = 0.04187$ atm, $P_2 = 10.0$ atm, $p_1 = 31.82$ mm and p_2 is to be determined. (Note that P must be in atm and $\overline{V}$ in cm^3 $mole^{-1}$ if R is in cm^3 atm deg^{-1} $mole^{-1}$, but that the units of p are immaterial as long as they are the same for both p_1 and p_2.) Therefore we have:

$$\ln (p_2/31.82) = [18.09/82.06(303.2)](10.0 - 0.0) = 0.00727$$

giving $p_2 = 32.08$ mm.

PROBLEMS

1. The data of Table 5-1 refer to the substance water which contracts on melting. What qualitative differences would there be for the corresponding table for a substance which expands on melting?
2. The melting point of potassium increases with pressure at the rate of 0.0167 deg atm^{-1}. If the densities of K(s) and K(l) are 0.851 and 0.830 g cm^{-3} at the normal melting point, 63.7°, find the heat fusion per gram.
3. Given the following sublimation and vapor pressure data for hydroquinone, use the "idealized" Clausius-Clapeyron relation to determine the heat of sublimation. ΔH_s, the heat of vaporization, ΔH_v, the heat of fusion, ΔH_f and the triple point temperature and pressure. The first two pairs of data refer to the solid state, the second two to the liquid.

$t(°C)$	132.4(s)	163.5(s)	192.0(l)	216.5(l)
P(mm)	1.00	10.00	40.00	100.00

4. Derive an expression for log P as a function of T where P is the vapor pressure of a liquid at temperature T and where it is assumed that $\overline{V}_g - \overline{V}_1 = \overline{V}_g$, that the vapor is ideal, and that $\overline{C}_P(g) - \overline{C}_P(l) = \Delta C_P$ = constant at all temperatures and pressures. Ignore the variation of enthalpy with pressure.

5. The slope of the log P vs. $1/T$ line for C_6H_6 is $-1693.3°K$, and it has been shown that d log $P/d(1/T) = -\Delta H/2.303zR\,[1 - (\overline{V}_1/\overline{V}_g)]$. Given that the true value for ΔH for the vaporization of $C_6H_6(l)$ at $353.4°K$ and 1 atm is 7400 cal mole^{-1}, and assuming that $\overline{V}_1/\overline{V}_g$ is negligible compared with unity, find z for C_6H_6 under these conditions.

6. Given the following virial equation of state for $CH_4(g)$ at $20°$ (when P is in atmospheres and $\overline{V}$ in liters) find its fugacity at that temperature and a pressure of 300 atm:

$$P\overline{V} = 24.055 - 4.8678(10^{-2})P + 8.956(10^{-5})P^2 + 10.486(10^{-10})P^4$$

7. For the vapor pressure of CO(l) as a function of T, W. F. Giauque (*J. Am. Chem. Soc.*, 54, 2610 (1932)) gives log P (cm) $= -477.3/T + 11.23721 - 0.064129T + 2.5911(10^{-4})T^2$. The molar volume is 35 cm^3 mole^{-1} at the normal boiling point, $81.61°K$, where the heat of vaporization is 1444 cal mole^{-1}.

   (a) Find dP/dT and $\overline{V}_g$ at the normal boiling point. Compare with the ideal value.

   (b) Estimate the fugacity and activity coefficient of CO at its normal boiling point using Eq. (5-16).

8. For CH_4, $T_c = 190.7°K$ and $P_c = 45.8$ atm. Estimate f for this gas at $20.0°$ and 300 atm using the Berthelot equation and compare the result with the more accurate value found in Problem 6.

9. Show that, in general, the variation of fugacity with pressure at constant temperature is only slight for liquids and solids but appreciable for gases, whereas the variation with temperature at constant pressure is appreciable for liquids and solids but only slight for gases.

10. The fugacity of $CH_4(g)$ at 300 atm is 141.8 atm at $240°K$ and 167.7 atm at $260°K$. Find the average Joule-Thomson heat at 300 atm in the range 240 to $260°K$.

11. The vapor pressure of water at $50.0°$ is 92.51 mm. Predict its vapor pressure under a pressure of nitrogen of 200 atm, supposing the water vapor-nitrogen mixture to be ideal. The density of $H_2O(l)$ is 0.988 g cm^{-3} under these conditions and its molecular weight is 18.02 g mole^{-1}.

Solutions—partial molar properties— the phase rule

SOLUTIONS

It is now necessary to extend the previous concepts to systems involving solutions—phases of variable composition. Solutions can be gaseous, liquid or solid. They are often called mixtures, especially when gaseous, and we shall frequently use this term for them out of deference to popular usage, but thermodynamically they are solutions. Solid solutions, often called mix-crystals, are less familiar to the student, but many instances are known. If gold and silver, e.g., are melted together and the melt cooled, the resulting solid is a solid solution: it is solid because it is crystalline and yet it is a solution because it is both homogeneous and variable in composition.

PARTIAL MOLAR PROPERTIES

The application of thermodynamic concepts to solutions immediately requires the idea of a state function for a pure substance to be extended to include the state function for a substance in solution. This means the introduction of the **partial molar state function**.

Suppose, e.g., we are interested in ΔV for the change:

$$n_A \text{ moles of } A(l) + n_B \text{ moles of } B(l) \longrightarrow (n_A + n_B) \text{ moles of solution}$$

at a given temperature and pressure. The required ΔV is the sum of the changes in volume which A and B undergo in the mixing process. We are thus led to the concept of the volume of a substance in solution. Moreover, we are just as often interested in the fate of only one of the components of the solution, e.g., in the change:

$$HCl(g) \longrightarrow HCl(0.1m \text{ soln})$$

The value of ΔV for this change refers only to the HCl and not to the solvent (although it is determined in part by the solvent). All the above comments on ΔV apply equally well to ΔE, ΔH, ΔS, ΔA and ΔG. There is thus the need for thermodynamic functions which describe the volume, energy, enthalpy, work content and free energy of a component in solution.

Before defining such quantities it is of paramount importance to be able to interpret the symbolism used in work with solutions. This is a common source of difficulty for the student. Let us look again at the equation given above, viz.

$$HCl(g) \longrightarrow HCl(0.1m)$$

We shall assume that the right-hand side refers to an aqueous solution, although this is not essential. Such an equation stands for the addition of one mole of HCl(g) to such a large amount of 0.1m HCl solution that the latter is *still* 0.1m after the addition! Although water is present *its* properties show no change, for *its* concentration and environment have not changed. Only the HCl which was added has undergone change. (On the other hand, if we had written:

$$HCl(g) + 555.1 \ H_2O(l) \longrightarrow HCl \cdot 555.1 \ H_2O$$

we would mean that we are *forming* a 0.1m HCl solution, and ΔV, ΔE, ΔH, etc., involve the changes in these properties for *both* the HCl and the H_2O.)

Again, suppose we consider the change:

$$\tfrac{1}{2}H_2(g) + AgCl(s) \longrightarrow HCl(0.1m) + Ag(s)$$

Such a change concerns the formation of HCl in a solution that is *already* 0.1m in HCl and *remains* so throughout the acquisition of the one mole of HCl. Thus the water (solvent) does not appear explicitly in our calculations (although the values of ΔV, ΔE, etc. would be different for a different solvent).

The quantity which expresses the thermodynamic state function for a substance in solution is the **partial molar state function**. If we use the symbol J to stand for the state function (V, E, H, S, A or G) of a *solution* it is observed that J depends on P, T and the number of moles of each component present, i.e.

$$J = f(P, \ T, \ n_1, \ n_2, \ n_3 \ldots) \tag{6-1}$$

where n_1, n_2, etc. denote the number of moles of the respective components. The solvent is usually designated component 1. The partial molar state function for component 1, which we shall designate $\overline{\overline{J}}_1*$, is defined by

$$\overline{\overline{J}}_1 = (\partial J/\partial n_1)_{P,T,n_2,n_3\ldots} \tag{6-2}$$

The partial molar state function for component 2 is, similarly,

$$\overline{\overline{J}}_2 = (\partial J/\partial n_2)_{P,T,n_1,n_3\ldots} \tag{6-3}$$

Thus the partial molar volume of the HCl in a $0.1m$ solution in water is given by $\overline{\overline{V}}_{HCl} = (\partial V/\partial n_{HCl})_{P,T,n_{H_2O}}$. It is therefore the increase in volume suffered by (all of) a solution of $0.1m$ HCl on the addition of 1 mole of HCl, the pressure, temperature and number of moles of H_2O being kept constant and the concentration of the solution remaining at $0.1m$. This requires us, in principle, to add the mole of HCl to an infinitely large quantity of $0.1m$ solution. Alternatively one may imagine adding an infinitesimal quantity of HCl (dn_{HCl}) to a finite quantity of $0.1m$ HCl solution, observing the change in volume (dV) and then dividing dV by dn_{HCl} to find the increase in V per mole of added HCl. Similarly, the partial molar free energy of the water ($\overline{\overline{G}}_{H_2O}$) and the partial molar free energy of the HCl ($\overline{\overline{G}}_{HCl}$) in the $0.1m$ HCl solution are given, respectively, by:

$$\overline{\overline{G}}_{H_2O} = (\partial G/\partial n_{H_2O})_{P,T,n_{HCl}} \quad \text{and} \quad \overline{\overline{G}}_{HCl} = (\partial G/\partial n_{HCl})_{P,T,n_{H_2O}}.$$

As it is customary to use the term **chemical potential** in place of partial molar free energy, and the symbol μ in place of $\overline{\overline{G}}$ (with the appropriate subscript), or even in place of $\overline{G}$ for a pure substance, the above statements become

$$\mu_{H_2O} = (\partial G/\partial n_{H_2O})_{P,T,n_{HCl}} \quad \text{and} \quad \mu_{HCl} = (\partial G/\partial n_{HCl})_{P,T,n_{H_2O}}.$$

respectively. Of the various partial molar quantities, it is primarily the chemical potential which concerns us here.

We now have to show why μ for a given component is the quantity which, for a substance in solution, replaces $\overline{G}$ for a pure substance in our

---

*This symbolism is introduced to distinguish the state functions referring to *any* given quantity of pure substance or solution, J, one mole of pure substance or solution (with subscript if necessary), $\overline{J}$, and one mole of substance *in* solution (with subscript), $\overline{\overline{J}}$. Thus the volume of 10 g, say, of aqueous ethanol will be designated by V, the volume of 1 mole of this solution by $\overline{V}$, the volume of 1 mole of pure water (or ethanol) as $\overline{V}_{H_2O \text{ (or } C_2H_5OH)}$, and the partial molar volume of water (or ethanol) in the solution as $\overline{\overline{V}}_{H_2O(\text{or } C_2H_5OH)}$. Some texts use a single bar over a symbol for a molar property, whether it is for a component in solution or not; others reserve the bar for a component in solution and use large and small capitals to distinguish non-molar from molar ones. The system adopted in this book is felt to be more suitable for student purposes, and it makes for less ambiguity in written work.

thermodynamic relations. Observe first of all that μ for any given component in solution reduces to $\bar{G}$ anyway for that component *when it is pure*. Since, for a pure substance, $G = f(P,T,n)$, there being no need for a subscript on the n, $(\partial G/\partial n)_{P,\,T}$ is the increase in G suffered by all of a sample of the pure substance when another mole of the substance is added to it. But this is identical to the free energy of the mole of added substance, $\bar{G}$. Thus $\bar{G}$ for a *pure* substance is the same quantity as G. The same is true, of course, for all the state functions.

Let us examine the following change:

$$H_2O\,(\text{g, 20 mm}) \longrightarrow H_2O(0.2m\ H_2SO_4)$$

To determine whether such a change is reversible, spontaneous or forbidden at a given temperature and pressure we would want to find ΔG for it. Now this is *not* the ΔG for adding one mole of $H_2O(g)$ to the requisite amount of pure $H_2SO_4(l)$, (actually 0.353 g) to give a $0.2m$ solution; ΔG for this operation would tell us only whether a mole of $H_2O(g)$ dissolves spontaneously or not in 0.353 g of $H_2SO_4(l)$ to give $0.2m$ solution. Rather we would want to find the free energy change suffered by the water only, when one mole of it is transferred from the gaseous state at 20 mm to a solution of H_2SO_4 *already* $0.2m$. This ΔG is the difference between the free energy gained by the $0.2m$ solution on acquiring the mole of H_2O and the free energy lost by the disappearance of the mole of $H_2O(g)$, i.e., $\Delta G = \mu_{H_2O} - \bar{G}_{H_2O}(g)$. The same is true if we had wished to find the change in any other state function for this transfer: $\Delta V = \bar{V}_{H_2O} - \bar{V}_{H_2O(g)}$, $\Delta H = \bar{H}_{H_2O} - \bar{H}_{H_2O(g)}$, etc. We see, then, that in such transfer processes, where we are concerned with the individual components in a solution, it is essential to use the partial molar state functions, not the molar state functions. Clearly, both the molar properties and the partial molar properties are expressed in the same units.

Example 6-1 For each of the following changes write the expression for ΔV and ΔG using the symbolism described: (a) $H_2O\,(0.7m\ NaCl) \longrightarrow$ $H_2O(g)$, (b) $0.2C_6H_6(l) + 0.6C_6H_5\cdot CH_3(l) \longrightarrow$ Soln, (c) $CaCO_3(s) \longrightarrow$ $CaO(s) + CO_2(g,\ CO_2\text{-air mixture})$.

Ans. (a) $\Delta V = \bar{V}_{H_2O(g)} - \bar{V}_{H_2O}$; $\Delta G = \bar{G}_{H_2O(g)} - \mu_{H_2O}$. (b) $\Delta V = 0.2(\bar{V}_{C_6H_6} - \bar{V}_{C_6H_6(l)}) + 0.6(\bar{V}_{C_6H_5\cdot CH_3} - \bar{V}_{C_6H_5\cdot CH_3(l)})$; $\Delta G = 0.2(\mu_{C_6H_6} - \bar{G}_{C_6H_6(l)}) + 0.6(\mu_{C_6H_5\cdot CH_3} - \bar{G}_{C_6H_5\cdot CH_3(l)})$. (c) $\Delta V = \bar{V}_{CO_2} + \bar{V}_{CaO(s)} - \bar{V}_{CaCO_3(s)}$; $\Delta G = \mu_{CO_2} + \bar{G}_{CaO(s)} - \bar{G}_{CaCO_3(s)}$.

Example 6-2 (a) Find an expression for the partial molar volume of a gas in an ideal gas mixture at total pressure P and temperature T. (b) Use it to find the partial molar volume of argon in an ideal mixture of 0.50 mole Ar and 1.50 mole Ne at $0°$ and a total pressure of 0.20 atm.

Ans. (a) For the mixture, $PV = n_t RT$ where $n_t = n_1 + n_2 + n_3 + \ldots$, and the subscripts refer to the various species. For gas 1, we have:

$$\overline{\overline{V}}_1 = (\partial V / \partial n_1)_{P,\,T,\,n_2,\,n_3 \ldots}$$

$$= \frac{\partial}{\partial n_1}\left[\frac{(n_1 + n_2 + n_3 + \ldots)RT}{P}\right]_{P,\,T,\,n_2,\,n_3 \ldots} = RT/P$$

(b) $\overline{V}_{Ar} = 0.0821(273.2)/0.20 = 112$ liters.

Note The value of $\overline{V}$ is the same for all the gases of the ideal mixture and depends only on the temperature and total pressure. $\overline{V}_{Ar}$ must not be confused with the volume of gas mixture which contains one mole of Ar. This latter quantity is given by $RT/$partial pressure of Ar.

We have seen in the earlier chapters numerous expressions for the dependence of the state functions for pure substances on temperature and pressure, and other relations. Analogous expressions for the partial molar state functions can readily be found by differentiation. Let us suppose, for simplicity, that only two components are present in the solution, although this is not essential. Eq. (1-8), e.g., can be differentiated with respect to n_1 at constant T, P and n_2 giving:

$$\left[\frac{\partial}{\partial n_1}\left(\frac{\partial H}{\partial T}\right)_P\right]_{P,\,T,\,n_2} = \left[\frac{\partial C_P}{\partial n_1}\right]_{P,\,T,\,n_2}$$

or, reversing the order of differentiation.

$$\left[\frac{\partial}{\partial T}\left(\frac{\partial H}{\partial n_1}\right)_{P,\,T,\,n_2}\right]_P = \overline{\overline{C}}_{P_1}$$

or

$$(\partial \overline{\overline{H}}_1 / \partial T)_P = \overline{\overline{C}}_{P_1}$$

The last differentiation is made at constant composition as well as at constant pressure, since the original differentiation, $(\partial H / \partial T)_P$, carried this implication. As a reminder of this it is better to write $(\partial \overline{\overline{H}}_1 / \partial T)_{P,X} = \overline{\overline{C}}_{P_1}$. If, instead, we had differentiated with respect to n_2, we should have found $(\partial \overline{\overline{H}}_2 / \partial T)_{P,X} = \overline{\overline{C}}_{P_2}$. In a similar fashion Eqs. (4-27), (4-28), (5-21), (4-12), etc. lead, respectively, to $(\partial \overline{\overline{V}}_i / \partial T)_{P,X} = -(\partial \overline{\overline{S}}_i / \partial P)_{T,X}$, $(\partial \mu_i / \partial P)_{T,X} = \overline{\overline{V}}_i$, $(\partial \ln f_i / \partial P)_{T,X} = \overline{\overline{V}}_i / RT$, $\mu_i = \overline{\overline{H}}_i - T\overline{\overline{S}}_i$, etc., where i refers to the component in question. *In this way the thermodynamic relations become applicable to components in solution.*

Example 6-3 The partial molar volume of ethanol in a 52.5% (by weight) aqueous solution at $25°$ is $57.0 \text{ cm}^3 \text{ mole}^{-1}$. By how much does its chemical potential in this solution increase for every atmosphere increase in the total pressure on the solution at 25°? (Ignore the compressibility of the solution.)

Ans. By Eq. (4-28), modified as shown, we have $(\partial \mu_{EtOH}/\partial P)_T = \bar{\bar{V}}_{EtOH}$ or $\Delta \mu_{EtOH} = 57.0 \ \Delta P$. Therefore μ_{EtOH} increases by 57.0 cm^3 atm $mole^{-1}$ or 1.38 cal $mole^{-1}$ per atm rise in pressure.

THE FUNDAMENTAL EQUATIONS OF PARTIAL MOLAR PROPERTIES

We now show certain fundamental relationships which exist among the partial molar properties. The total differential of any state function J is, from Eq. (6-1),

$$dJ = (\partial J/\partial P)_{T,X}dP + (\partial J/\partial T)_{P,X}dT + (\partial J/\partial n_1)_{T,P,n_2...}dn_1$$
$$+ (\partial J/\partial n_2)_{T,P,n_1...}dn_2 + ... \qquad (6\text{-}4)$$

When P and T are both constant this becomes:

$$dJ = \bar{\bar{J}}_1 dn_1 + \bar{\bar{J}}_2 dn_2 + ... \qquad (6\text{-}5)$$

Integration *at constant composition* gives:

$$J = \bar{\bar{J}}_1 n_1 + \bar{\bar{J}}_2 n_2 + ... \qquad (6\text{-}6)$$

or, for one mole of solution,

$$\bar{J} = \bar{\bar{J}}_1 X_1 + \bar{\bar{J}}_2 X_2 + ... \qquad (6\text{-}7)$$

If we now take the total differential of Eq. (6-6) we obtain:

$$dJ = \bar{\bar{J}}_1 dn_1 + \bar{\bar{J}}_2 dn_2 + ... + n_1 d\bar{\bar{J}}_1 + n_2 d\bar{\bar{J}}_2 + ...$$
$$= dJ + n_1 d\bar{\bar{J}}_1 + n_2 d\bar{\bar{J}}_2 + ...$$

by Eq. (6-5). Therefore we have:

$$n_1 d\bar{\bar{J}}_1 + n_2 d\bar{\bar{J}}_2 + ... = 0 \qquad (6\text{-}8)$$

Dividing through by $(n_1 + n_2 + ...)$ gives:

$$X_1 d\bar{\bar{J}}_1 + X_2 d\bar{\bar{J}}_2 + ... = 0 \qquad (6\text{-}9)$$

These relationships, as applied to particular state functions such as V or G, are useful in the thermodynamics of solutions. For free energy considerations, e.g., Eqs. (6-5), (6-7) and (6-9) become:

$$dG = \mu_1 dn_1 + \mu_2 dn_2 + ... = \sum_i \mu_i dn_i \qquad (6\text{-}10)$$

$$\bar{G} = \mu_1 X_1 + \mu_2 X_2 + ... = \sum_i \mu_i X_i \qquad (6\text{-}11)$$

and

$$X_1 d\mu_1 + X_2 d\mu_2 + ... = 0 = \sum_i X_i d\mu_i \qquad (6\text{-}12)$$

They will be illustrated shortly. Suffice for the present to note that Eq. (6-11), e.g., shows that each component contributes $\mu_i X_i$ to the molar free energy of the solution. Eq. (6-12) shows that any variation in the chemical potential of one component in a solution at constant T and P affects that of all the others in a prescribed manner. It is known as the **Gibbs-Duhem equation.**

Example 6-4 (a) When 1.158 moles of water are dissolved in 0.842 moles of ethanol the volume of the solution is 68.16 cm^3 at 25°. If $\bar{\bar{V}}_{H_2O} = 16.98$ cm^3 $mole^{-1}$ in this solution find $\bar{\bar{V}}_{C_2H_5OH}$. (b) Compare the partial molar volumes of the components with their molar volumes, if H_2O (l) and $C_2H_5 \cdot OH$ (l) have molecular weights of 18.02 and 46.07 g $mole^{-1}$, and densities of 0.9970 and 0.7852 g cm^{-3}, respectively, at this temperature.

Ans. (a) By Eq. (6-6) applied to volume, $V = \bar{\bar{V}}_{H_2O} n_{H_2O} + \bar{\bar{V}}_{C_2H_5OH} \cdot n_{C_2H_5OH}$, so 68.16 = (1.158)(16.98) + 0.842 $\bar{\bar{V}}_{C_2H_5OH}$ or $\bar{\bar{V}}_{C_2H_5OH} =$ 57.60 cm^3 $mole^{-1}$. (b) $\bar{\bar{V}}_{H_2O} = 18.02/0.9970 = 18.05$ cm^3 $mole^{-1}$ (cf. 16.98). $\bar{\bar{V}}_{C_2H_5OH} = 46.07/0.7852 = 58.67$ cm^3 $mole^{-1}$ (cf. 57.60). The partial molar volumes of both components are smaller than the molar volumes (in this case).

THE MEASUREMENT OF PARTIAL MOLAR PROPERTIES

It will be recalled that the absolute values of certain state functions (e.g., V and S) can be determined while those of others cannot (e.g., H and G). The same is true for the corresponding partial molar functions, so we shall find it possible to measure such quantities as $\bar{\bar{V}}_1$ and $\bar{\bar{V}}_2$, but not $\bar{\bar{H}}_1$ and $\bar{\bar{H}}_2$. Differences such as $\bar{\bar{H}}_1' - \bar{\bar{H}}_1''$, however, where, e.g., the two quantities refer to two different concentrations, can be measured.

In principle any partial molar property, $\bar{\bar{J}}_i = (\partial J/\partial n_i)$, for a given component i in a given solution, can be determined by measuring the increase in the value of J for the solution when one mole of i is added to an infinitely large amount of it—or when an infinitesimal amount of i, dn_i, is added to a finite amount of it, from which the quotient $\partial J/\partial n_i$ can be calculated. In practice, however, neither of these methods is feasible, for only finite quantities of component and solution can be used. Consequently $\partial J/\partial n_i$ must be found by some method of slope determination, either analytically or graphically.

DETERMINATION OF PARTIAL MOLAR VOLUME

If, from density measurements of a series of solutions of various known concentrations at constant T and P (usually 1 atm) it is possible to express the volume of a solution as an analytical function of n_1, n_2, n_3, etc., it is easy to find $\bar{\bar{V}}_1$, e.g., by differentiation of the function with respect to n_1, keeping n_2, n_3, etc. constant. More commonly, and more conveniently, the volume of the solution is expressed as a function of molality, m, the volume V being that of a solution containing m moles of solute in 1000 g of solvent. With, e.g., NaCl for solute in aqueous solution at 25° and 1 atm, $V = 1002.94 + 16.40m + 2.140m^{3/2} + 0.0027m^{5/2}$, and $\overline{V}_{NaCl}$ is found immediately by differentiation with respect to m to give $\overline{V}_{NaCl} = 16.40 + 3.210m^{1/2} + 0.0068m^{3/2}$. This is because $dV/dm = (\partial V/\partial n_{NaCl})_{n_{H_2O}}$, since molality implies that n_{H_2O} has been fixed at 1000/18.016, the number of moles of H_2O in 1000 g. When an analytical function is not available dV/dm can be found by determining $\Delta V/\Delta m$ for consecutive finite increments of m and estimating dV/dm by a smoothing process. Having found $\overline{V}_{NaCl}$, $\overline{V}_{H_2O}$ may then be determined by use of Eq. (6-6), where n_2 is replaced by m and n_1 is replaced by 1000/18.016 = 55.51. We have, then, $V = 1002.94 + 16.40m + 2.140m^{3/2} + 0.0027m^{1/2} = 55.51\overline{V}_{H_2O} + m\overline{V}_{NaCl} = 55.51\overline{V}_{H_2O} + m(16.40 + 3.210m^{1/2} + 0.0068m^{3/2})$ from which $\overline{V}_{H_2O} = 18.07 - 1.928(10^{-2})m^{3/2} - 7.4(10^{-5})m^{5/2}$.

Example 6-5 (a) Using the expressions for V as a function of m for aqueous NaCl at 25° already given, find $\overline{V}_{NaCl}$ and $\overline{V}_{H_2O}$ in $1m$ solution. (b) Given that the molar volumes of NaCl(s) and H_2O(l) are 27.00 and 18.07 cm^3 mole^{-1}, respectively, find ΔV°_{298} for

(i) $\dfrac{1000}{18.016}$ H_2O(l) + NaCl(s) $\longrightarrow$ Solution ($1m$)

(ii) NaCl(s) $\longrightarrow$ NaCl($1m$)

(iii) H_2O(l) $\longrightarrow$ H_2O($1m$)

Ans. (a) In $1m$ solution at 25° $\overline{V}_{NaCl} = 16.40 + 3.210(1^{1/2}) + 0.0068 \times (1^{3/2}) = 19.61$ cm^3 mole^{-1} and $\overline{V}_{H_2O} = 18.07 - 1.928(10^{-2})(1^{3/2}) - 7.4 \times (10^{-5})(1^{5/2}) = 18.05$ cm^3 mole^{-1}. (b) (i) $\Delta V^{\circ}_{298} = V_{soln} - [(1000/18.016) \times \overline{V}_{H_2O(l)} + m\overline{V}_{NaCl(s)}]$. But $V_{soln} = 1002.94 + 16.40(1) + 2.140(1^{3/2}) + 0.0027(1^{5/2}) = 1021.48$ cm^3, so $\Delta V^{\circ}_{298} = 1021.48 - [55.51(18.07) + 1(27.00)] = -8.6$ cm^3.

(ii) $\Delta V^{\circ}_{298} = \overline{V}_{NaCl} - \overline{V}_{NaCl(s)} = 19.61 - 27.00 = -7.39$ cm^3.

(iii) $\Delta V^{\circ}_{298} = \overline{V}_{H_2O} - \overline{V}_{H_2O} = 18.05 - 18.07 = -0.02$ cm^3.

Example 6-6 An aqueous solution saturated with NaCl(s) at 25° is $6.18m$. In this solution $\overline{V}_{NaCl}$ is 24.5 cm^3 mole^{-1}. The molar volume of NaCl(s) at 25° is 27.00 cm^3 mole^{-1}. Does the solubility of NaCl in water at 25° increase or decrease with increase in total pressure?

Ans. For NaCl(s) $\longrightarrow$ NaCl($6.18m$), $\Delta G_{298} = 0$ at 1 atm, since the undissolved and dissolved forms of NaCl are in equilibrium. But $\Delta V_{298} = \overline{V}_{NaCl} - \overline{V}_{NaCl(s)} = 24.5 - 27.00 = -2.5$ cm$^3 = (\partial \Delta G/\partial P)_{298}$ by Eq. (4-29). Therefore $(\partial \Delta G/\partial P)_{298} < 0$. It follows that ΔG decreases with P at 25°. Since it is 0 at 1 atm it will be <0 at higher pressures, and so the transfer of NaCl into $6.18m$ solution will become spontaneous. The solubility of NaCl will therefore increase with total pressure.

HEATS OF SOLUTION AND DILUTION

This subject was treated briefly in Chapter 1, but we are now able to examine it from the point of view of partial molar enthalpies. First, the reader is reminded that we may find $\Delta H = \overline{\overline{H}}_2' - \overline{H}_2$, but not $\overline{\overline{H}}_2'$ or $\overline{H}_2$.

Tabulated data on heats of solution are often given as heats of formation (ΔH_f) of the solution. Thus one will find, for 298°K and 1 atm, data such as given in Table 6-1 for NaOH and H_2O. Clearly, the first value

Table 6-1[a]

Heats of Formation of Aqueous NaOH at 25° and 1 atm (kcal mole^{-1})

NaOH(s)	−101.99	NaOH · $20H_2O$	−112.235
NaOH · $3H_2O$	−108.894	NaOH · $50H_2O$	−112.154
NaOH · $5H_2O$	−111.015	NaOH · $100H_2O$	−112.108
NaOH · $10H_2O$	−112.148	NaOH · $1000H_2O$	−112.139
NaOH · $15H_2O$	−112.228	NaOH · ∞H_2O	−112.236

[a]From "Selected Values of Chemical Thermodynamic Properties," Circular of the N.B.S. 500, U.S. Dept. of Commerce, 1952.

listed does not refer to a solution. The remaining ones, called **heats of formation of solution** *assume that the heat of formation of the solvent* (H_2O) *is zero.* By combining the value for NaOH(s) with any one of the others one can readily find the total heats of solution, as shown in the following:

$$Na(s) + \tfrac{1}{2}O_2(g) + \tfrac{1}{2}H_2(g) \longrightarrow NaOH(s) \qquad \Delta H = -101.99 \text{ kcal}$$

$$Na(s) + \tfrac{1}{2}O_2(g) + \tfrac{1}{2}H_2(g) + 3H_2O(l) \longrightarrow NaOH \cdot 3H_2O \quad \Delta H = -108.894 \text{ kcal}$$

By subtraction we obtain:

$$NaOH(s) + 3H_2O(l) \longrightarrow NaOH \cdot 3H_2O \quad \Delta H = -6.90 \text{ kcal}$$

The total heat of solution of NaOH(s) in NaOH · $3H_2O$ is thus $\Delta H = -6.90$ kcal mole^{-1}. On the other hand if the last equation be divided by three we find:

$$\tfrac{1}{3}NaOH(s) + H_2O(l) \longrightarrow \tfrac{1}{3}NaOH \cdot 1H_2O \quad \Delta H = -2.30 \text{ kcal}$$

so that the total heat of solution of $H_2O(l)$ in $\tfrac{1}{3}$NaOH · $1H_2O$ (or in NaOH· $3H_2O$, for it is only composition that is of interest here) is $\Delta H = -2.30$ kcal mole^{-1}. Similarly, combination of the heats of formation yields heats of dilution as shown in Chapter 1. For example, combination of ΔH_f for NaOH · $15H_2O$ with ΔH_f for NaOH · $50H_2O$ and with ΔH_f for NaOH · ∞H_2O gives:

$$NaOH \cdot 15H_2O + 35H_2O(l) \longrightarrow NaOH \cdot 50H_2O \quad \Delta H = +0.074 \text{ kcal}$$

and

$$NaOH \cdot 15H_2O + \infty H_2O(l) \longrightarrow NaOH \cdot \infty H_2O \quad \Delta H = -0.008 \text{ kcal}$$

(Observe that the sign of the heat of dilution is not always the same.)

Table 6-2

Total Heats of Solution of NaOH and H_2O at 25° and 1 atm (kcal mole^{-1})

n_{H_2O}/n_{NaOH} (1)	n_{NaOH}/n_{H_2O} (2)	m (3)	ΔH_{soln} per mole NaOH (4)	ΔH_{soln} per mole H_2O (5)
3	0.3333	18.503	-6.90	-2.30
5	0.2000	11.102	-9.03	-1.806
10	0.1000	5.551	-10.16	-1.016
15	0.06667	3.700	-10.24	-0.6827
20	0.05000	2.776	-10.25	-0.5050
50	0.02000	1.1102	-10.16	-0.2032
100	0.01000	0.5551	-10.12	-0.1012
1000	0.00100	0.05551	-10.15	-0.0105
∞	0	0	-10.25	0

In Table 6-2 are presented the total heats of solution of NaOH and H_2O for each of the concentrations given in Table 6-1 and calculated as shown previously. The concentrations are quoted as mole ratios and also as molalities.

Two *general* types of plots result from these data: (a) a plot of columns (1) vs. (4) or of (2) vs. (5), and (b) a plot of (1) vs. (5) or of (2) vs. (4). Data in column (3) can be used as a substitute for those in (2) since molality is proportional to n_{NaOH}/n_{H_2O}. In Fig. 6-1 column (2) is plotted vs. column (5). Since saturation is reached when $n_{NaOH}/n_{H_2O} = 0.51$ or $m = 2.83$ the graph comes to an end at this concentration. The irregularities in the trends of the values noted above would be more evident in a plot of column (2) vs. column (4).

We proceed now to the determination of partial heats of solution of sol-

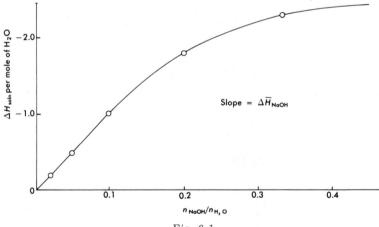

Fig. 6-1

vent and solute, designated by $\Delta\bar{H}_1$ and $\Delta\bar{H}_2$, respectively, or in the present example, by $\Delta\bar{H}_{H_2O}$ and $\Delta\bar{H}_{NaOH}$. By analogy with $\bar{\bar{H}}_1 = (\partial H/\partial n_1)_{P,\,T,\,n_2}$ and $\bar{\bar{H}}_2 = (\partial H/\partial n_2)_{P,\,T,\,n_1}$ from Eqs. (6-2) and (6-3) these quantities are defined by

$$\Delta\bar{H}_1 = (\partial\Delta H_{soln}/\partial n_1)_{P,\,T,\,n_2} \qquad (6\text{-}13)$$

and

$$\Delta\bar{H}_2 = (\partial\Delta H_{soln}/\partial n_2)_{P,\,T,\,n_1} \qquad (6\text{-}14)$$

In these ΔH_{soln} can refer to *any* values of n_1 and n_2 so long as the ratios n_1/n_2 or n_2/n_1 are for the composition in question. The differentiation, however, must be made keeping n_2 constant for $\Delta\bar{H}_1$ and n_1 constant for $\Delta\bar{H}_2$. It should be realized that $\Delta\bar{H}_1$ and $\Delta\bar{H}_2$ are the respective values of ΔH for the transfers:

Solvent $\longrightarrow$ Solvent (given solution)

and

Solute $\longrightarrow$ Solute (given solution)

i.e., we have:

$$\Delta\bar{H}_1 = \bar{\bar{H}}_1 - \bar{H}_1 \qquad (6\text{-}15)$$

and

$$\Delta\bar{H}_2 = \bar{\bar{H}}_2 - \bar{H}_2 \qquad (6\text{-}16)$$

The values of $\Delta\bar{H}_{NaOH}$ may thus be determined from the slope of the line in Fig. 6-1 at the given concentration. Similarly $\Delta\bar{H}_{H_2O}$ can be found from the slope of the line in which columns (1) and (4) of Table 6-2 are plotted. The values of $\Delta\bar{H}_{H_2O}$ and $\Delta\bar{H}_{NaOH}$ in the various solutions are given in Table 6-3 for rounded molalities. They are, however, often

Table 6-3

Partial Heats of Solution of NaOH and
H$_2$O at 25° and 1 atm[a]

m	$\Delta\bar{H}_{H_2O}$ (kcal mole^{-1})	$\Delta\bar{H}_{NaOH}$ (kcal mole^{-1})
0	0	−10.25
1	0.0017	−10.296
5	−0.0473	−9.630
8	−0.2098	−8.265
10	−0.3915	−7.145
12	−0.6715	−5.750
14	−0.897	−4.760
16	−1.159	−3.780

[a]Calculated mainly by interpolation of relative partial molal enthalpies given by G. Åkerlöf and G. Kegeles, *J. Am. Chem. Soc.*, **62**, 620 (1940).

determined by somewhat different techniques. It may be noticed by comparison of these data with those in Table 6-2 that the total heats of solution approach the partial heats of solution with increasing dilution and in the limit become equal to them.

RELATIVE ENTHALPIES

The preceding tabulations have listed only *differences* in enthalpy, but it is desirable to be able to list thermal properties of the dissolved substances themselves. As the absolute values of $\bar{H}_i$ cannot be found the next best thing is to choose a suitable state of reference with which other enthalpies may be compared. Conventionally the **reference state** for enthalpies of dissolved substances is the infinitely dilute solution, indicated by the superscript zero. The difference between $\bar{H}_i$ in the given state and $\bar{H}_i$ in the infinitely dilute solution ($\bar{H}_i{}^0$) is called the **relative partial molar enthalpy**, symbolized by $\bar{L}_i$ for a substance in solution. The analogous quantity for a pure substance (undissolved) is indicated by $\bar{L}_i$, the **relative molar enthalpy**. We have, then, for substances in solution,

$$\bar{L}_1 = \bar{H}_1 - \bar{\bar{H}}_1^\circ \quad \text{and} \quad \bar{L}_2 = \bar{H}_2 - \bar{\bar{H}}_2^\circ \tag{6-17}$$

Clearly, $\bar{L}_1$ and $\bar{L}_2$ are state functions. Furthermore, we have:

$$\bar{L}_1^\circ = \bar{\bar{L}}_2^\circ = 0 \tag{6-18}$$

The **relative molar enthalpy of pure solute** will be given by:

$$\bar{L}_2 = \bar{H}_2 - \bar{\bar{H}}_2^\circ \tag{6-19}$$

For pure solvent, however, since it is identical to the reference state, we write:

$$\bar{L}_1 = \bar{H}_1 - \bar{\bar{H}}_1^\circ = 0 \tag{6-20}$$

We may also speak of the **relative molar enthalpy of a solution**, $L_{\text{soln}} = H_{\text{soln}} - H_{\text{soln}}^\circ = (n_1\bar{\bar{H}}_1 + n_2\bar{\bar{H}}_2) - (n_1\bar{\bar{H}}_1^\circ + n_2\bar{\bar{H}}_2^\circ) = n_1(\bar{H}_1 - \bar{\bar{H}}_1^\circ) + n_2(\bar{H}_2 - \bar{\bar{H}}_2^\circ)$, or:

$$L_{\text{soln}} = n_1\bar{L}_1 + n_2\bar{L}_2 \tag{6-21}$$

It will be seen that, for any change, the following applies:

$$\Delta H = \Delta L \tag{6-22}$$

Let us apply this concept to heats of dilution to infinite dilution and reexamine the following equation given earlier:

$$NaOH \cdot 15H_2O + \infty H_2O(l) \longrightarrow NaOH \cdot \infty H_2O \quad \Delta H = -0.008 \text{ kcal}$$

Now $L = 0$ for both $NaOH \cdot \infty H_2O$ and $\infty H_2O(l)$. Therefore L for $NaOH \cdot 15H_2O = +0.008$ kcal. Writing ΔH for the heat of dilution to infinite dilution we see immediately that $_{c \to 0}$

$$\Delta H_{c \to 0} = -L_{\text{soln}} \tag{6-23}$$

regardless of how much solution is being considered. In this way L_{soln} may be found.

Now the properties we really wish to find for tabulation purposes are the $\bar{L}_i$'s which, through Eq. (6-21), contribute to L_{soln}. These may be found from partial heats of solution as follows. Application of Eq. (6-17) to both $\bar{H}_1$ and $\bar{H}_1$ gives $\bar{\bar{H}}_1 = \bar{L}_1 + \bar{\bar{H}}_1^{\circ}$ and $\bar{H}_1 = \bar{L}_1 + \bar{H}_1^{\circ}$. Substitution of these in Eq. (6-15) yields, with the help of Eq. (6-20),

$$\bar{L}_1 = \Delta \bar{H}_1 \tag{6-24}$$

Similar treatment for the solute (without the use of Eq. (6-20) leads to

$$\bar{L}_2 = \Delta \bar{H}_2 + \bar{L}_2 \tag{6-25}$$

Eq. (6-24) shows that partial heats of solution of solvent are identical to relative partial molar enthalpies of solvent. For the solute, however, we need also to know $\bar{L}_2$, as seen from Eq. (6-25). This is readily found by measuring the heat of solution of solute at infinite dilution, which refers to

Solute $\longrightarrow$ Solute (infinitely dilute solution).

For this transfer $\Delta H = \Delta \bar{H}_{2(\text{inf diln})} = \bar{\bar{L}}_{2(\text{inf diln})} - \bar{\bar{L}}_2 = \bar{\bar{L}}_2^{\circ} - \bar{\bar{L}}_2 = -\bar{L}_2$ or $\bar{L}_2 = -\Delta \bar{H}_{2(\text{inf diln})}$, so we have:

$$\bar{L}_2 = \Delta \bar{H}_2 - \Delta \bar{H}_{2(\text{inf diln})} \tag{6-26}$$

Alternatively, we may find $\bar{\bar{L}}_1$ from $\Delta H_{c \to 0}$ and $\bar{\bar{L}}_2$, or $\bar{\bar{L}}_2$ from $\Delta H_{c \to 0}$ and $\bar{\bar{L}}_1$, when the data are available, by means of Eqs. (6-21) and (6-23). Values of $\bar{L}_{H_2O}$ and $\bar{L}_{NaOH}$ for various concentrations are included in Table 6-4.

Table 6-4

Relative Partial Molar Enthalpies in NaOH
Solutions at 25° and 1 atm[a]

m	$m^{1/2}$	$\bar{L}_{H_2O}$ (cal mole^{-1})	$\bar{L}_{NaOH}$ (cal mole^{-1})
0	0	0	0
0.00111	0.0333	0.0	(16)
0.00555	0.0745	0.0	(35)
0.0555	0.2356	0.0	(97)
1.000	1.000	1.7	−46
5.000	2.236	−47.3	+620
8.000	2.828	−209.8	1985
10.000	3.162	−391.5	3105
12.000	3.464	−671.5	4500
14.000	3.741	−897	5490
16.000	4.000	−1159	6470

[a]See footnote to Table 6-3.

Example 6-7 (a) Find the values of $\bar{L}_{H_2O}$, $\bar{L}_{NaOH}$ and $\bar{L}_{soln}$ for $5m$ NaOH at 25° and 1 atm using the data in Table 6-3. (b) Find ΔH for each of the following changes. $\bar{L}_{NaOH(s)}$ is 10.25 kcal mole^{-1}.

(i) $5NaOH(s) + 55.51H_2O(l) \longrightarrow$ Solution
(ii) $NaOH(s) \longrightarrow NaOH(5m,\text{solution})$
(iii) $H_2O(l) \longrightarrow H_2O(5m \text{ solution})$
(iv) $NaOH \cdot 11.10H_2O + \infty H_2O(l) \longrightarrow NaOH \cdot \infty H_2O$
(v) $NaOH(s) \longrightarrow NaOH(\text{infinitely dilute solution})$
(vi) $NaOH(s) + 11.10H_2O(l) \longrightarrow$ Solution

Ans. (a) For $5m$ NaOH, $\Delta\bar{H}_{H_2O} = -0.0473$, $\Delta\bar{H}_{NaOH} = -9.630$ and $\Delta\bar{H}_{NaOH(\text{inf diln})} = -10.25$ kcal mole^{-1}. Therefore, by Eqs. (6-24) and (6-25), $\bar{L}_{H_2O} = -0.0473$ kcal mole^{-1} and $\bar{L}_{NaOH} = -9.630 + 10.25 = 0.62$ kcal mole^{-1}. In a solution containing 1000 g (55.51 moles) of H_2O and 5 moles of NaOH, $L_{soln} = 55.51(-0.0473) + 5(0.62) = 0.47$ kcal. For 1 mole of solution $L_{soln} = \bar{L}_{soln} = 0.47/(55.51 + 5) = 0.0078$ kcal mole^{-1}.

(b) (i) $\Delta H = \Delta L = 0.47 - [5(10.25) + 55.51(0)] = -50.78$ kcal.
(ii) $\Delta H = \Delta\bar{H}_{NaOH} = -9.630$ kcal.
(iii) $\Delta H = \Delta\bar{H}_{H_2O} = -0.0473$ kcal.
(iv) $\Delta H = \Delta H_{c\to 0} = -L_{soln} = -0.47/5 = -0.094$ kcal.
(v) $\Delta H = \Delta L = \bar{L}^\circ_{NaOH} - \bar{L}_{NaOH(s)} = 0 - 10.25 = -10.25$ kcal.
(vi) $\Delta H = \Delta L = 0.47/5 - [10.25 + 11.10(0)] = -10.16$ kcal.

Example 6-8 Given that ΔG_{298} for NaOH($10m$ solution) $\longrightarrow$ NaOH ($1m$ solution) is -4666 cal find ΔG_{299} with the help of the data in Table 6-4.

Ans. By the Gibbs-Helmholtz relation, Eq. (4-34), $(\partial\Delta G/\partial T)_P = (\Delta G - \Delta H)/T$. Now $\Delta H = \Delta L = \bar{L}_{NaOH(1m)} - \bar{L}_{NaOH(10m)} = -46 - 3105 = -3151$ cal mole^{-1}. Therefore $(\partial\Delta G/\partial T)_P = (-4666 + 3151)/298 = -5.08$ cal mole^{-1} deg^{-1} at 298°K, so ΔG decreases by 5.08 cal for every degree rise in temperature in the immediate neighborhood of 298°K. ΔG_{299} therefore equals $-4666 - 5.08 = -4671$ cal.

Regardless of which of the several ways of finding $\bar{L}_1$ and $\bar{L}_2$ are used experimentally, it is advisable to ensure that the values found are consistent with Eq. (6-8) in which J is replaced by L. For a two-component solution this becomes:

$$n_1 d\bar{L}_1 + n_2 d\bar{L}_2 = 0 \qquad (6\text{-}27)$$

Rearranging and integrating gives:

$$\int_{m=0}^{m=m} d\bar{L}_1 = \int_{m=0}^{m=m} -(n_2/n_1)d\bar{L}_2$$

Now $\bar{L}_1$ is zero at $m = 0$, so we have:

$$\bar{L}_1 = \int_{m=0}^{m=m} -(n_2/n_1)d\bar{L}_2 \qquad (6\text{-}28)$$

$\bar{L}_1$ values can thus be found from values of $\bar{L}_2$ by measuring the area under the curve obtained by plotting n_2/n_1 vs. $\bar{L}_2$. Eq. (6-28) is valid with subscripts interchanged since $\bar{L}_2$ is also zero at $m = 0$.

THE CRITERION OF HETEROGENEOUS EQUILIBRIUM

The most important partial molar state function is the chemical potential, because the most convenient criterion of spontaneity involves the free energy viz. $dG_{P,\,T} < 0$. Illustrations of the application of the free energy criterion, Eq. (4-23), have been given for systems in which solutions were absent. When, however, solution phases comprise a part or all of the closed system it is necessary to use the partial molar free energy, μ. Consider, e.g., an ethanol-water solution in equilibrium with a vapor phase. The vapor will be a gas solution since both components are volatile. When we say that dG for this system is zero to what (infinitesimal) change do we refer? Now there are really two equilibria involved here, viz.

$$\text{C}_2\text{H}_5\text{OH}(\text{liquid solution}) \longrightarrow \text{C}_2\text{H}_5\text{OH}(\text{gas solution})$$

and

$$\text{H}_2\text{O}(\text{liquid solution}) \longrightarrow \text{H}_2\text{O}(\text{gas solution})$$

and for the *system* to be at equilibrium *both* of these changes (which are better described as transfers) must be at equilibrium. Suppose that an infinitesimal amount of $\text{C}_2\text{H}_5\text{OH}$ were to be transferred at constant T and P from the liquid to the vapor when the system is at equilibrium. For this to produce no change in the free energy of the system, i.e. for dG to be zero, $\mu_{\text{C}_2\text{H}_5\text{OH}}$ in the liquid must equal $\mu_{\text{C}_2\text{H}_5\text{OH}}$ in the vapor (or gas) solution. Similarly $\mu_{\text{H}_2\text{O}}$ in the liquid must equal $\mu_{\text{H}_2\text{O}}$ in the vapor for the transfer of an infinitesimal amount of H_2O if dG is to be zero. Given constant T and P, then, the equality of the μ's for each component in both phases is the necessary condition for true equilibrium. Notice that we may not speak of an equilibrium between $\text{C}_2\text{H}_5\text{OH}$ and H_2O in either phase, for to have an equilibrium one must have a process and there is no process for converting $\text{C}_2\text{H}_5\text{OH}$ into H_2O! The question of whether the $\text{C}_2\text{H}_5\text{OH}$ or H_2O have the same potential is thus irrelevant. The two components must be treated separately. One further point should be made: the equality of the $\mu_{\text{C}_2\text{H}_5\text{OH}}$'s and the equality of the $\mu_{\text{H}_2\text{O}}$'s does not mean that the molar free energy of the liquid solution is equal to the molar free energy of the vapor. This may be seen by applying Eq. (6-11) to the present situation as follows:

for the vapor:

$$\bar{G}^{\text{v}} = \mu_{\text{H}_2\text{O}}{}^{\text{v}} X_{\text{H}_2\text{O}}{}^{\text{v}} + \mu_{\text{C}_2\text{H}_5\text{OH}}{}^{\text{v}} X_{\text{C}_2\text{H}_5\text{OH}}{}^{\text{v}}$$

and for the liquid:

$$\bar{G}^{\text{l}} = \mu_{\text{H}_2\text{O}}{}^{\text{l}} X_{\text{H}_2\text{O}}{}^{\text{l}} + \mu_{\text{C}_2\text{H}_5\text{OH}}{}^{\text{l}} X_{\text{C}_2\text{H}_5\text{OH}}{}^{\text{l}}$$

In general, $X_{H_2O}^v \neq X_{H_2O}^l$ and $X_{C_2H_5OH}^v \neq X_{C_2H_5OH}^l$ (even though the system is at equilibrium). Since, however, $\mu_{H_2O}^v = \mu_{H_2O}^l$ and $\mu_{C_2H_5OH}^v = \mu_{C_2H_5OH}^l$ we cannot expect, at the same time, that $\overline{G}^v = \overline{G}^l$.

This argument can be extended to a system at equilibrium containing any number of components in any number of phases: the essential result is the same, viz. *in a system in thermodynamic equilibrium the chemical potential of any one component is the same in all the phases which contain that component.*

The fundamental conclusion just reached is often shown to be true as follows. Let the system consist of $\mathcal{C}$ components, indicated by the subscripts 1, 2, 3, ... and $\mathcal{P}$ phases, indicated by the superscripts a, b, c, ... The free energy of the system will be the sum of the free energies of the phases or $G_{system} = \sum_0^{\mathcal{P}} G_{phase}$, so $dG_{system} = \sum_0^{\mathcal{P}} dG_{phase}$. But,

by Eq. (6-10), each $dG_{phase} = \mu_1 dn_1 + \mu_2 dn_2 + \mu_3 dn_3 + \ldots = \sum_0^{\mathcal{C}} \mu_i dn_i$, so

$dG_{system} = \sum_0^{\mathcal{P}} \left(\sum_0^{\mathcal{C}} \mu_i dn_i \right)$. At equilibrium, since $dG_{system} = 0$, we have:

$$\sum_0^{\mathcal{P}} \left(\sum_0^{\mathcal{C}} \mu_i dn_i \right) = 0 \qquad (6\text{-}29)$$

At the same time, however, the sum of all the dn_i's for each component must be zero since the system is a closed one. We then have:

$$\sum_0^{\mathcal{P}} dn_1 = \sum_0^{\mathcal{P}} dn_2 = \sum_0^{\mathcal{P}} dn_3 = \ldots = 0 \qquad (6\text{-}30)$$

Now both Eqs. (6-29) and (6-30) cannot be valid in general unless $\mu_1^a = \mu_1^b = \mu_1^c = \ldots$, $\mu_2^a = \mu_2^b = \mu_2^c = \ldots$, $\mu_3^a = \mu_3^b = \mu_3^c = \ldots$, etc., as already stated in words instead of symbols.

It may seem appropriate to discuss at this point the evaluation of free energy changes involving μ_i's, thus paralleling our treatment of $\overline{H}_i$'s. It is more convenient, however, to postpone such a discussion until the subject of ideal solutions has been introduced in the next chapter.

THE PHASE RULE

The equality of chemical potentials at equilibrium, discussed above, was shown by J. Willard Gibbs to lead to a highly important generalization underlying all systems at equilibrium regardless of their complexity.

Consider a system of $\mathcal{P}$ phases and containing $\mathcal{C}$ components. For our purpose it will suffice to define $\mathcal{C}$ as the smallest *number* of independently variable constituents needed to express the composition of every phase. We shall suppose that every phase has some of every component in it, but this assumption is not necessary. Every phase is at the same temperature T and the same total pressure P. The number of independent concentration variables in each phase is $\mathcal{C} - 1$, since fixing the concentration of all but one of the components fixes that of all of them. (Concentrations are assumed to be in mole or weight fraction.) As there are $\mathcal{P}$ phases the total number of independent concentration variables is $(\mathcal{C} - 1)\mathcal{P}$. Counting the variables T and P which are the same for every phase the total number of independent variables, N, is

$$N = (\mathcal{C} - 1)\mathcal{P} + 2 \qquad (6\text{-}31)$$

The system is at equilibrium, however, so μ for each component is the same in every phase. If there are three phases (a, b and c), e.g., then, for component 1, $\mu_1{}^a = \mu_1{}^b$ and $\mu_1{}^b = \mu_1{}^c$, a total of two equalities. ($\mu_1{}^a = \mu_1{}^c$ is redundant.) If there are four phases (a, b, c and d) then, for component 1, $\mu_1{}^a = \mu_1{}^b$, $\mu_1{}^b = \mu_1{}^c$ and $\mu_1{}^c = \mu_1{}^d$, a total of three equalities. It is seen that for component 1 there are one fewer equalities than the number of phases. For each component, then, there are $\mathcal{P} - 1$ equalities. For the $\mathcal{C}$ components there are $(\mathcal{P} - 1)\mathcal{C}$ equalities. Each equality has the effect of removing a variable from N in Eq. (6-31). The net number of independent variables which the system still possesses is then given by:

$$N - (\mathcal{P} - 1)\mathcal{C} \quad \text{or} \quad (\mathcal{C} - 1)\mathcal{P} + 2 - (\mathcal{P} - 1)\mathcal{C} = \mathcal{C} - \mathcal{P} + 2$$

This quantity, which is the number of independent variables of temperature, pressure and concentration which the system still possesses even though it is at equilibrium, is known as the **number of degrees of freedom** or **variance** of the system, $\mathcal{F}$, and so we have:

$$\mathcal{F} = \mathcal{C} - \mathcal{P} + 2 \qquad (6\text{-}32)$$

Alternatively $\mathcal{F}$ is the number of variables of temperature, pressure and concentration which the experimenter can vary independently without changing the number of phases, or it is the number of these variables which have to be fixed in order to define the system completely. It will be seen that the terms "invariant", "univariant" and "bivariant", used at the beginning of Chapter 5, refer to systems in which $\mathcal{F} = 0$, 1 and 2, respectively. Eq. (6-32) is the famous **phase rule** of Gibbs. This rule is valid only at equilibrium.

Example 6-9 (a) Show that a pure substance consisting of coexisting liquid and vapor phases at equilibrium is univariant. (b) Show why we do not expect to find four different phases of a pure substance coexisting at equilibrium.

Ans. (a) For a pure substance in two phases $\mathcal{C} = 1$ and $\mathcal{P} = 2$. By the phase rule $\mathcal{F} = 1 - 2 + 2 = 1$. (b) If $\mathcal{C} = 1$ and $\mathcal{F} = \mathcal{C} - \mathcal{P} + 2$ then $\mathcal{F} = 3 - \mathcal{P}$. If $\mathcal{P} = 4$, $\mathcal{F} < 0$. Negative values of $\mathcal{F}$ are hardly to be expected!

Note In one-component phase diagrams, e.g. Figs 5-1 and 5-2, areas might well be labelled "$\mathfrak{F} = 2$," lines labelled "$\mathfrak{F} = 1$" and points labelled "$\mathfrak{F} = 0$." For a conceivable system in which $\mathfrak{F} = -1$ see H. Halliwell and S. Nyberg, *J. Phys. Chem.*, 64, 855 (1960).

Example 6-10 A solution of ethanol in water is in equilibrium with vapor, also containing ethanol and water. (a) Name all the possible conventional variables in this system. (b) How many of these are independent variables? (c) If the temperature is fixed how many independent variables are there left?

Ans. (a) Pressure, temperature, concentration of ethanol in the liquid, concentration of ethanol in the vapor, concentration of water in the liquid and concentration of water in the vapor. (b) The number of variables which are independent is the same as the variance, $\mathfrak{F} = 2 - 2 + 2 = 2$. (c) 1.

Note The answer to (b) tells us that if any two of the six variables stated in (a) are fixed the other four variables are automatically fixed.

BEHAVIOR OF PARTIAL MOLAR PROPERTIES AT HIGH DILUTION

Eq. (6-9) relates isothermal, isobaric variations in the partial state functions for one component to those for the other component in a binary solution. As a consequence the two state functions, $\overline{V}_1$ and $\overline{V}_2$ say, cannot vary independently. This interrelated variation is of particular interest in the range of composition in the neighborhood of 100% of one of the components, let us say component 1. Now if X_2 be thought of as the independent variable Eq. (6-9) may be written:

$$X_1(\partial\overline{J}_1/\partial X_2)_{P,\,T} + X_2(\partial\overline{J}_2/\partial X_2)_{P,\,T} = 0 \qquad (6\text{-}33)$$

or

$$(\partial\overline{J}_1/\partial X_2)_{P,\,T}/(\partial\overline{J}_2/\partial X_2)_{P,\,T} = -X_2/X_1 \qquad (6\text{-}34)$$

We note, first, that $(\partial\overline{J}_1/\partial X_2)$ and $(\partial\overline{J}_2/\partial X_2)$ must have opposite signs since their ratio is negative. Plots of $\overline{J}_1$ and $\overline{J}_2$ vs. X_2, then, must always have *slopes of opposite sign* at any given composition. Secondly, at $X_2 = 0.5$, $X_1 = 0.5$ too and so $-X_2/X_1 = -1$. The two slopes must there be equal and opposite in sign. Thirdly, as X_2 approaches zero both sides of Eq. (6-34) approach zero. Experimentally this is found to occur in at least four ways, indicated in Table 6-5, which also includes examples of partial molar state functions which fall in the various categories. The different behaviors are indicated schematically in Fig. 6-2, where the relative positions of the two lines in each plot, i.e., whether one is above or below the other, are of no consequence.

Example 6-11 Using the analytical expressions for $\overline{V}_{H_2O}$ and $\overline{V}_{NaCl}$ in NaCl solutions at 25° and 1 atm given in the section entitled "Determination of Partial Molar Volume" show that the behavior is that of Type 4 of Table 6-5.

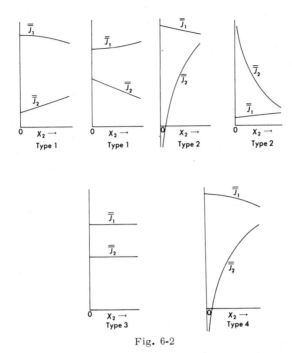

Fig. 6-2

Ans. $\overline{V}_{H_2O} = 18.07 - 1.928(10^{-2})m^{3/2} - 7.4(10^{-5})m^{5/2}$, so $d\overline{V}_{H_2O}/dm = -2.89(10^{-2})m^{1/2} - 18.5(10^{-5})m^{3/2}$. Clearly $\lim\limits_{m \to 0} d\overline{V}_{H_2O}/dm = 0$. Since,

at high dilution, $X_2 \propto m$, $dX_2 = $ (constant) (dm) so $\lim\limits_{X_2 \to 0}$ $(\partial \overline{V}_{H_2O}/\partial X_{NaCl})_{P, T} = 0$. $\overline{V}_{NaCl} = 16.40 + 3.210m^{1/2} + 0.0068m^{3/2}$, so $d\overline{V}_{NaCl}/dm = 1.605m^{-1/2} + 0.0102m^{1/2}$. Here, however, $\lim\limits_{m \to 0} d\overline{V}_{NaCl}/dm = \infty = \lim\limits_{X_2 \to 0} (\partial \overline{V}_{NaCl}/\partial X_{NaCl})_{P, T}$. Therefore, this system falls into Type 4 as far as $\overline{V}_i$'s are concerned.

Table 6-5

Limiting Behavior of $(\partial \overline{J}_i/\partial X_2)_{P, T}$

Type	$\lim\limits_{X_2 \to 0} (\partial \overline{J}_1/\partial X_2)_{P, T}$	$\lim\limits_{X_2 \to 0} (\partial \overline{J}_2/\partial X_2)_{P, T}$	Examples
1	zero	finite and non-zero	$\overline{H}_i$; $\overline{V}_i$ in solutions of nonelectrolytes
2	finite and non-zero	infinite	μ_i and $\overline{S}_i$
3	zero	zero	$\overline{V}_i$ and $\overline{H}_i$ in ideal solutions
4	zero	infinite	$\overline{V}_i$ in solutions of strong electrolytes

PROBLEMS

1. (a) Aqueous $4.42m$ KCl is saturated with KCl(s) at $18°$ and 1 atm. The partial heat of solution of KCl in this solution is $\Delta \bar{H}_{KCl} = 3.830$ kcal mole^{-1} and the absolute entropy of KCl(s) under these conditions is 19.76 eu mole^{-1}. Find the partial molar entropy of KCl in the saturated solution.

(b) Prove from these data that the solubility of KCl(s) in water at 1 atm increases with rise in temperature in the neighborhood of $18°$.

2. For a solution of ethanol in water at $25°$ in which $X_{EtOH} = 0.375$ the density is 0.8859 g cm^{-3} and $\overline{V}_{EtOH} = 57.4$ cm^3 mole^{-1}. Find $\overline{V}_{H_2O}$ in this solution. The molecular weights of $H_2O(l)$ and $EtOH(l)$ are 18.02 and 46.07, respectively.

3. The total heat of solution of H_2SO_4 in water at $25°$ at various compositions is as follows:

Composition	ΔH_{total} (kcal mole $H_2SO_4{}^{-1}$)	Composition	ΔH_{total} (kcal mole $H_2SO_4{}^{-1}$)
$H_2SO_4 \cdot 2H_2O$	-10.02	$H_2SO_4 \cdot 5H_2O$	-13.87
$H_2SO_4 \cdot 3H_2O$	-11.71	$H_2SO_4 \cdot 6H_2O$	-14.52
$H_2SO_4 \cdot 4H_2O$	-12.92		

(a) Estimate the partial heat of solution of H_2SO_4 in $H_2SO_4 \cdot 4H_2O$ at this temperature and compare it with the total heat of solution.

(b) Write the equations to which these partial and total heats of solution refer.

4. You are given the following values of the relative partial molar enthalpies of H_2SO_4 and H_2O in sulfuric acid solutions of various molalities, m, at $25°$**. The relative molar enthalpy of $H_2SO_4(l)$ is $23,540$ cal mole^{-1}.

m	$n_{H_2O}/n_{H_2SO_4}$	$\overline{L}_{H_2O}$ (cal mole^{-1})	$\overline{L}_{H_2SO_4}$ (cal mole^{-1})
1.1101	50	-5.70	$+6065$
2.2202	25	-24.4	6681
3.7004	15	-89.8	7896

Find (a) the partial heat of solution of H_2SO_4 in $1.1101\,m$ H_2SO_4, (b) the integral heat of solution of H_2SO_4 in $1.1101m$ H_2SO_4 and (c) the heat evolved on adding 35 moles $H_2O(l)$ to a solution containing 1 mole of H_2SO_4 in 15 moles of H_2O.

5. (a) From the data of Problem 4 above find the heat effect on diluting a solution which contains 2 moles H_2SO_4 in 50 moles H_2O to infinite dilution at $25°$.

(b) What is the relative enthalpy of the undiluted solution?

**Quoted from Glasstone's *Thermodynamics*, Copyright 1947, D. Van Nostrand Company, Inc., Princeton, N. J.

6. Ether and water are shaken together in a sealed, otherwise evacuated container so as to give two liquid layers and a vapor. All three phases contain ether and all three contain water. The temperature is maintained at 25°.

    (a) Use the phase rule to determine whether this system is defined.

    (b) What relationships, if any, exist among the chemical potentials (i) of the ether in the various phases (ii) of the water in the various phases (iii) of the ether and the water?

7. In Fig. 6-3 $\overline{\overline{V}}_{EtOH}$ is plotted against X_{EtOH} for ethanol-water solutions at room temperature.

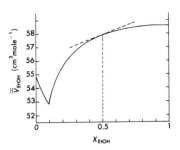

Fig. 6-3. (Adapted from *Thermodynamics* by G. N. Lewis and M. R. Randall, revised by K. S. Pitzer and L. Brewer. Copyright 1961 by the McGraw-Hill Book Company, Inc. Used by permission of McGraw-Hill Book Company.)

(a) On the basis of Eq. (6-34) predict qualitatively the course of the analogous curve for $\overline{\overline{V}}_{H_2O}$ against X_{EtOH}, given that $\overline{V}_{H_2O}$ is 18.1 cm^3 mole^{-1} and that $\overline{\overline{V}}_{H_2O}$ at $X_{EtOH} = 1$ is 13.7 cm^3 mole^{-1}.

(b) Into which of the types described in Table 6-5 does this system fall?

7

Ideal solutions—
chemical equilibrium in ideal solution

IDEAL SOLUTIONS

A solution is said to be **ideal** or **perfect** when the fugacity of each component in it is directly proportional to its mole fraction at all concentrations, and at constant temperature and total pressure. Since, then, $f_i \propto X_i$, $f_i = $ (constant) (X_i). However, if this is to obtain even when $X_i = 1$, the proportionality constant must be $f_i^{\bullet}$, the fugacity of the pure ith component* *in the same state of aggregation*, so we have:

$$f_i = f_i^{\bullet} X_i \qquad (P, T \text{ constant}) \qquad (7\text{-}1)$$

This is known as **Raoult's law** and is the thermodynamic criterion of ideal solutions whether they be gaseous, liquid or solid. The constant total pressure requirement is particularly important for gas solutions.

To relate chemical potential to composition for ideal gas, liquid *or* solid solutions we recall Eq. (5-10) which, as applied to the ith component of a solution, becomes:

$$\mu_i = RT \ln f_i + B_i \qquad (7\text{-}2)$$

*A dot used as a superscript with such symbols as μ, p and f will indicate that the quantity refers to the pure component.

where $\lim_{P \to 0} (f_i/p_i) = 1$, p_i being the partial pressure. For ideal solutions at a given temperature and total pressure we may combine this with Eq. (7-1) to give $\mu_i = RT \ln f_i^{\bullet} X_i + B_i = RT \ln X_i + RT \ln f_i^{\bullet} + B_i$ or:

$$\mu_i = RT \ln X_i + \text{constant} \qquad (P, T \text{ constant}) \qquad (7-3)$$

The chemical potential is seen to decrease with the concentration and, as the latter is diminished indefinitely, to approach minus infinity (cf. Type 2 of Table 6-5 and Fig. 6-2). The unknown value of μ_i is reflected in the unknown value of the constant. To find the *difference* between the chemical potentials of a given component at two different concentrations let μ_i and μ_i' be the potentials when the mole fractions are X_i and X_i', respectively. Then $\mu_i = RT \ln X_i + \text{constant}$ and $\mu_i' = RT \ln X_i' + \text{constant}$ so we have:

$$\Delta G = \mu_i - \mu_i' = RT \ln (X_i/X_i') \qquad (7-4)$$

which is the free energy change for the transfer of *1 mole* of the ith component from an infinitely large quantity of solution in which its mole fraction is X_i' to an infinitely large quantity of solution in which its mole fraction is X_i, temperature and total pressure being the same in both states.

Example 7-1 Assume that benzene(l)-in-toluene(l) solutions are ideal. Consider two such solutions, one in which $X_{C_6H_6} = 0.80$ and another in which $X_{C_6H_6} = 0.40$, both at $25°$ and a total pressure of 1 atm. (a) In which solution does the benzene have the greater chemical potential? (b) Evaluate this difference. (c) Find ΔG_{298}° for the transfer of 2 moles of benzene from the first to the second solution.

Ans. (a) By Eq. (7-3), $\mu_{C_6H_6}$ is greater in the solution for which $X_{C_6H_6} = 0.80$.
(b) By Eq. (7-4) $\mu_{C_6H_6}(X_{C_6H_6} = 0.40) - \mu_{C_6H_6}(X_{C_6H_6} = 0.80) = RT \ln (0.40/0.80) = 1.99(298) \ln 0.50 = -410 \text{ cal mole}^{-1}$.
(c) For the transfer of 2 moles $\Delta G = 2(-410) = -820$ cal.

Note This transfer is spontaneous as expected: a component will diffuse spontaneously to a region of lower potential or to a region of lower concentration. Although liquid solutions were considered, the working of the problem and the results would have been identical for ideal gas solutions.

When X_i' in Eq. (7-4) is unity, $\mu_i' = \mu_i^{\bullet}$, where $\mu_i^{\bullet}$ is the chemical potential of the pure ith component. We have

$$\Delta G = \mu_i - \mu_i^{\bullet} = RT \ln X_i \qquad (P, T \text{ constant}) \qquad (7-5)$$

for the transfer, at constant T and P, of *one mole* of pure ith component to a solution in which its mole fraction is X_i. Eqs. (7-4) and (7-5) are expressions for **free energy of dilution** when $X_i' > X_i$.

Example 7-2 Solid solutions of $p\text{-C}_6\text{H}_4\text{BrCl}$ in $p\text{-C}_6\text{H}_4\text{Br}_2$ are practically ideal at 50°. Find ΔG_{323}° for the change:

$$p\text{-C}_6\text{H}_4\text{BrCl(s)} \rightleftharpoons p\text{-C}_6\text{H}_4\text{BrCl(Solid solution,}\ X_{p\text{-C}_6\text{H}_4\text{BrCl}} = 0.30)$$

Ans. By Eq. (7-5), $\Delta G_{323}^\circ = RT \ln 0.30 = 1.99(323) \ln 0.30 = -772$ cal.

In applying Eqs. (7-3), (7-4) and (7-5) to gas solutions it is often more convenient to express μ_i in terms of partial pressure. The fugacity and partial pressure of a given component are now identical, and Eq. (7-2) becomes:

$$\mu_i = RT \ln p_i + B_i \tag{7-6}$$

(Observe that the chemical potential of an ideal gas in an ideal gas mixture at a given temperature *depends only on its partial pressure.*) Eq. (7-4) becomes:

$$\Delta G = \mu_i - \mu_i' = RT \ln (p_i/p_i') \tag{7-7}$$

equivalent to Eq. (7-4), except that the stipulation of constant total pressure has been dropped. If the partial pressure in the state indicated by the primes is 1 atm, the ideal gas is in its standard state and we have:

$$\mu_i - \mu_i^\circ = RT \ln p_i \tag{7-8}$$

p_i being in atm.

Example 7-3 An ideal gas mixture at 400°K contains $\text{H}_2(g)$ at a partial pressure of 2.0 atm. A second ideal gas mixture at the same temperature contains $\text{H}_2(g)$ at a partial pressure of 5.0 atm. Find the free energy of transfer of 0.50 mole of H_2 from the first to the second mixture.

Ans. By Eq. (7-7) $\Delta G = 0.50(1.99)(400) \ln (5.0/2.0) = 364$ cal.

The simplicity of the equation of state for ideal gases readily permits one to find an expression for the variation of chemical potential with total pressure. Eq. (4-28), applied to a component of a solution becomes:

$$(\partial \mu_i/\partial P)_{T,X} = \overline{\overline{V}}_i \tag{7-9}$$

as shown earlier. However, $\overline{\overline{V}}_i$ for a gas in an ideal mixture is given by RT/P, as shown in Example 6-2. We thus have:

$$(\partial \mu_i/\partial P)_{T,X} = RT/P \tag{7-10}$$

Since RT/P is the same for all gases of a given mixture it follows that the rate of change of the chemical potential with total pressure is the same for every gas present regardless of the relative amounts of the gases! By contrast we may differentiate Eq. (7-6) with respect to partial pressure at constant temperature to give:

$$(\partial \mu_i/\partial p_i)_T = RT/p_i \tag{7-11}$$

which, though similar in form to Eq. (7-10), has a very different meaning. Observe that there is no need to stipulate constant total pressure in

Eq. (7-11) because μ_i is independent of P (except as P determines p_i). The partial pressure may be changed isothermally by changing the composition and/or the total pressure. Eq. (7-11) covers all these possibilities.

Even for non-ideal liquid solutions, e.g., free energy changes can be treated by means of Eqs. (7-6), (7-7) and (7-8) *if* their vapors are ideal, and provided p_i and p_i' refer to the partial pressures in the vapors *that are in equilibrium with* the liquid solutions. Suppose we wish to find ΔG for the transfer A(soln, $X_A = X_A$) $\longrightarrow$ A(soln, $X_A = X_A'$) in which A is a volatile component of both solutions, neither of them being ideal. Because of this we may *not* use Eq. (7-4). If, however, we know the partial pressures of A (p_A and p_A') in the vapors which are in equilibrium with the respective solutions, and *if* the vapor may still be assumed to be ideal (even though the liquid solutions are not) then we may imagine the transfer to be conducted by way of the vapor state as follows:

$$A(\text{soln}, X_A = X_A) \xrightarrow{(1)} A(\text{g}, p_A = p_A) \xrightarrow{(2)} A(\text{g}, p_A = p_A') \xrightarrow{(3)} A(\text{soln}, X_A = X_A')$$

The required $\Delta G = \Delta G$ for (1) $+ \Delta G$ for (2) $+ \Delta G$ for (3). But ΔG for (1) $= \Delta G$ for (3) $= 0$, and ΔG for (2) $= RT \ln (p_A'/p_A)$ so ΔG for the overall transfer is $RT \ln (p_A'/p_A)$. In this way *data on equilibrium partial pressures enable us to evaluate ΔG in spite of the non-ideality of the liquid solutions.* In general it is acceptable to assume that vapors of non-ideal liquid and solid solutions are ideal provided the pressures are not too large.

Example 7-4 Solutions of acetone (A) in chloroform (C) at 35° in which $X_A = 0.640$ and 0.339 have equilibrium partial pressures of A equal to 200.8 and 79.2 mm, respectively. Neither solution is ideal. Find ΔG_{308} for A($X_A = 0.640$) $\longrightarrow$ A($X_A = 0.339$).

Ans. $\Delta G_{308} = 1.987(308)(2.303) \log(79.2/200.8) = -570$ cal.

Note Eq. (7-4) would have given a value of -389 cal.

THERMODYNAMICS OF MIXING

When two or more components are mixed to give an *ideal* gas, liquid or solid solution the changes in the state functions for such mixing or dissolving processes can be readily found. It is understood that the components being mixed are *in the same state of aggregation as the final solution*. Consider the mixing, at constant temperature T and constant total pressure P, of n_A moles of A, n_B moles of B, n_C moles of C, etc. to give a solution in which the respective mole fractions are X_A, X_B, X_C, etc. The mixing process is then written $n_A A + n_B B + n_C C + \ldots \longrightarrow n_t$ moles solution, where $n_t = n_A + n_B + n_C + \ldots$, the total number of moles of solution formed. We wish to find ΔG, ΔV, ΔS, etc. for this change.

Eq. (6-6) applied to free energy, is:

$$G = \mu_A n_A + \mu_B n_B + \ldots = \sum \mu_i n_i \tag{6-6}$$

where G refers to the solution (*all* of it!). For the mixing process, then, $\Delta G^M = G - (n_A \mu_A^\bullet + n_B \mu_B^\bullet + \dots) = (\mu_A n_A + \mu_B n_B + \dots) - (\mu_A^\bullet n_A + \mu_B^\bullet n_B + \dots) = n_A(\mu_A - \mu_A^\bullet) + n_B(\mu_B - \mu_B^\bullet) + \dots$. However, for each component, $\mu_i - \mu_i^\bullet = RT \ln X_i$ by Eq. (7-5), so $\Delta G^M = \Sigma n_i RT \ln X_i$ and

$$\Delta \overline{G}^M = RT \sum X_i \ln X_i \qquad (7\text{-}12)$$

We note that, since each $X_i < 1$, $\Delta G^M < 0$; the mixing process is always spontaneous. We also note that ΔG^M depends only on the temperature and the composition—not on the total pressure, as long as it is the same for both the unmixed and mixed components.   For binary (two-component) solutions, since $X_A + X_B = 1$, the following applies:

$$\Delta \overline{G}^M = RT [X_B \ln X_B + (1 - X_B) \ln (1 - X_B)] \qquad (7\text{-}13)$$

This quantity is plotted against X_B for such solutions at 298°K and at 400°K in Fig. 7-1. The curve is symmetric. It is now easy to find the

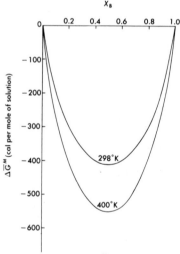

Fig. 7-1

volume change on mixing. Recalling Eq. (4-29), and observing from Eq. (7-12) that ΔG^M is independent of P (as long as P is constant) we see that $(\partial \Delta G^M / \partial P)_T$ must be zero and so we have:

$$\Delta V^M = 0 \qquad (7\text{-}14)$$

Similarly, recalling Eq. (4-33) and observing from Eq. (7-12) that $(\partial \Delta \overline{G}^M / \partial T)_P = R \Sigma X_i \ln X_i$, we see that the following is true:

$$\Delta \overline{S}^M = -R \sum X_i \ln X_i \qquad (7\text{-}15)$$

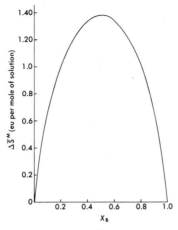

Fig. 7-2

Notice that $\Delta S^M > 0$, so the mixing process is accompanied by an entropy increase. This is to be expected in the light of Chapter 3, for mixing is attended by an increase in probability. For binary solutions $\Delta \overline{S}^M = -R\,[X_B \ln X_B + (1 - X_B) \ln (1 - X_B)]$, plotted in Fig. 7-2. For given compositions $\Delta \overline{S}^M$ is the same for all temperatures and pressures (as long as they are constant). Furthermore, by Eq. (4-13), $\Delta \overline{H}^M = RT \, \Sigma \, X_i \ln X_i + T\,(-R \, \Sigma \, X_i \ln X_i)$ or we have:

$$\Delta \overline{H}^M = 0 \tag{7-16}$$

Moreover, by Eq. (1-6), $\Delta \overline{H}^M = \Delta \overline{E}^M + P\Delta \overline{V}^M$ provided P is constant, so with the help of Eqs. (7-14) and (7-16) we obtain:

$$\Delta \overline{E}^M = 0 \tag{7-17}$$

Finally, by Eq. (4-14) $\Delta \overline{G}^M = \Delta \overline{A}^M + P\Delta \overline{V}^M$ provided P is constant, so with the help of Eqs. (7-12) and (7-14), we arrive at the following:

$$\Delta \overline{A}^M = RT \sum X_i \ln X_i \tag{7-18}$$

It will be seen that Eqs. (7-14), (7-16) and (7-17) imply that all components in an ideal solution contribute the same amounts to the volume, enthalpy and energy as they contribute to these properties for the pure components or $\overline{V}_i = V_i$, $\overline{H}_i = H_i$ and $\overline{E}_i = E_i$. Furthermore, since $\Delta G^M = \Delta H^M - T\Delta S^M$, and $\Delta H^M = 0$, the spontaneity of the mixing process is entirely an entropy effect—the molecules have more space in which to move after mixing than they do before. The same applies to transfer processes to which Eqs. (7-4) and (7-5) refer.

Although $\overline{\overline{V}}_i$, $\overline{\overline{H}}_i$ and $\overline{\overline{E}}_i$ are all independent of composition in ideal solutions, μ_i does depend on composition as given by Eq. (7-5). To complete the picture we ask whether $\overline{\overline{S}}_i$ is independent of composition.

Evidently not, since $\Delta S^M \neq 0$. The exact dependence is obtained readily by differentiation of Eq. (7-5) with respect to T at constant composition and pressure to give:

$$(\partial \mu_i / \partial T)_{P,X} - (\partial \mu_i^\bullet / \partial T)_{P,X} = R \ln X_i$$

By Eq. (4-30), however, $(\partial \mu_i / \partial T)_{P,X} = -\overline{\overline{S}}_i$ and $(\partial \mu_i^\bullet / \partial T)_{P,X} = -\overline{S}_i$ so we have:

$$\overline{\overline{S}}_i = \overline{S}_i - R \ln X_i \tag{7-19}$$

Example 7-5 (a) Find ΔG, ΔV, ΔS, ΔH, ΔE and ΔA for the solution of 2.0 moles of $SnCl_4(l)$ in 3.0 moles of $CCl_4(l)$ at 298°K and 1 atm to give an ideal solution. (b) If the entropies of $SnCl_4(l)$ and $CCl_4(l)$ under these conditions are 61.8 and 51.3 eu mole^{-1}, respectively, find the entropy of the solution formed in (a). (c) Find the partial molar entropy of $SnCl_4$ in the solution in (a).

Ans. (a) In the resulting solution $X_{SnCl_4} = 0.40$ and $X_{CCl_4} = 0.60$. Therefore $\Delta \overline{G}^M = 1.99(298)(0.40 \ln 0.40 + 0.60 \ln 0.60) = -398$ cal per mole of solution. ΔG^M is therefore $(2.0 + 3.0)(-398) = -1990$ cal for the 5 moles formed. $\Delta A^M = -1990$ cal too. $\Delta V^M = \Delta H^M = \Delta E^M = 0$. $\Delta \overline{S}^M = -1.99(0.40 \ln 0.40 + 0.60 \ln 0.60) = 1.34$ eu per mole of solution, so $\Delta S^M = 5.0(1.34) = 6.70$ eu for the 5 moles formed.
(b) The total entropy of the unmixed liquids is $2(61.8) + 3(51.3) = 277.5$ eu. The entropy of the solution is 6.70 eu larger than this or 284.2 eu.
(c) By Eq. (7-19), $\overline{\overline{S}}_{SnCl_4} = 61.8 - 1.99 \ln 0.40 = 63.6$ eu mole^{-1}.

Example 7-6 Use the data of Example 6-4 to find the volume of a solution of 1.158 moles cf $H_2O(l)$ in 0.842 moles of $C_2H_5OH(l)$ at 25° *if* the solution were ideal.

Ans. If the solution were ideal ΔV^M would be zero and so V would be given by $n_{H_2O} \overline{V}_{H_2O} + n_{C_2H_5OH} \overline{V}_{C_2H_5OH}$ (as well as $n_{H_2O} \overline{\overline{V}}_{H_2O} + n_{C_2H_5OH} \overline{\overline{V}}_{C_2H_5OH}$). Therefore $V = (1.158)(18.05) + (0.842)(58.67) = 70.30$ cm^3.

Note The actual volume of the solution is 68.16 cm^3, so there is a contraction on mixing, or $\Delta V^M_{actual} < 0$.

Example 7-7 Find ΔG_{273} for the following processes in which ideal solutions may be assumed to be formed. Both A and B are ideal.

(a) $2A(g, 5 \text{ atm}) + 3B(g, 5 \text{ atm}) \longrightarrow$ Mixture $(g, P = 5 \text{ atm})$
(b) $2A(g, 2 \text{ atm}) + 3B(g, 3 \text{ atm}) \longrightarrow$ Mixture $(g, P = 5 \text{ atm})$

Ans. (a) Since this is at constant total pressure and temperature we use Eq. (7-13). In the resulting mixture $X_A = 0.4$ and $X_B = 0.6$. Therefore $\Delta \overline{G}^M = (2.0)(273)[0.4 \ln 0.4 + 0.6 \ln 0.6] = -360$ cal per mole of mixture and $\Delta G^M = 5(-360) = -1800$ cal for the 5 moles formed.

(b) This is not a constant total pressure process. However, in the resulting mixture the partial pressure of each gas is the same as its initial pressure. Therefore $\Delta G^M = 0$.

CHEMICAL EQUILIBRIUM IN IDEAL GAS SYSTEMS

The relationship between chemical potential and partial pressure given by Eq. (7-8) has important consequences. Consider the general chemical change in which *ideal* gases A, B, etc. react to give *ideal* gases C, D, etc. according to the equation:

$$aA(g,\ p = p_A) + bB(g,\ p = p_B) + \ldots \longrightarrow cC(g,\ p = p_C)$$
$$+ dD(g,\ p = p_D) + \ldots$$

where the p's are partial pressures. We may compute the free energy change, ΔG, as follows:

$$\Delta G = (c\mu_C + d\mu_D + \ldots) - (a\mu_A + b\mu_B + \ldots)$$

By Eq. (7-8), however, $\mu = \mu° + RT \ln p$ for each gas, so we have:

$$\Delta G = [c(\mu_C° + RT \ln p_C) + d(\mu_D° + RT \ln p_D) + \ldots]$$
$$- [a(\mu_A° + RT \ln p_A) + b(\mu_B° + RT \ln p_B) + \ldots]$$
$$= [(c\mu_C° + d\mu_D° + \ldots) - (a\mu_A° + b\mu_B° + \ldots)] + [(cRT \ln p_C$$
$$+ dRT \ln p_D + \ldots) - (aRT \ln p_A + bRT \ln p_B + \ldots)]$$
$$= \Delta G° + RT \ln (p_C{}^c)(p_D{}^d)\ldots/(p_A{}^a)(p_B{}^b)\ldots$$

Representing $(p_C{}^c)(p_D{}^d)\ldots/(p_A{}^a)(p_B{}^b)\ldots$ by Q we have:

$$\Delta G = \Delta G° + RT \ln Q_P \qquad (7\text{-}20)$$

known as the **reaction isotherm** or **van't Hoff isotherm**. This is useful for finding ΔG for any given change from $\Delta G°$ for that change. Q_P is called the **reaction quotient**. The result shown in Eq. (7-20) is valid whether or not the reactants A, B, etc. are in the form of a gas mixture and whether or not the products C, D, etc. are in the form of a gas mixture, as long as the values of p used in Q_P are the given partial pressures. Both ΔG and $\Delta G°$ refer to a *complete* conversion of a moles of A and b moles of B, etc., to c moles of C and d moles of D, etc. Furthermore, noting that Eq. (7-8), on which the above derivation is based, is a special case of Eq. (7-7), we see that all the p's involved in the expression for Q_P are really ratios of given pressures to standard state pressures. These ratios are thus dimensionless and so Q_P must be dimensionless. If, on the other hand, we express the p's in some other unit, millimeters, e.g., when computing Q_P, we are implying that the standard state to which $\Delta G°$ refers is now a pressure of 1 mm for each gas. The numerical value will, of course, vary depending on the units in which pressure is expressed. This may be indicated in parentheses following Q_P.

*Example 7-8*** If ΔG_{298} for H_2(g, 1.00 atm) + I_2(g, 1.00 atm) $\longrightarrow$ 2HI(g, 1.00 atm) is – 4.01 kcal find ΔG_{298} for:

$$H_2(g, 1.00(10^{-4}) \text{ atm}) + I_2(g, 3.00(10^{-4}) \text{ atm}) \longrightarrow 2HI(g, 4.00(10^{-4}) \text{ atm})$$

Ans. We are given that $\Delta G_{298}^{\circ} = -4.01$ kcal so, by Eq. (7-20), $\Delta G_{298} = -4,010 + 1.987(298) \ln 4.00^2(10^{-8})/1.00(10^{-4})(3.00)(10^{-4}) = 5.90$ kcal.

Note (1) The value of ΔG calculated above is valid whether the H_2(g) and I_2(g) are mixed (and temporarily unreactive) or separated, as long as the given p's are the partial pressures.
(2) If we wish to use the ΔG's as criteria of spontaneity we must recall that this may be done only when the total pressure is constant. If the H_2 and I_2 are imagined to be present initially in the same vessel (of fixed volume) it is seen that the total initial pressure, $1.00(10^{-4}) + 3.00(10^{-4}) = 4.00(10^{-4})$ atm would be the same as that of the HI. One may conclude validly that, since $\Delta G > 0$, the product is thermodynamically less stable than the reactants.

It was just shown that, for the reaction of Example 7-8, the product was less stable than the reactant, but only by about 6 kcal. It will now be shown that there are other states, consisting of a gas mixture of H_2, I_2 and HI which are even more stable than either the reactants or the products.   Furthermore, there is one of these states that is the most stable, referred to as an **equilibrium mixture** of reactants and products.

We begin by considering a simple chemical interconversion of one gaseous substance, A, into an isomer, B, according to

$$A(g) \rightleftharpoons B(g)$$

The molar free energies of A and B are not known, of course, but we may suppose that they have the values $\mu_A^{\bullet}$ and $\mu_B^{\bullet}$, respectively, at 298°K and a pressure of P atm. Let us suppose that $\mu_A^{\bullet}$ and $\mu_B^{\bullet}$ are 800 and 400 cal mole^{-1}, respectively. Half a mole of each gas *unmixed* would have a combined free energy of $(800/2) + (400/2) = 600$ cal. If, however, they were mixed, the total pressure of the mixture also being P atm and the temperature still 298°K, the free energy of the mole of mixture would, according to Eq. (7-13), be less than that of the unmixed gases by $-1.99(298)(0.5 \ln 0.5 + 0.5 \ln 0.5)$ or 410 cal, and so $\overline{G}_{\text{soln}}$ would equal $600 - 410 = 190$ cal. In a similar fashion we could find $\overline{G}_{\text{soln}}$ for all possible mixtures of A and B. A plot of these data is shown in Fig. 7-3, in which the dotted line gives the free energy of *one* mole (altogether) of the unmixed gases and the solid line that of one mole of the mixed gases. It is seen that the former is straight (i.e. the free energy is additive, as for all mechanical mixtures) but that the latter is curved, exhibiting a minimum. The position of this minimum can be located readily as will be shown later (Ex. 7-12). In the example under discussion it is found to lie

---

**In this and in subsequent examples of this chapter all the gases are assumed to behave ideally.

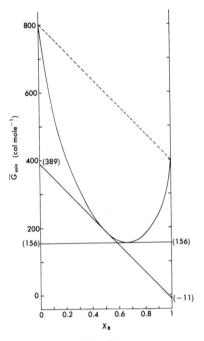

Fig. 7-3

at $X_B = 0.663$ and $\overline{G}_{soln} = 156$ cal mole^{-1}. The chemical potentials of A and B in this solution will then be, by Eq. (7-5), $\mu_A = 800 + RT \ln (1 - 0.663) = 156$ cal and $\mu_B = 400 + RT \ln 0.663 = 156$ cal. (It should come as no surprise that $\mu_A = \mu_B$ for A and B are in equilibrium here). We note also that, by Eq. (6-11), $\overline{G}_{soln} = (1 - 0.663)(156) + 0.663(156) = 156$ cal, as already stated. We see, therefore, that even though the chemical potential of B is less than that of A, the chemical potential of the mixture for which $X_B = 0.663$ is less than that of both and, in fact, less than that of all other mixtures. Since A and B are interconvertible a mixture of composition $X_B = 0.663$ will form regardless of whether we start with pure A, pure B, or any mixture of them.

We observe that the minimum in Fig. 7-3 will be nearer to that side of the diagram for which the $\mu^{\bullet}$ has the smaller value. When $\mu_A{}^{\bullet}$ and $\mu_B{}^{\bullet}$ are widely different the minimum will lie practically on one of the vertical axes. If, e.g., $\mu_A{}^{\bullet} \gg \mu_B{}^{\bullet}$ the minimum will be effectively at $X_B = 1$, and, at equilibrium, the change A $\longrightarrow$ B will be effectively complete.

One other feature of Fig. 7-3 is worthy of mention. It can be proven that if the tangent to the curve at any given composition be drawn, then its intercepts on the vertical axes, where $X_A = 1$ and $X_B = 1$, are equal to μ_A and μ_B, respectively, in the given solution. (The same principle applies to a plot of any molar property of a solution vs. mole fraction, and is valid whether the solution be ideal or not.) Clearly, the tangent at the minimum has intercepts of 156 and 156 cal mole^{-1}, as expected. For $X_B = 0.5$, $\mu_A = 389$ and $\mu_B = -11$ cal mole^{-1}, as shown by the sloping tangent in the figure.

We shall not pursue the graphical approach any further. Rather, let us turn our attention to the means of locating the composition of the equilibrium state, as exemplified by the minimum of Fig. 7-3.

Suppose the homogeneous ideal system:

$$a\text{A(g)} + b\text{B(g)} + \ldots \rightleftharpoons c\text{C(g)} + d\text{D(g)} + \ldots$$

has come to equilibrium. In this condition the values of partial pressure will have acquired particular values, $\mathcal{P}$, depending on what they were initially. At the same time ΔG will have become zero. That is, for

$$a\text{A(g, } p = \mathcal{P}_A) + b\text{B(g, } p = \mathcal{P}_B) + \ldots \rightleftharpoons c\text{C(g, } p = \mathcal{P}_C) +$$
$$+ d\text{D(g, } p = \mathcal{P}_D) + \ldots$$

$\Delta G = 0$. Eq. (7-20) becomes, therefore:

$$-\Delta G^\circ = RT \ln (\mathcal{P}_C{}^c)(\mathcal{P}_D{}^d)\ldots/(\mathcal{P}_A{}^a)(\mathcal{P}_B{}^b)\ldots \qquad (7\text{-}21)$$

But ΔG° is a constant at a given temperature. Therefore $(\mathcal{P}_C{}^c)(\mathcal{P}_D{}^d)\ldots/$ $(\mathcal{P}_A{}^a)(\mathcal{P}_B{}^b)\ldots$ is also a constant. Denoting it by K_P we have:

$$K_P = (\mathcal{P}_C{}^c)(\mathcal{P}_D{}^d)\ldots/(\mathcal{P}_A{}^a)(\mathcal{P}_B{}^b)\ldots \qquad (7\text{-}22)$$

where K_P is a true constant called the **equilibrium constant**. Eq. (7-21) may thus be written:

$$\Delta G^\circ = -RT \ln K_P \qquad (7\text{-}23)$$

and Eq. (7-20) becomes:

$$\Delta G = RT \ln (Q_P/K_P) \qquad (7\text{-}24)$$

Eq. (7-22) is sometimes the **law of mass action** or the **mass law**. K_P is seen to be the particular value of Q_P for which $\Delta G = 0$. Since ΔG° is independent of total pressure, so is K_P, by Eq. (7-23), but both depend on temperature, as will be seen later. There are an infinite number of sets of values of $\mathcal{P}$ which satisfy Eq. (7-22), so one cannot speak of the equilibrium partial pressure of any one of the several gases, except under specific conditions.

There are several other important aspects of K_P.

(1) Its value, even for a given temperature, is always associated with a particular reaction. If one chooses to write the reaction:

$$c\text{C(g)} + d\text{D(g)} \rightleftharpoons a\text{A(g)} + b\text{B(g)}$$

then K_P is now $(\mathscr{P}_A{}^a)(\mathscr{P}_B{}^b)/(\mathscr{P}_C{}^c)(\mathscr{P}_D{}^d)$, i.e. the reciprocal of what it was before.

(2) Its value depends on the coefficients used. If we write:

$$(c/2)C(g) + (d/2)D(g) \rightleftharpoons (a/2)A(g) + (b/2)B(g)$$

then K_P is the square root of what it was in (1).

(3) The value of K_P is dimensionless because it is special kind of Q_P (cf. discussion of Q_P).

(4) The value of K_P will, however, depend in general on the units in which the $\mathscr{P}$'s are expressed. If they are in atmospheres, then $\Delta G°$ refers to each substance at 1 atm; if millimeters, $\Delta G°$ refers to each substance at 1 mm. Tabulated values of $\Delta G°$, however, always imply 1 atm.

The constancy of K_P may be illustrated by the data in Table 7-1 which show the final pressures of H_2, I_2 and HI attained when a vessel contain-

Table 7-1

Expt.	Initial Partial Pressures (atm $\times 10^5$)			Equilibrium Partial Pressures (atm $\times 10^5$)			$\mathscr{P}_{HI}{}^2/\mathscr{P}_{H_2}\mathscr{P}_{I_2}$
	p_{H_2}	p_{I_2}	p_{HI}	$\mathscr{P}_{H_2}$	$\mathscr{P}_{I_2}$	$\mathscr{P}_{HI}$	
1	10.00	10.00	0	0.63	0.63	18.74	880
2	0	0	10.00	0.32	0.32	9.36	860
3	20.00	30.00	20.00	0.39	10.39	59.22	870
4	20.00	0	30.00	20.05	0.05	29.90	900

ing various initial partial pressures of some or all of these gases is brought to equilibrium. In all cases the final values of $\mathscr{P}$ are such as to give the same value for $\mathscr{P}_{HI}{}^2/\mathscr{P}_{H_2}\mathscr{P}_{I_2}$, as seen in the last column.

Example 7-9 (a) Find K_P for $H_2(g) + I_2(g) \rightleftharpoons 2HI(g)$ if $\Delta G°_{298} = -4.01$ kcal. (b) Find K_P for $2HI(g) \rightleftharpoons H_2(g) + I_2(g)$. (c) Find K_P for $\frac{1}{2}H_2(g) + \frac{1}{2}I_2(g) \rightleftharpoons HI(g)$.

Ans. (a) By Eq. (7-23), $-4010 = -1.987(298) \ln K_P$, or $K_P = 870$. (b) $K_P = 1/870 = 0.00115$. (c) $K_P = 870^{1/2} = 295$.

Note If, as here, the number of moles of products in the equation equals the number of moles of reactants, K_P has the same value regardless of the pressure units used, but this is a special case.

Example 7-10 For $N_2O_4(g) \rightleftharpoons 2NO_2(g)$ K_P at 298°K is 86.3(mm). (a) Find ΔG_{298} for $N_2O_4(g, 1 \text{ mm}) \rightarrow 2NO_2(g, 1 \text{ mm})$. (b) Find K_P (atm) at 298°K.

148   *Chemical equilibrium in ideal solution*

Ans. (a) By   Eq. (7-23), $\Delta G_{298}^{\circ} = -1.987(298) \ln 86.3 = -2641$ kcal.
(b) K_P (atm) $= (\mathscr{P}_{NO_2}(mm)/760)^2/\mathscr{P}_{N_2O_4}(mm)/760) = K_P(mm)/760 =$
$86.3/760 = 0.1136$.

Example 7-11 Using the answer to Ex. 7-10(b) find ΔG_{298} for

$$N_2O_4(g, \ 0.50 \text{ atm}) \longrightarrow 2NO_2(g, \ 0.20 \text{ atm})$$

Ans. Since $K_P = 0.1136$ and $Q_P = 0.20^2/0.50 = 0.080$ we have, from
Eq. (7-24), $\Delta G_{298} = 1.987(298) \ln (0.080/0.1136) = -208$ cal.

OTHER FORMS OF THE EQUILIBRIUM FUNCTION

The partial pressure $(\mathscr{P}_i)$ of a gas in a mixture is a measure of its concentration. We may, however, find it more convenient to express concentration in terms of moles per liter $(\mathcal{C}_i)$. Since, by the ideal gas law, $\mathscr{P}_i = \mathcal{C}_i RT$, Eq. (7-22) may be written:

$$K_P = \frac{(\mathcal{C}_C{}^c)(\mathcal{C}_D{}^d)\cdots}{(\mathcal{C}_A{}^a)(\mathcal{C}_B{}^b)} (RT)^{(c+d+\dots)-(a+b+\dots)}$$

where the $\mathcal{C}$'s are concentrations *at equilibrium*. Substituting $\Delta n = (c + d + \dots) - (a + b + \dots)$, the increase in the number of moles of gas for the reaction *as written*, and

$$K_c = \frac{(\mathcal{C}_C{}^c)(\mathcal{C}_D{}^d)\cdots}{(\mathcal{C}_A{}^a)(\mathcal{C}_B{}^b)\cdots} \tag{7-25}$$

the above expression for K_p may be written:

$$K_p = K_c(RT)^{\Delta n} \tag{7-26}$$

Since K_p, R, T and Δn are independent of the total pressure, so is K_c. This, like K_p, is therefore a true equilibrium constant. If, as for the example of Table 7-1, $\Delta n = 0$, then $K_p = K_c$. It can be readily shown that Eq. (7-23) becomes:

$$\Delta G^{\circ} = -RT \ln K_c \tag{7-27}$$

where, however, ΔG° is the free energy change when every gas is *at a concentration of one mole per liter*, instead of at a pressure of 1 atm. Observe that, since concentrations are in moles per liter and pressures are in atmospheres, R in Eq. (7-26) must be in liter-atmospheres per mole per degree. On the other hand, R in Eq. (7-27), and in Eqs. (7-21), (7-23) and (7-24) must be in calories per mole per degree if ΔG° is to be in calories.

There are two other expressions, similar in form to K_p and K_c, which may be called equilibrium functions but not equilibrium constants. Since $\mathscr{P}_i = X_i P$, X_i being the mole fraction of the ith gas *in the equilibrium mixture* at total pressure P, we may express each $\mathscr{P}_i$ in Eq. (7-22) in terms of X_i and find that we have:

$$K_p = K_X P^{\Delta n} \tag{7-28}$$

where

$$K_X = \frac{(X_C{}^c)(X_D{}^d) \cdots}{(X_A{}^a)(X_B{}^b) \cdots} \tag{7-29}$$

Furthermore, since $X_i = n_i/n_t$, n_t being the total number of moles of gas *in the equilibrium mixture*, we may express each X_i in Eq. (7-29) in terms of n_i and obtain:

$$K_X = K_n n_t{}^{-\Delta n} \tag{7-30}$$

where

$$K_n = \frac{(n_C{}^c)(n_D{}^d) \cdots}{(n_A{}^a)(n_B{}^b) \cdots} \tag{7-31}$$

Combination of Eqs. (7-28) and (7-30) yields:

$$K_p = K_n P^{\Delta n} n_t{}^{-\Delta n} \tag{7-32}$$

The functions K_X and K_n are useful in computations but depend on P, and so are not constants, except when $\Delta n = 0$.

Example 7-12 Show that the minimum in Fig. 7-3 lies at $X_B = 0.663$, supposing that, for $A \rightleftharpoons B$, $\mu_A{}^{\bullet} = 800$ and $\mu_B{}^{\bullet} = 400$ cal mole^{-1}, and that the total pressure is P throughout and the temperature 298°K.

Ans. Since $\Delta n = 0$, $K_p = K_X$ from Eq. (7-28). It follows from Eq. (7-23) that $\Delta G° = -RT \ln K_X$. However, ΔG is independent of total pressure since, in Eq. (4-29), $\Delta V = 0$. Therefore ΔG at pressure P, viz. $400 - 800 = -400$ cal, equals ΔG at 1 atm ($\Delta G°$), so $-400 = -1.987(298) \ln (X_B/X_A) = -1.987(298) \ln X_B/(1 - X_B)$. Solving gives $X_B = 0.663$.

COMPUTATIONS INVOLVING EQUILIBRIUM

There are so many types of computations posed in the study of equilibrium that no "standard treatment" can be given. The following illustration will be found useful, however, in clarifying the meaning of the various equilibrium functions and demonstrating how a problem can often be attacked. Let us suppose that we are given that four ideal gases, A, B, C and D interact according to

$$A(g) + 2B(g) \rightleftharpoons 3C(g) + D(g)$$

and that 2.0 moles of A, 3.0 of B, none of C and 1.0 of D are brought together in a vessel at 300°K and held at a total pressure of 0.8 atm until equilibrium is attained. At this time 1.2 moles of D, let us say, are found to be present. We wish to find K_p, K_c, K_n and K_X. In the approach to equilibrium the quantities of each gas will increase or decrease, but always in accordance with the stoichiometry of the equation. We reason as follows: since the amount of D increased from 1.0 to 1.2 moles, an increase of 0.2, the amount of C must have increased by 3(0.2) or 0.6 moles. This must have resulted in the disappearance of 0.2 moles of A and 2(0.2) or 0.4 moles of B, so that the quantities of A, B and C remaining must have been 2.0 – 0.2 or 1.8 moles, 3.0 – 0.4 or 2.6 moles and 0 + 0.6 or 0.6 moles, respectively. In order to keep these quantities clearly in mind it is strongly recommended that they be recorded in the following tabular fashion. (It is important that the amounts present be not confused with the coefficients of the equation.)

	A	B	C	D	
Initial	2.0	3.0	0	1.0	moles
Decrease	0.2	0.4	—	—	moles
Increase	—	—	0.6	0.2	moles
Final	1.8	2.6	0.6	1.2	moles

The last row of data corresponds to the n's of Eq. (7-31) and so $n_t = 1.8 + 2.6 + 0.6 + 1.2 = 6.2$ moles. K_n is thus $(0.6)^3(1.2)/(1.8)(2.6)^2 = 0.021$ and K_X is $0.021(6.2)^{-1} = 0.0034$, by Eq. (7-30), since $\Delta n = (3 + 1) - (1 + 2) = 1$. By Eq. (7-28) $K_p = 0.0034(0.8)^1 = 0.0027$ (atm). Finally, by Eq. (7-26), $K_c = 0.0027[0.082(300)]^{-1} = 0.000110$. The order in which the various quantities in the above tabulation are obtained will, of course, depend on the available information. Frequently K_p is given and the other quantities are desired, requiring the solution of equations which may be quadratic or of higher order. In the solution of these equations approximations may often be made.

Example 7-13 For $H_2(g) + I_2(g) \rightleftharpoons 2HI(g)$, K_p is 870 at 298°K. (a) How many moles of HI are formed if 0.250 moles of $H_2(g)$ and 0.250 moles of $I_2(g)$ are mixed and brought to equilibrium at that temperature? (b) How many moles of H_2 are formed if 0.250 moles of I_2 and 0.350 moles of HI are mixed and brought to equilibrium? (Assume that no solid iodine is formed in (a) or (b).)

Ans. (a) Letting x be the number of moles of H_2 (and therefore of I_2) used up in reaction, and tabulating the data as suggested above gives the following:

	H_2	I_2	HI	
Initial	0.250	0.250	0	moles
Decrease	x	x	—	moles
Increase	—	—	$2x$	moles
Final	$0.250 - x$	$0.250 - x$	$2x$	moles

Moreover, since $\Delta n = 0$, $K_p = 870$. Therefore $K_n = (2x)^2/(0.250 - x)^2 = 870$. Taking the square root of both sides and solving gives $x = 0.234$ and 0.268 for the two roots. Clearly the second of these has no physical meaning, for it implies that more H_2 and I_2 disappears than was present initially. Retaining the first root means that 2(0.234) or 0.468 moles of HI are formed.

(b) Letting x be the number of moles of H_2 formed, we have:

	H_2	I_2	HI	
Initial	0	0.250	0.350	moles
Decrease	—	—	$2x$	moles
Increase	x	x	—	moles
Final	x	$0.250 + x$	$0.350 - 2x$	moles

Therefore $(0.350 - 2x)^2/x \, (0.250 + x) = 870$. Cross multiplying and solving the resulting quadratic equation gives $x = -0.253$ and 0.00056. The first root is discarded. There are thus 0.00056 moles of H_2 formed.

Note It is common to make the arithmetic in part (a) unnecessarily complicated by failing to take the square root as indicated.

DEGREE OF DISSOCIATION

The term **degree of dissociation**, α, is widely used when one molecule of reactant can give more than one molecule of product, e.g. $A \rightleftharpoons 2B$ or $A \rightleftharpoons B + C$ or $A \rightleftharpoons 2B + C$. Consider the *first* of these. If n_o moles of A dissociate completely, $2n_o$ moles of B will form and $\alpha = 1$. If no dissociation occurs, $\alpha = 0$. Let us suppose that at equilibrium only 25% of the A dissociates ($\alpha = 0.25$) when the total pressure is 3 atm. We then have:

	A	B	
Initial	n_o	0	moles
Decrease	$0.25 \, n_o$	—	moles
Increase	—	$0.50 \, n_o$	moles
Final	$0.75 \, n_o$	$0.50 \, n_o$	moles

Since $n_t = 1.25n_o$, $K_p = [(0.50n_o)^2/0.75n_o](3^1)(1.25n_o)^{-1}$. The n_o's are seen to cancel. In this way it may be shown that, in general, for the type $A \rightleftharpoons 2B$ we have:

$$K_p = \frac{(2\alpha n_o)^2 \, P}{(1 - \alpha)n_o} \, [(1 + \alpha)n_o]^{-1}$$

which simplifies to:

$$K_p = \frac{4\alpha^2}{1 - \alpha^2} \, P \qquad (7\text{-}33)$$

Observe that n_o is absent from the expression. We may thus find α if only K_p and P are known. It is seen that α depends upon P even though K_p does not. If $\alpha \ll 1$ we may write $K_p = 4\alpha^2 P$. For the type $A \rightleftharpoons B + C$ repetition of the above procedure gives:

$$K_p = \frac{\alpha^2}{1 - \alpha^2} \, P \qquad (7\text{-}34)$$

It may be noted that Eq. (7-34) is valid only when B and C are absent initially or present initially in stoichiometric amounts. For the type A $\rightleftharpoons$ 2B + C the relationship between α, K_p and P is more complicated.

Example 7-14 If K_p is 0.64 (atm) for $N_2O_4(g) \rightleftharpoons 2NO_2(g)$ at 318°K find the degree of dissociation under a total pressure of 2.0 atm.

Ans. By Eq. (7-33) $0.64 = [4\alpha^2/(1 - \alpha^2)]2.0$. Solving gives $\alpha = \pm 0.27$ or 27%. The negative root is rejected for obvious reasons.

EQUILIBRIA INVOLVING IDEAL GAS AND PURE LIQUID OR SOLID PHASES

A common type of equilibrium arises when one or more of the substances in a reaction system is a *pure* phase, i.e., a phase of fixed composition, as in the following:

$$CO_2(g) + C(graphite) \rightleftharpoons 2CO(g)$$
$$I_2(s) + H_2S(g) \rightleftharpoons 2HI(g) + S(s)$$
$$CaCO_3(s) \rightleftharpoons CaO(s) + CO_2(g)$$

The thermodynamic treatment of such equilibria is, in some respects, simpler than that of homogeneous systems provided an approximation is accepted. As in the development of Eq. (7-20) let us consider the general change:

$$aA(g, p = p_A) + bB(s, p = p_B) \longrightarrow cC(s, p = p_C) + dD(g, p = p_D)$$

Both B and C are pure solids at pressures p_B and p_C, respectively. By Eq. (7-8) $\mu = \mu° + RT \ln p$ for A and D and, since μ for **condensed phases**, i.e., liquids or solids, changes negligibly with pressure over not too large a range (cf. Ex. 4-14), we have:

$$\Delta G = (c\mu_C + d\mu_D) - (a\mu_A + b\mu_B) \cong [c(\mu_C°) + d(\mu_D° + RT \ln p_D)]$$
$$- [a(\mu_A° + RT \ln p_A) + b(\mu_B°)] = \Delta G° + RT \ln (p_D{}^d/p_A{}^a)$$

or

$$\Delta G \cong \Delta G° + RT \ln Q_p' \qquad (7\text{-}35)$$

analogous to Eq. (7-20) with the difference that Q_p' contains only those substances present as gases. The approximation involved in this expression is a close one and usually ignored. $\Delta G°$ refers to the free energy change for the reaction *as written*, i.e., with B and C being pure solids. At equilibrium Eq. (7-35) then becomes:

$$\Delta G° \cong -RT \ln K_p' \qquad (7\text{-}36)$$

analogous to Eq. (7-23), where K_p', sometimes called a **condensed equilibrium constant**, is given by:

$$K_p' = \frac{p_D{}^d \cdots}{p_A{}^a \cdots} \qquad (7\text{-}37)$$

and includes the equilibrium partial pressures, $\mathscr{P}$, only for those substances present solely as gases. Thus for the three equilibria mentioned at the beginning of this section we have, respectively, $K_p' = \mathscr{P}_{CO}^{2}/\mathscr{P}_{CO_2}$; $K_p' = \mathscr{P}_{HI}^{2}/\mathscr{P}_{H_2S}$; $K_p' = \mathscr{P}_{CO_2}$. Finally, combination of Eqs. (7-35) and (7-36) gives:

$$\Delta G \cong RT \ln (Q_p'/K_p') \qquad (7\text{-}38)$$

Example 7-15 If $CaCO_3(s)$, $CaO(s)$ and $CO_2(g)$ are in equilibrium at 800° when the pressure of CO_2 is 167 mm find K_p' (atm) and $\Delta G°$ at this temperature for:

$$CaCO_3(s) \rightleftharpoons CaO(s) + CO_2(g)$$

Ans. $K_p' = \mathscr{P}_{CO_2} = 167/760 = 0.220$ (atm). $\Delta G° = -1.987(1073) \ln 0.220 =$ 3230 cal.

Note This equilibrium pressure of 167 mm is said to be the **dissociation pressure** of $CaCO_3$ at 800°. When $p_{CO_2} < 167$ mm $Q_p' < K_p'$ and $\Delta G < 0$ by Eq. (7-38). $CaCO_3(s)$ will thus be unstable at 800° when exposed to an atmosphere in which the partial pressure of CO_2 is less than 167 mm. It may be added that at 898° $\mathscr{P}_{CO_2} = 760$ mm. At this temperature, therefore, $CaCO_3$ dissociates very rapidly in an open system at 1 atm. The two situations just described are analogous, respectively, to (1) the evaporation of water at room temperature in a dry atmosphere and (2) the boiling of water at 100° when exposed to air at 1 atm.

Example 7-16 When $H_2NCOONH_4(s)$ is introduced into an evacuated vessel at 30° the total pressure resulting from the attainment of the following equilibrium is found to be 125 mm. Find K_p'.

$$H_2NCOONH_4(s) \rightleftharpoons 2NH_3(g) + CO_2(g)$$

Ans. The NH_3 and CO_2 must have been formed in the ratio of $2:1$. Neither gas was present initially so they must also be present in the ratio $2:1$ at equilibrium. Therefore $\mathscr{P}_{NH_3} = 2\mathscr{P}_{CO_2}$ and $\mathscr{P}_{NH_3} + \mathscr{P}_{CO_2} = 125$ mm. Solving gives $\mathscr{P}_{NH_3} = 83$ mm and $\mathscr{P}_{CO_2} = 42$ mm, so $K_p' = 83^2(42) = 2.89(10^5)$ (mm).

Example 7-17 The vapor pressure of $H_2O(l)$ is 380 mm at 81.7°. Find K_p' and $\Delta G°$ at this temperature for $H_2O(l) \rightleftharpoons H_2O(g)$.

Ans. $K_p' = \mathscr{P}_{H_2O} = 380/760 = 0.500$ (atm) and $\Delta G° = -1.987(354.9) \ln 0.500 = 489$ cal.

Note Vapor (and sublimation) pressures of pure liquids (and solids) are really a form of condensed equilibrium constant. We may therefore expect to find that the variation of K_p' with T is similar to the Clausius-Clapeyron relation, Eq. (5-3). (cf. Eq. (7-41).)

VARIATION OF POSITION OF EQUILIBRIUM WITH PRESSURE

We have seen that, according to Eq. (7-23), $\Delta G° = -RT \ln K_p$, and that, since $\Delta G°$ is independent of P at a given temperature, K_p must also be independent of P, which leads to:

$$(\partial \ln K_p/\partial P)_T = 0 \qquad (7\text{-}39)$$

Moreover, by differentiation of Eq. (7-26) $(\partial \ln K_p/\partial P)_T = (\partial \ln K_c/\partial P)_T$, so we have:

$$(\partial \ln K_c/\partial P)_T = 0 \qquad (7\text{-}40)$$

This does not mean, of course, that an equilibrium does not shift with change in pressure, but only that K_p and K_c remain constant.

Example 7-18 In Ex. 7-14 K_p for $N_2O_4(g) \rightleftharpoons 2NO_2(g)$ at 318°K is given as 0.64 (atm), and $\alpha = 0.27$ at a total pressure of 2.0 atm. Find (a) K_p and (b) α at a total pressure of 1.0 atm.

Ans. (a) K_p is 0.64 (atm) at all pressures.
(b) By Eq. (7-33) $[4\alpha^2/(1 - \alpha^2)]\,1.0 = 0.64$, the solution of which is $\alpha = 0.37$ or 37%.

VARIATION OF POSITION OF EQUILIBRIUM WITH TEMPERATURE

Although K_p and K_c are independent of pressure they do vary with temperature. The dependence of K_p on T is obtained immediately by combining the Gibbs-Helmholtz relation, Eq. (4-35), with Eq. (7-23) in the form $\Delta G°/T = -R \ln K_p$ to give $[\partial(-R \ln K_p)/\partial T]_P = -\Delta H°/T^2$ or:

$$(\partial \ln K_p/\partial T)_P = \Delta H°/RT^2$$

Since, however, K_p is independent of P there is no need for the partial notation, so we have:

$$d \ln K_p/dT = \Delta H°/RT^2 \qquad (7\text{-}41)$$

known as the **van't Hoff equation**. (It is common to omit the superscript from $\Delta H°$ because, for systems consisting only of ideal gases, $\Delta H° = \Delta H$, enthalpy then being independent of pressure. Even for non-ideal gases, and for systems with condensed phases, $\Delta H°$ and ΔH are nearly identical.) We see immediately that whether K_p increases or decreases with increase in T depends on whether ΔH is $>$ or < 0. The extent of the change is obtained by integration of Eq. (7-41). If the temperature change is small, or if $\Delta H°$ is independent of T, it may be integrated to give:

$$\log K_p = (-\Delta H°/2.303 R)(1/T) + \text{constant} \qquad (7\text{-}42)$$

(cf. the integration of Eq. (5-3) to give Eq. (5-5)). A plot of $\log K_p$ vs. $1/T$ will therefore be linear (under these conditions) with a slope of $-\Delta H/2.303\,R$, from which ΔH may be found. Alternatively, Eq. (7-41) may be integrated between temperatures T_1 and T_2, still assuming ΔH independent of T, to give

$$\log \frac{K_p(\text{at } T_2)}{K_p(\text{at } T_1)} = \frac{\Delta H^\circ}{2.303\,R}\left(\frac{T_2 - T_1}{T_1 T_2}\right) \tag{7-43}$$

The discussion relating to Fig. 5-4, especially the method of finding the slopes of such lines, should be reviewed at this point. By means of Eq. (7-43) any one of the five quantities K_p at T_2, K_p at T_1, ΔH°, T_2 or T_1 can be found if the other four are known, provided ΔH is independent of T.

Example 7-19 For $H_2(g) + I_2(g) \rightleftharpoons 2HI(g)$, $K_p = 870$ at $298°K$ and $\Delta H^\circ_{298} = -2.48$ kcal. Find K_p at $328°K$, assuming ΔH is constant in this temperature range.

Ans. Substitution in Eq. (7-43) yields:

$$\log K_p \text{ (at } 328°K) - \log 870 = \frac{-2480}{2.303\,R}\left(\frac{328 - 298}{298(328)}\right),$$

from which we find that K_p at $328°K$ is 593.

Note Since $\Delta H < 0$, K_p decreases with rise in T.

When, however, ΔH° varies significantly with temperature we must express it as a function of T before integrating Eq. (7-41). If the function is of the form given by Eq. (1-22) we proceed as follows. Substitution of Eq. (1-22) in Eq. (7-41) gives, on integration:

$$\ln K_p = \int (1/RT^2)(\Delta H^\circ_I + \Delta a T + (\Delta b/2)T^2 + (\Delta c/3)T^3 + \ldots)\mathrm{d}T + I$$

or

$$\ln K_p = -\frac{\Delta H^\circ_I}{RT} + \frac{\Delta a}{R}\ln T + \frac{\Delta b}{2R}T + \frac{\Delta c}{6R}T^2 + \ldots + I \tag{7-44}$$

where I is an integration constant. This result permits finding K_p at any temperature, T, within the range of validity of the parameters a, b, c, $\ldots$ for each of the substances involved, provided the parameters and the two integration constants, I and ΔH_I, are all known. The value of I is found by determining K_p (or ΔG°) at any one temperature.

Example 7-20 For $2HCl(g) + \frac{1}{2}O_2(g) \rightleftharpoons H_2O(g) + Cl_2(g)$, $\Delta G^\circ_{298} = -9.098$ kcal, $\Delta H^\circ_{298} = -13.672$ kcal and the heat capacities ($\overline{C}_p$, cal mole^{-1} deg^{-1}) vary with T in the range 298 to $1500°K$ as follows:

$$HCl(g), \overline{C}^\circ_P = 6.7319 + 0.4325(10^{-3})T + 3.697(10^{-7})T^2$$
$$O_2(g), \overline{C}^\circ_P = 6.0954 + 3.2533(10^{-3})T - 10.171(10^{-7})T^2$$
$$H_2O(g), \overline{C}^\circ_P = 7.219 + 2.374(10^{-3})T + 2.67(10^{-7})T^2$$
$$Cl_2(g), \overline{C}^\circ_P = 7.5755 + 2.4244(10^{-3})T - 9.650(10^{-7})T^2$$

Find K_p at $500°K$ and ΔG°_{500}.

Ans. Combination of the heat capacity data (cf. Example 1-34) leads to Δa°, Δb°, and Δc° to give:

$$\Delta C_P^\circ = -1.7170 + 2.3067(10^{-3})T - 9.288(10^{-7})T^2$$

Use of Eq. (1-22) then leads to $\Delta H_I^\circ = -13,254$ cal. Moreover, $\Delta G_{298}^\circ = -9098$ cal $= -1.987(298.2 \ln K_p)$, giving $\ln K_p$ at $298°K = 15.352$. Substitution in Eq. (7-44) gives:

$$15.352 = \frac{13,254}{1.987(298.2)} - \frac{1.7170}{1.987} \ln 298.2 + \frac{2.3067(10^{-3})}{2(1.987)} 298.2$$
$$- \frac{9.288(10^{-7})}{6(1.987)} 298.2^2 + I \qquad \text{or} \qquad I = -2.263$$

At any temperature T, then, we have:

$$\ln K_p = \frac{13,254}{1.987T} - \frac{1.7170}{1.987} \ln T + \frac{2.3067(10^{-3})}{2(1.987)} T - \frac{9.288(10^{-7})}{6(1.987)} T^2 - 2.263$$

Substituting $T = 500°$ gives K_p at $300°K = 394$ and $\Delta G^\circ = -1.987(500) \ln 394 = -5940$ cal.

The effect of a change in temperature on the *quantities* of substances present at equilibrium may now be illustrated. Suppose we have an equilibrium system consisting of 0.102 moles of $H_2(g)$, 0.332 moles of $I_2(g)$, and 5.43 moles of $HI(g)$ at equilibrium at $298°K$ where $K_p = 870$ for $H_2(g) + I_2(g) \rightleftharpoons 2HI(g)$. How much of these substances will be present if the above system is brought to a new equilibrium at $328°K$ where K_p is 593, as shown in Example 7-19? Proceeding in the usual way we have:

	H_2	I_2	HI	
Initial	0.102	0.332	5.43	moles
Decrease	x	x	—	moles
Increase	—	—	$2x$	moles
Final	$0.102 - x$	$0.332 - x$	$5.43 + 2x$	moles

From $K_p = K_n = (5.43 + 2x)^2/(0.102 - x)(0.332 - x) = 593$ we find x to be -0.0314, so the final mixture consists of 0.133 moles of H_2, 0.363 moles of I_2 and 5.37 moles of HI. The rise in temperature has thus shifted the equilibrium to the left.

The variation of K_c with temperature is obtained by taking the logarithm of both sides of Eq. (7-26) and differentiating with respect to temperature to yield d $\ln K_p/dT = $ d $\ln K_c/dT + \Delta n/T$. But d $\ln K_p = \Delta H^\circ/RT^2$ by Eq. (7-41), so d $\ln K_c/dT = \Delta H^\circ/RT^2 - \Delta n/T = [\Delta H^\circ - \Delta n(RT)]/RT^2$. Therefore we obtain:

$$d \ln K_c/dT = \Delta E^\circ/RT^2 \qquad (7\text{-}45)$$

This equation is used in the same way as Eq. (7-41).

Finally it may be pointed out that when *pure* solid or liquid phases participate along with ideal gases Eqs. (7-41) to (7-45) are still accept-able (within the validity of the approximation used in finding Eq. (7-35)).

EFFECT OF ADDITION OF INERT GAS

A type of stress on a system at equilibrium, not previously mentioned, is the addition to it of an inert gas—one which does not participate directly in the chemical reactions. The addition, assumed to be at constant tem-perature, may be made in two principal ways: at constant volume and at constant total pressure. If the gases are ideal addition at constant vol-ume will have no effect on the position of the equilibrium because for each reacting gas $p_i = (n_i/V)RT$, and none of the quantities on the right is being altered. Addition at constant total pressure, on the other hand, may shift the equilibrium even though K_p is unaltered. Reference to Eq. (7-32) will show that, since the addition of inert gas changes n_t, and since K_p and P remain the same, K_n must alter. Assuming that the addition of gas increases the volume of the system it is seen that n_t increases and, if $\Delta n > 0$, an increase in K_n results, with a corresponding shift in the equilibrium from left to right. If $\Delta n < 0$ the shift is in the opposite direc-tion. The effect of added inert gas at constant total pressure thus dupli-cates the effect of increase of volume.

Example 7-21 A system at equilibrium consists of three substances A, B and C which interact according to $A(g) \rightleftharpoons B(g) + C(g)$. A particular equilibrium composition at a total pressure of 1.000 atm and a fixed tem-perature contains 0.200, 0.100 and 0.300 moles of A, B and C, respec-tively. If 0.600 moles of an inert gas G is now added, without changing the total pressure or temperature, what quantities of A, B and C result?

Ans. At the given temperature $K_p = [0.100(0.300)/0.200](1.000)^1 \times (0.600)^{-1} = 0.250$ (atm), by Eq. (7-32). Let the addition of G cause x moles of A to disappear. We now have:

	A	B	C	G	
Initial	0.200	0.100	0.300	0	moles
Decrease	x	—	—	—	moles
Increase	—	x	x	0.600	moles
Final	$0.200 - x$	$0.100 + x$	$0.300 + x$	0.600	moles

The new n_t, equal to the sum of the last row of quantities, is $1.200 + x$ moles, so we have:

$$K_p = 0.250 = \frac{(0.100 + x)(0.300 + x)}{0.200 - x}(1.000)^1 (1.200 + x)^{-1},$$

the solution of which is $x = 0.043$. The new quantities present are thus 0.157 moles of A, 0.143 moles of B and 0.343 moles of C.

Note K_n has increased but K_p is still 0.250 (atm).

PROBLEMS

1. (a) Find ΔG°_{298} for each of the following, assuming all solutions to be ideal:
   (i) $SnCl_4(l) \longrightarrow SnCl_4 \; (X_{SnCl_4} = 0.60)$
   (ii) $0.60\; SnCl_4(l) + 0.40\; CCl_4(l) \longrightarrow$ Solution
   (b) Find ΔS for (i) above.
2. (a) Show that ΔG_{273} for the mixing process of Example 7-7 (b) is zero by first converting each of the unmixed gases to a pressure of 5 atm and then mixing them.
   (b) Find ΔV^M for the mixing process of Example 7-7 (b).
3. The standard entropies of n-$C_4H_{10}(g)$ and iso-$C_4H_{10}(g)$ at $298°K$ are 74.10 and 70.42 eu mole^{-1}, respectively. If an equilibrium mixture of these gases (assuming they are interconvertible) has the composition $X_{iso} = 0.714$ and $X_{normal} = 0.286$ find the entropy of one mole of this mixture.
4. Consider the possible equilibrium n-$C_4H_{10}(g) \rightleftharpoons$ iso-$C_4H_{10}(g)$. The standard free energies of formation of normal and isobutane at $298°K$ are -3.754 and -4.296 kcal mole^{-1}, respectively.
   (a) If we arbitrarily assign a value of zero to $\bar{G}^\circ$ for the normal compound $(\bar{G}^\circ_n)$ show that this means assigning a value of -542 cal mole^{-1} to the iso compound $(\bar{G}^\circ_{iso})$.
   (b) Assuming, first, that neither gas shows any tendency to become the other find the chemical potential of a system consisting of 0.300 moles of the iso and 0.700 moles of the normal in which the gases are *unmixed*, but each at a pressure of 1 atm.
   (c) Repeat (b) for the case in which the gases, both still supposed to be inert are mixed at a total pressure of 1 atm.
   (d) Find the chemical potential of each gas in this mixture.
   (e) Suppose, now, that the isomers equilibrate readily. What would be the composition of the equilibrium mixture? Would it depend on the total pressure?
   (f) What is the chemical potential of each gas in this equilibrium mixture?
   (g) What is the total free energy of the equilibrium mixture?
5. (a) The value of K_p for $Cl_2(g) \rightleftharpoons 2Cl(g)$ is 0.570 at $2000°K$. Find K_c and K_X when the total pressure is 2 atm. Which of these three "K's" are true equilibrium constants, assuming ideal behavior?
   (b) Find ΔG_{2000} for $Cl_2(g, c = 1$ mole liter$^{-1}) \longrightarrow 2Cl(g, c = 1$ mole liter$^{-1})$.
6. Given that K_p for $2H_2O(g) \rightleftharpoons 2H_2(g) + O_2(g)$ is $6.9(10^{-15})$ (atm) at $1000°$ find the degree of dissociation, α, of steam at this temperature and a total pressure of 2 atm.
7. (a) If ΔG°_{298} for $Na_2SO_4 \cdot 10H_2O(s) \rightleftharpoons Na_2SO_4(s) + 10H_2O(g)$ is 21.80 kcal find K'_p and the equilibrium partial pressure of $H_2O(g)$.
   (b) What partial pressure of $H_2O(g)$ permits the coexistence of $Na_2SO_4(s)$, and $Na_2SO_4 \cdot 10H_2O(s)$ at $25°$?

(c) If an attempt be made to decrease the pressure of a system consisting of $Na_2SO_4(s)$, $Na_2SO_4 \cdot 10H_2O(s)$ and $H_2O(g)$ at equilibrium by increasing the volume of the system what happens to the partial pressure of $H_2O(g)$ in the system?

8. (a) At $250°$ $PCl_5(g)$ dissociates according to $PCl_5(g) \rightleftharpoons PCl_3(g) + Cl_2(g)$ to the extent of 80% under a total pressure of 1 atm. A mixture of 0.20 moles of PCl_5, 0.80 moles of PCl_3 and 0.80 moles of Cl_2 will therefore be at equilibrium at 1 atm and $250°$. Find K_p, the total volume of the system and the concentration of each gas in mole liter^{-1}.
(b) If, to this mixture, 0.50 moles of Cl_2 be added, keeping the total pressure constant, how many moles of each gas will be present when a new point of equilibrium is reached? What is the new total volume? What is the new concentration of each gas?
(c) What would have been the new concentration of Cl_2 *if* there had been no equilibrium shift?

9. (a) If $SbCl_5(g)$ is 71.8% dissociated at $521°K$ and a total pressure of 1 atm find K_p for $SbCl_5(g) \rightleftharpoons SbCl_3(g) + Cl_2(g)$ under these conditions.
(b) What is (i) K_p and (ii) the degree of dissociation at $521°K$ and a total pressure of 10 atm?

10. Given that $\Delta G_{298}^\circ = 28.6440$ kcal and $\Delta H_{298}^\circ = 41.2204$ kcal for $CO_2(g) + C(graphite) \rightleftharpoons 2CO(g)$, find ΔG° and K_p' at $1000°K$. The heat capacities (cal deg^{-1} mole^{-1}) vary with T according to the following:

$CO(g)$ $\quad \bar{C}_P^\circ = 6.3424 + 1.8363(10^{-3})T - 2.801(10^{-7})T^2$
$CO_2(g)$ $\quad \bar{C}_P^\circ = 6.369 + 10.100(10^{-3})T - 34.05(10^{-7})T^2$
$C(graphite)$ $\bar{C}_P^\circ = -1.265 + 14.008(10^{-3})T - 103.31(10^{-7})T^2$
$$+ 2.751(10^{-9})T^3$$

11. Given that K_c for $N_2O_4(g) \rightleftharpoons 2NO_2(g)$ is $5.48(10^{-3})$ at $25°$ and $2.44(10^{-2})$ at $45°$ find the average ΔE° in this temperature range.

12. A gas mixture which is 76.2% H_2, 23.5% N_2 and 0.3% Ar (by volume) is equilibrated at $400°$ and a total pressure of 50 atm and found to contain 15.11% NH_3 (by volume). Find K_p for:

$$\frac{3}{2}H_2(g) + \frac{1}{2}N_2(g) \rightleftharpoons NH_3(g)$$

assuming ideal behavior.

8

Phase equilibria in ideal binary systems

VAPORIZATION EQUILIBRIA FOR COMPLETELY MISCIBLE LIQUIDS

We will now consider the equilibrium between an ideal liquid solution of two volatile components, A and B, and its vapor, also assumed to be ideal. The vapor will contain both components too, with partial pressures p_A and p_B, respectively. The assumption of ideality implies that Raoult's law, Eq. (7-1), applies to both A and B in both phases. Let us imagine a series of ideal solutions of A and B, all at $25°$, and ranging from pure A to pure B. The total pressure will vary from $p_A^{\bullet}$ to $p_B^{\bullet}$, but we will ignore this in applying Raoult's law (cf. Eq. (5-21)). Since, then, $(f_i)_{\text{liquid}} = (f_i^{\bullet})_{\text{liquid}} X_i$, where X refers to the liquid phase, and since $(f_i)_{\text{liquid}} = (f_i)_{\text{vapor}} = p_i$, we have:

$$p_i = p_i^{\bullet} X_i \text{ (constant } T) \tag{8-1}$$

Eq. (8-1) is the commonly quoted form of Raoult's law, the slight approximation noted above being usually overlooked entirely. For the binary system A-B it becomes:

$$p_A = p_A^{\bullet} X_A \text{ (constant } T) \tag{8-2}$$

and

$$p_B = p_B^{\bullet} X_B \text{ (constant } T) \tag{8-3}$$

Both p_A and p_B thus vary linearly with X_A and with X_B at constant T.

If, at a certain temperature, $p_A^\bullet = 100$ mm and $p_B^\bullet = 400$ mm, $p_A = 100X_A$ mm and $p_B = 400X_B$ mm. For a solution in which $X_B = 0.400$, $p_A = 60$ and $p_B = 160$ mm so the total pressure P (= $p_A + p_B$) is 220 mm. If Y_i is the mole fraction of the ith component in the *vapor* phase $Y_A = 60/220 = 0.273$ and $Y_B = 0.727$, since the following is true:

$$p_i = PY_i \tag{8-4}$$

by Dalton's law. Clearly $X_A \neq Y_A$ and $X_B \neq Y_B$, so the vapor composition differs from the equilibrium liquid composition except for the pure components. In general, then, since $P = p_A^\bullet X_A + p_B^\bullet X_B = p_A^\bullet(1 - X_B) + p_B^\bullet X_B$, we have:

$$P = p_A^\bullet + (p_B^\bullet - p_A^\bullet)X_B \tag{8-5}$$

which means a linear relation also between P and X_B with a slope of $p_B^\bullet - p_A^\bullet$. In Fig. 8-1 p_A, p_B and P for a given temperature, 100°, are plotted against mole fraction. The uppermost line is called a **liquidus**

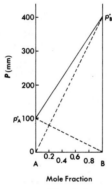

Fig. 8-1

since it relates liquid composition to total pressure. The mole fraction of B (Y_B) in the *vapor* which is in equilibrium with a liquid in which the mole fraction of B is X_B, is seen by Eq. (8-4) to be p_B/P, where p_B is given by Eq. (8-3) and P by Eq. (8-5), so we have:

$$Y_B = p_B^\bullet X_B/[p_A^\bullet(1 - X_B) + p_B^\bullet X_B] \tag{8-6}$$

Fig. 8-2 (an **isotherm**) shows two lines, a plot of P vs. X_B (the liquidus already indicated in Fig. 8-1) and a plot of P vs. Y_B (called the **vaporus**) when $p_A^\bullet = 100$ mm and $p_B^\bullet = 400$ mm. The position of one point on each line has been calculated earlier ($P = 220$ mm, $X_B = 0.400$ and $Y_B = 0.727$). If the total pressure and composition are such as to

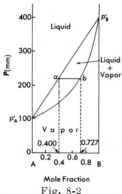

Fig. 8-2

give, on plotting, a point above the liquidus, the system is at a pressure which exceeds the vapor pressure of a liquid of that composition, so the formation of vapor is not possible. This region is therefore appropriately labelled "liquid." For a similar reason the area below the vaporus is labelled "vapor." Points falling in the lenticular region represent systems consisting of both liquid and vapor.

Example 8-1 Two liquids A and B form an ideal solution and at a given temperature $p_A{}^\bullet = 200$ mm and $p_B{}^\bullet = 400$ mm. What is the composition of a liquid which is in equilibrium with a vapor in which the concentration of B is 80 mole percent?

Ans. $Y_B = 0.80$.   By Eq. (8-6), $0.80 = 400(X_B)/[200(1 - X_B) + 400X_B]$, the solution of which is $X_B = 0.67$.

If one of the components, say A, is non-volatile Fig. 8-2 reduces to Fig. 8-3, the lenticular area becomes triangular and the vapor region reduces to the vertical right-hand axis, since $X_B = 1$ for *all* vapors.

If, instead of considering the dependence of total pressure on composition at a fixed temperature one considers the dependence of temperature

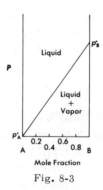

Fig. 8-3

on composition at a fixed total pressure, say 1 atm, Fig. 8-4 is obtained. We shall suppose that $p_A{}^{\bullet}$ is 1 atm at 350°K and that $p_B{}^{\bullet}$ is 1 atm at 300°K. These temperatures are therefore the normal boiling points. Liquid A with the higher boiling point is thus the one with the lower vapor pressure at a given temperature, and so corresponds *qualitatively* to the relationship A and B bear to each other in Fig. 8-2. We may plot a liquidus and a vaporus curve for a given pressure on one graph, Fig. 8-4, analogous to Fig. 8-2, and label it as shown. Such a diagram is called an isobar and labelled analogously. Both lines on isobars are *curved*, even for ideal behavior. The quantitative relationships between X_i and T and between Y_i and T are obtained as follows.

In any given equilibrium the chemical potential of a component (μ_i) will be the same in both phases so $(\mu_i)_1 = (\mu_i)_v$, where the subscripts 1 and v

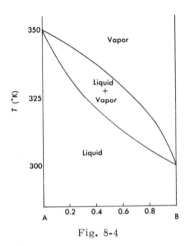

Fig. 8-4

indicate the liquid and vapor phases, respectively. Since P = constant we may use Eq. (7-5) for each phase and write:

$$(\mu_i{}^{\bullet})_1 + RT \ln X_i = (\mu_i{}^{\bullet})_v + RT \ln Y_i$$

rearrangement of which gives:

$$\frac{(\mu_i{}^{\bullet})_1}{T} - \frac{(\mu_i{}^{\bullet})_v}{T} = R \ln(Y_i/X_i)$$

Differentiation of this with respect to T at constant P yields, with the help of Eq. (4-32), written with partial molar quantities,

$$-\frac{(\overline{H}_i)_1}{T^2} + \frac{(\overline{H}_i)_v}{T^2} = R \left[\frac{\partial \ln (Y_i/X_i)}{\partial T}\right]_P$$

Since both phases are ideal we write:

$$\left[\frac{\partial \ln(Y_A/X_A)}{\partial T}\right]_P = \frac{\Delta H_A}{RT^2} \tag{8-7}$$

and

$$\left[\frac{\partial \ln(Y_B/X_B)}{\partial T}\right]_P = \frac{\Delta H_B}{RT^2} \tag{8-8}$$

where ΔH is the molar heat of vaporization. Integration of Eq. (8-7) between the limits $T = T$ and $T = T_A$, where T_A is the boiling point of A at the pressure of the isobar, assuming ΔH_A to be independent of T and recognizing that when $T = T_A$, $X_A = Y_A = 1$, gives:

$$\int_{T_A}^{T} d \ln (Y_A/X_A) = \int_{T_A}^{T} (\Delta H_A/RT^2)\, dT$$

or

$$\ln (Y_A/X_A) = \frac{\Delta H_A}{R}\left(\frac{T - T_A}{(T)(T_A)}\right) \tag{8-9}$$

Similarly, integration of Eq. (8-8) between the limits $T = T$ and $T = T_B$, where T_B is the boiling point of B at the pressure of the isobar gives:

$$\ln (Y_B/X_B) = \frac{\Delta H_B}{R}\left(\frac{T - T_B}{(T)(T_B)}\right) \tag{8-10}$$

Example 8-2 Two volatile liquids, A and B, form an ideal system. The normal boiling points are 350 and 300°K, and the heats of vaporization 7.00 and 6.00 kcal mole^{-1}, respectively. Calculate the equilibrium compositions of liquid and vapor at 310, 325 and 340°K, and draw the 1-atm isobar.

Ans. At 310°K substitution in Eq. (8-9) gives:

$$\log(Y_A/X_A) = \frac{7000}{2.303(1.987)}\left[\frac{310 - 350}{310(350)}\right]$$

from which $Y_A/X_A = 0.273$. Substitution in Eq. (8-10) gives, similarly:

$$\log(Y_B/X_B) = \frac{6000}{2.303(1.987)}\left[\frac{310 - 300}{310(300)}\right]$$

from which $Y_B/X_B = 1.383$. But $X_A + X_B = 1$ and $Y_A + Y_B = 1$, so we have four equations in four unknowns. The solutions are readily found to be:

$$X_A = 0.34 \quad X_B = 0.66 \quad Y_A = 0.09 \quad \text{and} \quad Y_B = 0.91$$

Repetition of the above computation at 325 and 340°K, and plotting of the results gives Fig. 8-4.

VAPORIZATION EQUILIBRIUM FOR COMPLETELY IMMISCIBLE LIQUIDS

When the restriction is imposed that the two liquids be immiscible there can now be no liquid phases with a composition other than that of pure A or pure B. If both of these are volatile the vapor phase can still vary, however, from $Y_B = 0$ to $Y_B = 1$. The following combinations of phases are possible: A(l) + Vapor, B(l) + Vapor, A(l) + B(l) + Vapor. When both A(l) and B(l) are present $p_A = p_A^{\bullet}$ and $p_B = p_B^{\bullet}$ so $P = p_A^{\bullet} + p_B^{\bullet}$ *regardless of the quantities of each liquid phase present.* On the other hand, if, e.g., only A(l) and vapor are present $p_A = p_A^{\bullet}$ but $p_B \neq p_B^{\bullet}$ and $P = p_A^{\bullet} + p_B$. Moreover, since the vapor is ideal, we have:

$$Y_B = 1 - Y_A = 1 - (p_A^{\bullet}/P) \tag{8-11}$$

Similarly, for the coexistence of only B(l) and vapor, $p_B = p_B^{\bullet}$, $P = p_A + p_B^{\bullet}$ and we write:

$$Y_B = p_B^{\bullet}/P \tag{8-12}$$

If, e.g., $p_A^{\bullet}$ and $p_B^{\bullet}$ are 20 and 80 mm at 1 atm, the isobar for 1 atm will consist of the two curves shown in Fig. 8-5, as plotted from the data in

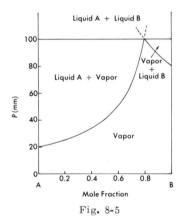

Fig. 8-5

Table 8-1. Each Y_B is calculated from an arbitrary value of P. The second-to-last row refers to the only vapor composition which is in equilibrium with *both* pure liquids. This composition appears as the point of intersection of the two curves. The pressure here is $p_A^{\bullet} + p_B^{\bullet}$. The labelling of the three resulting areas is self-evident. It is important and interesting to note that the position of the left-hand curve in Fig. 8-5

Table 8-1

P(mm)	Y_B	
	Liquid A + Vapor	Liquid B + Vapor
20	0	—
40	0.50	—
60	0.67	—
80	0.75	1.00
90	0.78	0.89
100	0.80	0.80
110	(0.82)	(0.73)

$p_A{}^\bullet$ = 20mm, $p_B{}^\bullet$ = 80 mm

depends only on the properties of A, not on those of B since, in Eq. (8-11), P is arbitrary and $p_A{}^\bullet$ is a property of A. An analogous statement applies to the right-hand curve.

For isobars in such systems, the quantitative relations are quickly obtained from Eq. (8-7) by putting $X_A = 1$ when the only liquid phase is A(l). Similarly we put $X_B = 1$ in Eq. (8-8) when the only liquid phase is B(l). We have, then, on integration, assuming ΔH independent of T,

$$\ln Y_A = \frac{\Delta H_A}{R}\left(\frac{T - T_A}{(T)(T_A)}\right) \qquad (8\text{-}13)$$

and

$$\ln Y_B = \frac{\Delta H_B}{R}\left(\frac{T - T_B}{(T)(T_B)}\right) \qquad (8\text{-}14)$$

in the respective situations. For given values of ΔH_A, ΔH_B, T_A and T_B it is easy to find the corresponding values of Y_A and Y_B at any temperature. When the last two are plotted against T two curves, one for each relation, result, giving the variation of vapor composition with temperature for vapors saturated with A(l) and B(l), respectively. When $T_A = 350°K$, $T_B = 300°K$, $\Delta H_A = 7.00$ kcal mole^{-1} and $\Delta H_B = 6.00$ kcal mole^{-1} (cf. Example 8-2), all at 1 atm, and the values of Y found for $T = 295$, 300 and 325°K are plotted, Fig. (8-6) is obtained. The left-hand curve may be described correctly as the **solubility curve** of A(l) in B(g) and the right hand curve that for B(l) in A(g). Since Eq. (8-13) contains no properties of B, the solubility curve of A obtained therefrom is independent of the nature of B (as long as it forms an ideal system with A and ΔH is independent of T). The reverse is true by considering Eq. (8-14). Attention may be drawn to the resemblance between these equations and others such as Eq. (5-6) and (7-43). Recognition of such similarities aids one's understanding of them.

The temperature of the horizontal in Fig. 8-6 is the boiling point of any mixture of the two liquids at the pressure of the isobar, viz. 1 atm. Those

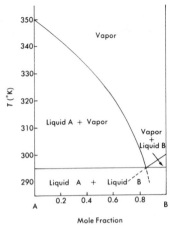

Fig. 8-6

familiar with **eutectic** systems will note the resemblance thereto, but Fig. 8-6 is not a eutectic system, since the latter requires solid phases to be present.

FUSION EQUILIBRIA FOR COMPLETELY MISCIBLE SOLID AND LIQUID COMPONENTS

The essential difference between this kind of system and the one considered at the beginning of this chapter is that what was there taken to be a vapor is now taken to be a liquid, and what was there taken to be a liquid is now taken to be a solid. Instead of applying Raoult's law to a vapor and a liquid we apply it to a liquid and a solid, since we are assuming the solid phase also to be ideal.

Solid-liquid equilibria differ from liquid-vapor equilibria in (1) their comparative insensitivity to changes in total pressure, (2) the inappropriateness of the use of partial pressures and (3) the use of heat of fusion instead of heat of vaporization. On account of the insensitivity to pressure we shall not consider isotherms. Isobars, however, have the appearance of Fig. 8-4, but the areas require relabelling. The quantitative relationships are still given by Eqs. (8-9) and (8-10) except that (1) Y_A and Y_B now refer to the liquid phase, (2) X_A and X_B now refer to the solid phase, (3) ΔH_A and ΔH_B now refer to the molar heats of fusion of A and B, and (4) T_A and T_B now refer to the melting points of A and B—all at the pressure of the isobar. Since, however, it is more common to use X's to refer to the *liquid* phase in solid-liquid studies we shall interchange the X's and the Y's. Rewriting Eqs. (8-9) and (8-10) in accordance with this we have:

$$\ln (X_A/Y_A) = \frac{\Delta H_A}{R} \left[\frac{T - T_A}{(T)(T_A)} \right] \qquad (8\text{-}15)$$

and

$$\ln \left(X_B/Y_B\right) = \frac{\Delta H_B}{R}\left[\frac{T - T_B}{(T)(T_B)}\right]$$

(8-16)

where X_A and X_B refer to the liquid phase, Y_A and Y_B refer to the solid phase and ΔH_A and ΔH_B are the molar heats of fusion. As shown for liquid-vapor equilibria, X_A, Y_A, X_B and Y_B can all be found for a given temperature, when ΔH, T_A and T_B are known, by the use of the above relations, recognizing also that $X_A + X_B = 1$ and $Y_A + Y_B = 1$. A typical schematic isobar is shown in Fig. 8-7.

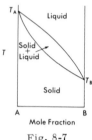

Fig. 8-7

FUSION EQUILIBRIA FOR COMPLETELY IMMISCIBLE SOLID BUT MISCIBLE LIQUID COMPONENTS—SOLUBILITY OF SOLIDS IN LIQUIDS

Following the pattern of the preceding section we return to Eqs. (8-13) and (8-14) and realize that they also apply to liquid compositions in equilibrium with A(s) and B(s), respectively. Since we are using X's rather than Y's for the liquid phase we write Eq. (8-13) as:

$$\ln X_A = \frac{\Delta H_A}{R}\left(\frac{T - T_A}{TT_A}\right)$$

(8-17)

and Eq. (8-14) as

$$\ln X_B = \frac{\Delta H_B}{R}\left(\frac{T - T_B}{TT_B}\right)$$

(8-18)

where ΔH_A afid ΔH_B are now the molar heats of fusion, assumed to be independent of T. Eq. (8-17) may be rewritten as follows:

$$\log X_A = -\frac{\Delta H_A}{2.303R}\left(\frac{1}{T}\right) + \text{constant}$$

(8-19)

and analogously for Eq. (8-18), so that a plot of $\log X_A$ vs. $1/T$ should be linear with a slope of $-\Delta H_A/2.303R$, at least over a small temperature range.

Eq. (8-17) gives the composition of liquids saturated with A(s) at various values of T and so gives the variation of the solubility of A(s) in

B(l) with temperature. Analogously Eq. (8-18) gives the variation of the solubility of B(s) in A(l). A typical isobar is presented schematically in Fig. 8-8, where the left- and right-hand curves are the solubility curves of A(s) and B(s), respectively. Again we note the independence of one of

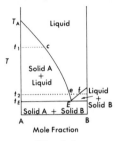

Fig. 8-8

the other so that the (ideal) solubility of A(s) in B(l) at a given temperature depends only on what A is, not upon what B is. Clearly, X_A increases with rise in T for the solubility of A(s) in B(l), and X_B increases with rise in T for the solubility of B(s) in A(l). Furthermore, referring to Eq. (8-17), an increase in T_A will lower X_A so, other things being equal, a solid with a higher melting point will have a lower (ideal) solubility at a given T than one with a lower melting point—a familiar observation. Similarly, if two solids have approximately the same melting point (T_A, e.g.) the one with the higher heat of fusion will have the greater (ideal) solubility at the same temperature.

The point of intersection (E) of the two curves is the only liquid saturated simultaneously with A(s) and B(s). Liquid of this composition is thus in equilibrium with A(s) and B(s). Such a system is said to be at its **eutectic point.**

Example 8-3   A certain solid melts at 87° and its heat of fusion is 2.50 kcal mole^{-1}. Find its ideal solubility at 57°.

Ans. It may be assumed from the fact that no mention is made of solid solution formation that there is none. Substitution in Eq. (8-17) gives:

$$\log X = \frac{2500}{1.987(2.303)} \left[\frac{330 - 360}{330(360)}\right] = -0.138$$

where X is the mole fraction of the substance in the saturated solution and therefore its solubility. Solving gives $X = 0.728$.

Note   This is the solubility regardless of the solvent used, provided the solvent forms an ideal solution with the substance.

FREEZING POINT VS. SOLUBILITY

It is important to realize that the solid-liquid isobars discussed in the two preceding sections give *both solubility and freezing point behavior.*

In Fig. 8-8, e.g., point c represents the composition of the liquid in equilibrium with A(s) at temperature t_1. Since the **solubility** of a substance in a liquid is its concentration in the liquid at saturation, the solubility of A(s) in B(l) is the value of X_A for point c. The freezing point of a solution, however, is the temperature at which the solution is in equilibrium with solid solvent. In a solution of composition c there is more A present than B so A would normally be regarded as the solvent. Thus t_1 is the freezing point of this particular solution in spite of the fact that it only begins to freeze at t_1. It finishes freezing (as the temperature is lowered) at t_E. Similarly t_2 is the freezing point of a solution of B(s) in A(l) denoted by e, and the freezing point of a solution of A(s) in B(l) denoted by f. We may also say that X_A for point e is the solubility of A(s) in B(l) at t_2 and that X_B for point f is the solubility of B(s) in A(l) at t_2.

PROBLEMS

Note: Assume that all heats of vaporization and fusion are independent of temperature.

1. At 69° the vapor pressure of liquid n-hexane (A) is 760 mm and that of liquid n-heptane (B) is 560 mm. Find the total pressure and the composition of the vapor which is in equilibrium with an ideal solution for which $X_A = 0.700$.

2. At 25° the vapor pressure of $H_2O(l)$ is 23.8 mm and that of $C_6H_5Cl(l)$ is 11.5 mm. The two are immiscible.
   (a) Find the total pressure and composition of the vapor in a system consisting of both liquids in equilibrium with vapor at 25°.
   (b) Find the total pressure of a system consisting of the vapor of both liquids in contact with only $C_6H_5Cl(l)$ at 25° if the mole fraction of H_2O in the vapor is 0.300.

3. The normal boiling points of $C_6H_5Cl(l)$ and $H_2O(l)$ are 131 and 100°, respectively. The heats of vaporization are 8.73 and 9.72 kcal mole^{-1}. Estimate the normal boiling point of the two-liquid system.

4. The substances p-$C_6H_4Br_2$ (A) and p-C_6H_4BrCl (B) have melting points of 87 and 65°, and heats of fusion of 4.908 and 4.484 kcal mole^{-1}, respectively. They form a complete series of solid solutions. Assuming that both the solid and liquid solutions are ideal find the mole fraction of B in the coexisting liquid and solid phases at 77°.

5. The melting point of $C_6H_6(s)$ is 5.4° and its heat of fusion 2.370 kcal mole^{-1}. The melting point of p-$C_6H_4Cl_2(s)$ is 53.1° and its heat of fusion 4340 kcal mole^{-1}. These two substances are miscible in the liquid but immiscible in the solid states. Find (a) the ideal solubility of p-$C_6H_4Cl_2(s)$ in $C_6H_6(l)$ at 26.8° and (b) the freezing point of an ideal solution of p-$C_6H_4Cl_2$ in $C_6H_6(l)$ in which $X_{p-C_6H_4Cl_2} = 0.091$.

9

Dilute real solutions of nonelectrolytes

The vast majority of binary systems are simply not ideal—they deviate in varying degrees from the ideal behavior discussed in the two preceding chapters. The thermodynamic relations developed there, when applied to non-ideal systems, will therefore sometimes give approximately correct results and sometimes very erroneous ones. Nevertheless we find that, provided relatively small modifications be made in the treatment, the relationships may still be applied to *dilute* solutions—those in which one of the two components is present in small concentration. The subject of the dilute solution becomes therefore a most important one. We shall confine ourselves to dilute *liquid* solutions. Dilute gas solutions require no special consideration for most of them are ideal anyway. Dilute solid solutions are comparatively unimportant.

RAOULT'S LAW AND HENRY'S LAW

Let us consider solutions in the system A-B where A and B may both be volatile. Unless otherwise stated we shall assume that the vapor phase is ideal, so $(f_i)_{vapor} = p_i$. Raoult's law, if and where valid, is:

$$p_i = p_i{}^{\bullet}X_i \text{ (constant } T) \tag{8-1}$$

for A and B, as in the preceding chapter. Suppose that at a given temperature the pressure-composition relations are as shown in Fig. 9-1 (a) and (b) (cf. Fig. 8.1). In (a) the deviations from ideal behavior are said to be

171

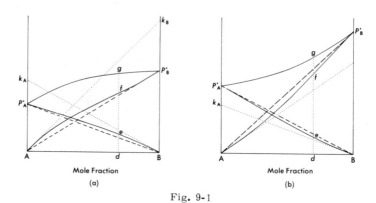

Mole Fraction

(a)

Mole Fraction

(b)

Fig. 9-1

positive, in (b) they are *negative*. The dashed lines show the ideal partial pressures, the solid lines the actual partial and total pressures, the latter still being equal to $p_A^\bullet + p_B^\bullet$ (e.g., $\overline{dg} = \overline{de} + \overline{df}$).* Although the system is far from ideal it is found *experimentally* that the observed partial pressure curve for A approaches the Raoult's law line tangentially as X_A approaches unity (the left-hand side of the diagram). Since the slope of the observed line is $(\partial p_A/\partial X_A)_T$ and that of the ideal line is $p_A/X_A = p_A^\bullet/1 = p_A^\bullet$ we may say

$$\lim_{X_A \to 1} (\partial p_A/\partial X_A)_T = p_A^\bullet \tag{9-1}$$

Now when X_A approaches unity we have dilute solutions of B in A, so that provided the solution is dilute enough Raoult's law, Eq. (8-1), holds for A. (The reader is reminded that the requirement of constant total pressure in Raoult's law, Eq. (7-1), was dropped as unimportant in Eq. (8-1).) Similarly, for the right-hand end of the other partial pressure curve, we have

$$\lim_{X_B \to 1} (\partial p_B/\partial X_B)_T = p_B^\bullet \tag{9-2}$$

and Raoult's law holds for B in sufficiently dilute solutions of A in B. Thus Raoult's law applies to that component in dilute solution which is playing the role of solvent.

Another important result is seen by examining the right-hand end of the observed partial pressure curve for A, where X_A is close to zero. *Experimentally* the curve has a finite, non-zero, limiting slope. We may say, then, the following:

$$\lim_{X_A \to 0} (p_A/X_A) = k_A \tag{9-3}$$

*The deviations may be such as to give a maximum or a minimum in the total pressure curve.

where k_A is a finite, non-zero constant which gives the limiting slope of the line as X_A approaches zero. If we draw a line representing this limiting slope it will intersect the $X_A = 1$ axis at k_A as shown by the dotted line.   Similarly,   for   the   left-hand end of the observed partial pressure curve of B, we have:

$$\lim_{X_B \to 0} (p_B/X_B) = k_B \tag{9-4}$$

Eqs. (9-3) and (9-4) show that p_i becomes directly proportional to X_i as X_i approaches zero, so we write, in general:

$$p_i = k_i X_i \qquad (T \text{ constant}) \tag{9-5}$$

for solutions in which X_i is very small. Eq.(9-5) is one form of Henry's law.   The quantity k_i is referred to as the Henry's law constant for i. If one writes Raoult's law in the form $p_i = p_i{}^{\bullet} X_i$ it will be evident that it may be regarded as a special case of Henry's law in which the proportionality constant is $p_i{}^{\bullet}$. In their application to dilute solutions in non-ideal systems, however, it is important to realize that *Raoult's law holds for the solvent and Henry's law for the solute*. We here encounter an ambiguity in terminology which is worth clarification. If we regard Raoult's law as the criterion of ideality then the dilute solutions we are considering are ideal with respect to the solvent but not with respect to the solute. Dilute solutions in non-ideal systems, or **dilute real solutions** are often considered to be ideal too, and referred to as ideal dilute solutions, but it should be understood that they are ideal only with respect to solvent: the solute does not follow Raoult's law, it follows Henry's law.

Eq.(9-5) is only one form of Henry's law. In its most general form we should really write it in terms of fugacities and restrict its application to constant temperature and total pressure (cf. Raoult's law, Eq. (7-1)):

$$f_i = k_i X_i \qquad (\text{constant } T \text{ and } P) \tag{9-6}$$

The importance of the constant pressure restriction will be apparent later when behavior at high pressure will be considered briefly. Ordinarily, though, as we pass from $X_B = 0$ to $X_B = 1$ in Fig. 9-1 the effect of the change in P is quite unimportant for liquids and solids (cf. Eq. (5-21)). Furthermore the vapor phase was taken to be ideal. For these reasons it was sufficient to write Eq. (9-6) as Eq. (9-5).

CHEMICAL POTENTIAL AND CONCENTRATION

The validity of Raoult's law for the solvent and Henry's law for the solute in dilute solution leads to simple relations between μ_i and X_i for both components.   For dilute solutions of B(solute) in A (solvent) it follows that, at constant temperature,

$$\mu_A = \mu_A{}^{\bullet} + RT \ln X_A \tag{9-7}$$

as shown in Chapter 7. It was also shown that, for the transfer of one mole of A from a dilute solution of B in A at one concentration X_A' to another at concentration X_A,

$$\Delta G = RT \ln (X_A/X_A') \qquad (9\text{-}8)$$

Similar but not identical relations hold for B in the liquid solution. Applying Eq. (7-2), which is always true, to this component means that $\mu_B = RT \ln f_B + \text{constant}$. Since f_B in the liquid equals f_B in the equilibrium vapor which in turn is virtually the same as p_B we have:

$$\mu_B = RT \ln p_B + \text{constant}$$

Since Henry's law applies to B we may write:

$$\mu_B = RT \ln (k_B X_B) + \text{constant} = RT \ln k_B + RT \ln X_B + \text{constant}$$

Combination of the two constant terms gives:

$$\mu_B = \text{constant}' + RT \ln X_B \qquad (9\text{-}9)$$

which is valid as long as Henry's law applies.

The similarity between Eqs. (9-7) and (9-9) is at once evident, but one reflects Raoult's law, the other Henry's law. It follows from Eq. (9-9) that, for the transfer of one mole of B from a dilute solution of B in A at one concentration X_B' to another at concentration X_B, we have:

$$\Delta G = RT \ln (X_B/X_B') \qquad (9\text{-}10)$$

Example 9-1 Find ΔG_{298} for (i) A $(X_A = 0.980) \longrightarrow$ A $(X_A = 0.950)$, and (ii) B $(X_A = 0.980) \longrightarrow$ B $(X_A = 0.950)$ where A and B are the only components in the two solutions. The system A-B is not, in general, ideal.

Ans. Both of these solutions are dilute, so (i) by Eq. (9-8), $\Delta G_{298} = 1.987(298) \ln (0.950/0.980) = -18.7$ cal and (ii) by Eq. (9-10), $\Delta G_{298} = 1.987(298) \ln (0.050/0.020 = 540$ cal.

Example 9-2 For B(l) $\longrightarrow$ B$(X_B = 0.050)$, where A and B do not in general form ideal solutions, why is ΔG not given by $RT \ln (0.05/1)$?

Ans. Eq. (9-10) is not applicable here because B(l) is not a dilute solution of B.

STANDARD STATES FOR SOLVENT AND SOLUTE

We have seen that the standard states for pure liquids are the liquids at 1 atm and the given temperature. These are also the logical standard states for the components of liquid solutions. Since, however, μ for components of condensed systems is insensitive to changes in pressure the 1 atm specification is usually disregarded and $\mu^\bullet$, which refers to any given pressure, and μ° (which refers to a pressure of 1 atm) are effectively interchangeable. For dilute solutions of B in A, Eq. (9-7) may thus be rewritten:

$$\mu_A = \mu_A^\circ + RT \ln X_A \qquad (9\text{-}11)$$

If we choose $X_B = 1$ for the standard state of B, however, μ_B becomes μ_B° when $X_B = 1$ and substitution in Eq. (9-9) gives $\mu_B^\circ = $ constant$'$, so $\mu_B = \mu_B^\circ + RT \ln X_B$. Now Eq. (9-9) is not applicable up to anywhere near as high a concentration as $X_B = 1$ so the result is not correct if μ_B° refers to pure B (1). Nevertheless a relation of the form of Eq. (9-9) is still desirable. The dilemma is resolved by the following argument. *Suppose* that $\mu_B = \mu_B^\circ + RT \ln X_B$ *were* to apply at $X_B = 1$. Then μ_B° would be the value of μ_B at that point. This corresponds to the intercept of the limiting tangent to the curve for p_B on the $X_B = 1$ axis in Fig. 9-1 where $p_B = k_B$ (if the vapor is not ideal f_B is plotted against X_B and the analogous intercept found.) It is therefore convenient to choose for the standard state of B *the hypothetical pure liquid B with a partial pressure (or fugacity) equal to the value it would have were Henry's law to hold up to* $X_B = 1$, viz. k_B. On this basis we may still write:

$$\mu_B = \mu_B^\circ + RT \ln X_B \qquad (9\text{-}12)$$

where μ_B° is the value of μ_B in this hypothetical standard state. We are thus led to the concept of a standard state for solvent which is real, and a standard state for solute which is hypothetical (but useful). Eq. (9-12) is still restricted in its application, however, to dilute solutions of B. If, on the other hand, B is present in high and A in low concentration it may be better to regard B as the solvent, in which case Raoult's law is applied to it and μ_B° is the value of μ_B in real, pure liquid B.

Solute concentrations are often conveniently stated in molality, m. Since in dilute solution $m \propto X_B$, Eq. (9-12) can be written $\mu_B = RT \ln m +$ constant. But the constant in *this* relation is the value of μ_B where $m = 1$ *if* Henry's law were to hold up to $m = 1$. We thus write

$$\mu_B = \mu_B^\circ + RT \ln m \qquad (9\text{-}13)$$

where the standard state of B is now B in a *hypothetical one-molal solution for which Henry's law is still valid.* The significance of this choice of standard state will be clearer from an examination of Fig. 9-2 (a) and (b) in which molality is plotted against p_B for positively and negatively deviating behavior, respectively. (The dashed lines depicting ideal behavior are now curved since the direct proportion between m and X_B does not extend to high concentrations.) The slopes of the experimental curves (solid lines) as m approaches zero are still finite and nonzero, as shown. This follows from Eq. (9-5) for, since $p_B \propto X_B$ and $X_B \propto m$, $p_B \propto m$ or:

$$p_B = k_B' m \qquad (9\text{-}14)$$

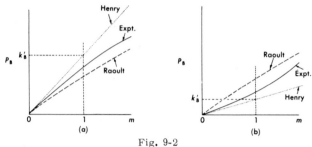

Fig. 9-2

which is Henry's law in still another form. The value which p_B would have at $m = 1$ were Henry's law still applicable at that concentration is thus given by k'_B shown in the diagrams.

VARIATION OF PARTIAL MOLAR PROPERTIES WITH CONCENTRATION

It was shown in Chapter 7 that, for ideal solutions, the more important state functions depend on concentration at constant T and P as follows:

$$\mu_i = \mu_i^\bullet + RT \ln X_i \tag{7-5}$$

$$\bar{S}_i = \bar{S}_i - R \ln X_i \tag{7-19}$$

$$\bar{V}_i = \bar{V}_i \text{ (therefore independent of } X_i) \qquad \text{(cf. Eq. (7-14))}$$

$$\bar{H}_i = \bar{H}_i \text{ (therefore independent of } X_i) \qquad \text{(cf. Eq. (7-16))}$$

It is appropriate to inquire whether these or similar relations hold also for components in dilute real solutions. Solvent and solute must now be treated separately. Since Raoult's law holds for the solvent *all the above relations are valid for the solvent in sufficiently dilute solution*. For the solute B, however, which obeys Henry's law, they require modification. We have seen:

$$\mu_B = \mu_B^\circ + RT \ln X_B \tag{9-12}$$

where μ_B° refers to the hypothetical pure (liquid) solute. If we take logarithms of both sides of Eq. (9-6) we obtain:

$$\ln f_B = \ln k_B + \ln X_B = \ln f_B^\circ + \ln X_B$$

since $k_B = f_B^\circ$. Differentiation of both sides with respect to T at constant P and composition gives, with the help of Eq. (5-22):

$$(\bar{\bar{H}}_B^* - \bar{\bar{H}}_B)/RT^2 = (\bar{\bar{H}}_B^* - \bar{\bar{H}}_B^\circ)/RT^2$$

or

$$\bar{\bar{H}}_B = \bar{\bar{H}}_B^\circ \tag{9-15}$$

Since $\bar{\bar{H}}_B^\circ$ is a constant $\bar{\bar{H}}_B$ *must be independent of concentration through-out the range of validity of Henry's law.* Since this range includes in-finite dilution, $\bar{\bar{H}}_B^\circ$ is also the partial molar enthalpy at infinite dilution. We conclude, therefore, that $\bar{\bar{H}}$ *for the solute in the hypothetical standard state is identical to that in the infinitely dilute solution.* Furthermore, recalling that a solute at infinite dilution was referred to in Chapter 6 as being in its reference state, we see that $\bar{\bar{H}}_B$ in the reference state is the same as $\bar{\bar{H}}_B$ in the standard state. Had we used Henry's law in the form $f_B = k'_B m$ (cf. Eq. (9-14) the same conclusion would have been reached.

We may now combine Eq. (9-12) with $\mu_B = \bar{\bar{H}}_B - T\bar{\bar{S}}_B$ (Eq. (4-12)) to yield immediately:

$$\bar{\bar{S}}_B = \bar{\bar{S}}_B^{\prime\circ} - R \ln X_B \tag{9-16}$$

It is to be emphasized that, in Eqs. (9-12), (9-15) and (9-16) the standard state is the hypothetical pure B, not the actual pure B.

VAPOR PRESSURE LOWERING

All the preceding discussions are also applicable in principle to systems in which only one of the components, e.g. A, is volatile, but since all values of p_B are then negligible certain simplifications ensue. When the liquid phase consists predominantly of the volatile solvent attention is focused on Raoult's law for solvent, since no solute pressures are measurable. With A standing for the solvent Raoult's law, Eq. (8-1), becomes $p_A/p_A{}^\bullet = X_A$. Subtracting both sides from unity gives:

$$\frac{p_A{}^\bullet - p_A}{p_A{}^\bullet} = X_B \tag{9-17}$$

Since only A is volatile, pressures of A are also total pressures, P, so we have:

$$(P_{\text{solvent}} - P_{\text{solution}})/P_{\text{solvent}} = X_B \tag{9-18}$$

valid only in solutions of B in A when Raoult's law holds for A. The numerator of the left side is known as the **lowering of the vapor pressure**, the whole left side as the **relative lowering of the vapor pressure**.

Example 9-3 When 9.00 g of a certain involatile polyhydric alcohol is dis-solved in 250 g of water a solution with a vapor pressure of 17.474 mm at 20° is formed. For H_2O (l) $p^\bullet$ is 17.535 mm at this temperature. Find the molecular weight of the alcohol.

Ans. The solution is dilute so Raoult's law will be expected to hold reason-ably well for the water. Furthermore only the water is volatile so we may use Eq. (9-18). Substitution gives $(17.535 - 17.474)/17.535 = X_B$ or $X_B = 0.00348$. But $X_B = (m_B/M_B)/(m_{H_2O}/M_{H_2O} + m_B/M_B)$ where m is mass and M is molecular weight, and $m_B = 9.00$ g, $m_{H_2O} = 250$ g and $M_{H_2O} = 18.02$, so $0.00348 = (9.00/M_B)/(9.00/M_B + 250/18.02)$ from which it is found that $M_B = 186$.

BOILING POINT ELEVATION

As shown in Fig. 8-3 for solutions of nonvolatile solutes in volatile solvents, the vapor pressure of the solution is lower than that of the solvent so that, for a given pressure, the boiling point of the solution is higher than that of the solvent. At the boiling point of the solution the latter is in equilibrium with the vapor. But the vapor has only A in it so:

$$(\mu_A)_v = (\mu_A{}^\bullet)_v = (\mu_A)_l$$

where the subscripts v and l refer to the two phases. If $P = 1$ atm $(\mu_A{}^\bullet)_v = (\mu_A^\circ)_v$. Moreover $(\mu_A)_l = (\mu_A^\circ)_l + RT \ln X_A$ if Raoult's law applies to A. Therefore $(\mu_A^\circ)_v = (\mu_A^\circ)_l + RT \ln X_A$ or we have:

$$(\mu_A^\circ)_v/T - (\mu_A^\circ)_l/T = R \ln X_A$$

Differentiating with respect to T at constant P and applying the Gibbs-Helmholtz equation, Eq. (4-32), gives:

$$-\frac{(\overline{H}_A^\circ)_v}{T^2} + \frac{(\overline{H}_A^\circ)_l}{T^2} = R \left[\frac{\partial \ln X_A}{\partial T} \right]_{P = 1 \text{ atm}} = -\frac{\Delta H_A}{T^2}$$

where ΔH_A is the heat of vaporization of A at the normal boiling point, or:

$$\left[\frac{\partial \ln X_A}{\partial T} \right]_{P = 1 \text{ atm}} = -\frac{\Delta H_A}{RT^2} \qquad (9\text{-}19)$$

which gives the rate of change of composition in the liquid with T under conditions in which the equilibrium vapor is at 1 atm. In other words it gives the variation of the normal boiling point (T) with X_A. Since ΔH_A is positive it is seen that T increases as X_A decreases or as X_B increases. As long as the solutions are *dilute* the temperature range considered is small and ΔH_A can be considered *independent* of T. We have, therefore, on integration *at constant pressure* (1 atm) between $X_A = X_A$, where the normal boiling point is T, and $X_A = 1$, where it is T_A°,

$$\int_1^{X_A} d \ln X_A = -\frac{\Delta H_A}{R} \int_{T_A^\circ}^T \frac{dT}{T^2}$$

or

$$\ln X_A = -\frac{\Delta H_A}{R} \left(\frac{T - T_A^\circ}{TT_A^\circ} \right) = \ln (1 - X_B) \qquad (9\text{-}20)$$

Additional approximations may now be made, all permissible at sufficient dilution. We shall (1) replace $T T_A^\circ$ by $T_A^{\circ 2}$ (e.g., if $T_A^\circ = 373.2$ and $T = 373.5$, $T T_A^\circ = 139,390$ and $T_A^{\circ 2} = 139,280$, indistinguishable within the usual accuracy of measurement) (2) replace $\ln (1 - X_B)$ by $-X_B$ since $\ln (1 - X_B)$ may be expanded into $- X_B - X_B^2/2 - X_B^3/3 - \ldots$, all terms except the first being negligible when $X_B \ll 1$. For example, if $X_B = 0.0300$, $\ln (1 - X_B) = -0.0304$ and $-X_B = -0.0300$. These give, on rearrangement and replacement of $T - T_A^\circ$ by ΔT_b, the boiling point elevation:

$$\Delta T_b = \frac{R T_A^{\circ 2}}{\Delta H_A} X_B \qquad (9\text{-}21)$$

Finally, this result may be expressed in terms of molality m. Since $X_B = n_B/(n_A + n_B)$ and $n_A \gg n_B$ (because of the dilution), $X_B \cong n_B/n_A = m/(1000 \div M_A)$, where M_A is the molecular weight of the solvent. Eq. (9-21) then becomes:

$$\Delta T_b = \left(\frac{R T_A^{\circ 2} M_A}{1000 \Delta H_A} \right) m \qquad (9\text{-}22)$$

The quantity in parentheses is called the **molal elevation constant**, K_b of the solvent—it contains no quantities characteristic of the solute. It may be thought of as the value of ΔT_b for a one-molal solution *if* Raoult's law and the above approximations are still valid at that concentration (which they aren't!). R and ΔH_A must be in consistent units. Clearly, ΔT_b is proportional to both X_B and m in very dilute solution. The *elevation* is the same whether the centigrade or Kelvin scales are used.

Example 9-4 A solution of 20.0 g of a certain solute (molecular weight = 168.1) in 1000 g of benzene (molecular weight = 78.1) has a normal boiling point of 80.40°. The normal boiling point of benzene is 80.10°. (a) Predict the normal boiling point of a solution of 10.0 g of the same solute in 1000 g of benzene. (b) Find the experimental value of K_b for benzene. (c) Calculate the value of K_b given that the heat of vaporization for benzene is 7.370 kcal mole^{-1} at its boiling point.

Ans. (a) Since $\Delta T_b \propto m$, the solution with only 10.0 g of solute per 1000 g of benzene will have half the elevation or $(80.40 - 80.10)/2 = 0.15°$. Therefore the normal boiling point will be $80.10 + 0.15 = 80.25°$. (b) Since $\Delta T_b = 80.40 - 80.10 = 0.30°$ when $m = 20.0/168.1 = 0.119$, $K_b = \Delta T_b/m = 0.30/0.119 = 2.52$. (c) $K_b = R T_A^{\circ 2} M_A/1000 \Delta H_A = 1.987 (80.10 + 273.15)^2 (78.1)/(1000) (7370) = 2.63$.

SOLUBILITY OF GASES IN LIQUIDS

The subject of gas solubility in liquids usually concerns solutions in which the liquid phase is predominantly the component that is relatively nonvolatile.   Thus in water which is saturated with nitrogen at $25°$ and 100 atm the mole fraction of water is still almost unity. In the gas phase, however, the mole fraction of water is negligibly small when the gas is at high pressure and the temperature low. The situation thus resembles that discussed in the preceding section in that in both phases one component predominates, but differs in that the predominating component is not the same one in both phases. Attention now is focused on Henry's law as it applies to the gas dissolved in the liquid phase. In determining whether the solute nitrogen follows Henry's law in this system two features are to be noted. First, high gas pressures dictate the use of fugacities instead of pressures.   Second, the condition of constant total pressure, dropped in Eq. (9-5), should be retained as in Eq. (9-6) if a wide range of pressure is to be considered.   Let us examine the data for nitrogen in water at $25°$** listed in Table 9-1. The mole fractions are, of course,

Table 9-1

p_{N_2} (atm)	0	50.00	100.0	200.0	300.0	500.0
f_{N_2} (atm)	0	49.65	99.2	202.1	315.2	595.7
$X_{N_2} \times 10^3$	0	0.542	1.015	1.812	2.455	3.558
f_{N_2} (atm) corr. to $P_{total} = 500$ atm	0	90.76	169.6	302.1	412.1	595.7

Adapted from I. R. Krichevsky and J. S. Kasarnovsky, *J. Am. Chem. Soc.*, **57, 2168 (1935).

those in the liquid phase.   The fugacities are the same for both phases but we shall think of them as referring to the nitrogen in the liquid solution.   The total pressure, which is virtually identical to p_{N_2}, is clearly different for each column of data, except for the last row which will be referred to later. If, as in Fig. 9-1, p_{N_2} be plotted against X_{N_2} or f_{N_2} against X_{N_2} a curved line is obtained.   This is shown in Fig. 9-3 (a) where rows 2 and 3 of Table 9-1 are plotted.   A graph of rows 1 and 3 would have been almost indistinguishable from this.   At first sight the curvature suggests that Henry's law does not hold for the dissolved nitrogen up to pressures as high as 500 atm. If, however, we calculate what the fugacities of the dissolved nitrogen would be were the *total* pressure P on the solution to be kept constant at, say, 500 atm, for all the solutions, we would reach a different conclusion.   Now the variation of f with P is given by Eq. (5-21), integration of which, assuming $\bar{V}$ independent of P, leads to:

$$\ln f_{N_2} (P = 500 \text{ atm}) = \ln f_{N_2} (P = P \text{ atm}) + \frac{\bar{\bar{V}}_{N_2}}{RT} (500 - P)$$

Using this equation and a value of $\bar{\bar{V}}_{N_2} = 32.8$ ml mole^{-1}, the data in the last row of Table 9-1 were calculated. If these corrected values be plotted against X_{N_2} as in Fig. 9-2 (b) the curvature disappears and we conclude

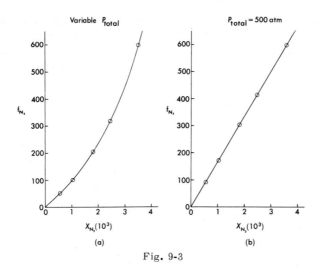

Fig. 9-3

that Henry's law holds, after all, up to $P = 500$ atm. The importance of the constant total pressure condition in Eq. (9-6) is thus apparent in a situation such as this. If pressure differences not greater than a few atmospheres are involved, however, there is no need to insist on constant total pressure.

Example 9-5 Describe the situation presented in Example 9-3 as the solubility of a gas in a liquid.

Ans. The solubility of water vapor in the liquid polyhydric alcohol, when the vapor is at a pressure of 17.474 mm, is 250 g of H_2O per 9.00 g of alcohol.

SOLUBILITY OF HIGHLY SOLUBLE SOLIDS IN LIQUIDS— FREEZING POINT DEPRESSION

This topic has been considered toward the end of the preceding chapter. It was there assumed that Raoult's law holds at all concentrations. Here we assume that it holds only for A in dilute solutions of B in A and that the solid phase which is in equilibrium with the given solution is *pure solid A*. The heat of fusion of A, ΔH_A, is still taken to be independent of T. We may then say that Eq. (8-17) is valid but only at high dilution:

$$\ln X_A = \frac{\Delta H_A}{R}\left(\frac{T - T_A}{T T_A}\right) \qquad (8\text{-}17)$$

Since T_A is constant this may be rewritten:

$$\log X_A = -\frac{\Delta H_A}{2.303R}\left(\frac{1}{T}\right) + \text{constant} \qquad (9\text{-}23)$$

so a plot of $\log X_A$ vs. $(1/T)$ should be linear with a slope of $-\Delta H_A/$ $2.303R$ within the validity of the above assumptions. Since the solutions are in equilibrium with A(s), X_A is the solubility of A(s) in B at temperature T. So far, then, little new has been added. We now wish to express concentration in terms of X_B or molality m. This is done by making substitutions and approximations in Eq. (8-17) as was done in converting Eq. (9-20) to Eq. (9-21) to give:

$$\Delta T_f = \frac{RT_A^{\,2}}{\Delta H_A} X_B \qquad (9\text{-}24)$$

where T_A is the melting point of A, ΔH_A its molar heat of fusion and $\Delta T_f = T_A - T$, not $T - T_A$. Clearly, in view of the approximations just made, Eq. (9-24) may be used only at high dilution. ΔT_f is called the **freezing point depression**. We further convert mole fraction to molality and find, as for Eq. (9-22):

$$\Delta T_f = \left(\frac{RT_A^{\,2}M_A}{1000\Delta H_A}\right)m \qquad (9\text{-}25)$$

where the quantity in parentheses is called the **molal depression constant**, K_f, of the solvent—it contains no quantities characteristic of the solute and represents the value of ΔT_f for a one-molal solution if Raoult's law and all the above approximations were to hold up to $m = 1$. ΔT_f is seen to be directly proportional to both X_B and m.

Example 9-6 Find the freezing point of a solution of sucrose $(M = 342)$ in water which is 2.00% solute by weight. The heat of fusion of ice $(M = 18.02)$ is 1.436 kcal mole^{-1}.

Ans. We assume that the solid phase in equilibrium with the solution is ice. Furthermore, the solution is dilute enough for Eq. (9-25) to hold. The molality will be $[1000(2.00)]/[98.00(342)]$ or 0.0597 so $\Delta T_f = [1.987(273.2^2)\,(18.02)/(1000)\,(1436)]\,0.0597 = 0.111$. The freezing point of the solution is therefore $0.000 - 0.111 = -0.111°$.

If K_f is written $RT_A M_A/1000\Delta S_A$, where ΔS_A is the entropy of fusion, it is seen that solvents which gain little entropy on melting give the largest values of ΔT_f, other things being equal. This is why camphor has been widely used in freezing point depression work.

SOLUBILITY OF SLIGHTLY SOLUBLE SOLIDS IN LIQUIDS

The difference between this situation and that of the preceding section will be evident qualitatively from Fig. 9-4 (which is of the same type as Fig. 8-8 but for a non-ideal system). Solution c, on the line ae is saturated with A(s) at temperature t_1 and is *high* in A content. Raoult's law may be taken as applying to A in this solution as discussed immediately above. Solution d, on the other hand, is on the line be, is saturated with

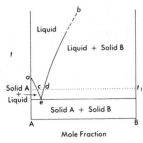

Fig. 9-4

B, but is *low* in B content, so we may *not* apply Raoult's law to B. Since B is the saturating phase we must work with B and must use Henry's law. This introduces some important differences in the treatment.

For these saturated solutions we use:

$$(\mu_B)_l = (\mu_B^{\bullet})_s$$

where the subscripts l and s refer to the two phases. However, $(\mu_B)_l = (\mu_B^{\circ})_l + RT \ln X_B$ by Eq. (9-12), $(\mu_B^{\circ})_l$ referring to the hypothetical standard state. This gives, on rearrangement and differentiation, as in the development of Eq. (9-19):

$$\frac{(\overline{\overline{H}}_B^{\circ})_l}{T^2} - \frac{(\overline{H}_B)_s}{T^2} = R\left[\frac{\partial \ln X_B}{\partial T}\right]_P$$

or

$$\left[\frac{\partial \ln X_B}{\partial T}\right]_P = \frac{\Delta H_B'}{RT^2} \qquad (9\text{-}26)$$

where $\Delta H_B' = (\overline{\overline{H}}_B^{\circ})_l - (\overline{H}_B)_s$ but is *not* a heat of fusion. (The stipulation of constant pressure is hardly necessary for we are dealing with a condensed system.) Since $\overline{\overline{H}}_B^{\circ}$ has been shown to be the partial molar enthalpy of B in an infinitely dilute solution, $\Delta H_B'$ is the *heat of solution of B(s) in the infinitely dilute solution in A*. Taking it to be independent of T over a small temperature range Eq. (9-26) may be integrated to give:

$$\log X_B = -\frac{\Delta H_B'}{2.303R}\left(\frac{1}{T}\right) + \text{constant} \qquad (9\text{-}27)$$

or integrated between $T = T$ where $X_B = X_B$ and $T = T'$ where $X_B = X_B'$ as follows:

$$\int_{X_B}^{X_B'} d \ln X_B = \frac{\Delta H_B'}{R}\int_{T}^{T'} dT/T^2$$

or

$$\log{(X'_B/X_B)} = \frac{\Delta H'_B}{2.303R}\left(\frac{T' - T}{TT'}\right) \tag{9-28}$$

(Why may we not integrate between $X_B = X_B$ and $X_B = 1$?) Again a straight line results when the logarithm of the solubility is plotted against $1/T$. The heat of solution is obtained from the slope. The ratio X'_B/X_B is the ratio of the solubilities of B at the two temperatures. Since $X_B \propto m$ one may replace X'_B/X_B by m'/m, the ratio of the corresponding molalities.

Example 9-7 The solubility of $SnI_4(s)$ in $CHCl_3(l)$ at three temperatures is as follows:

$T(°K)$	283.15	298.15	313.15
X_{SnI_4}	0.00981	0.01692	0.02747

Plot the data according to Eq. (9-27), determine whether the relation is linear and find the heat of solution of $SnI_4(s)$ in $CHCl_3(l)$ at infinite dilution.

Ans. Fig. 9-5 gives the desired plot. The line has a slight curvature but its average slope leads to $\Delta H'_{SnI_4} = 6.04$ kcal mole^{-1} which is therefore the desired heat of solution. The curvature may be the result of deviation from Henry's law and/or variation of heat of solution with temperature.

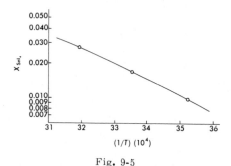

Fig. 9-5

Note The values of X_{SnI_4} are small enough for the application of Eq. (9-27) to be acceptable, at least as a first approximation.

Example 9-8 If 100 g of ethanol dissolves 0.225 g of anthracene(s) at 40° and 0.463 g at 60° find the heat of solution of anthracene in ethanol at infinite dilution at about 50°.

Ans. In such a solution the ratio of the number of grams of solute in a fixed quantity of solvent equals the ratio of the mole fractions. Substitution in Eq. (9-28) gives:

$$\log\,(0.225/0.463) = \frac{\Delta H'_B}{2.303R}\left[\frac{313 - 333}{313(333)}\right]$$

where B stands for anthracene. Solution of this equation gives $\Delta H'_B = 7.5\,\mathrm{kcal\,mole^{-1}}$.

Note The heat of fusion of anthracene is $6.6\,\mathrm{kcal\,mole^{-1}}$ implying that the heat of solution of *liquid* anthracene in an infinitely large amount of ethanol is $0.9\,\mathrm{kcal\,mole^{-1}}$.

OSMOTIC PRESSURE

The fugacity of the solvent in a solution is always less than that of the pure solvent at the same T and P. If, then, solution and solvent are separated by a membrane which is permeable only to solvent—called a **semipermeable membrane**—and if both are at the same T and P, the solvent will slowly flow through the membrane into the solvent. Such a flow is termed **osmosis**. Fig. 9-6 indicates schematically an osmotic cell the temperature of which is held constant. The crosshatched region represents the membrane and C a capillary. As solvent enters, the volume of the solution increases and the solution rises in the tube. When this occurs, however, the total pressure on the solution increases due to the increased hydrostatic pressure of the column of liquid in the tube. This in turn increases the fugacity of the solvent in the solution (since f increases with P, cf. Eq. (5-21)), and with sufficient increase in the length of the liquid column, f eventually becomes equal to that of the pure solvent, the total pressure on which has not changed, and osmosis then ceases. If the volume within the capillary is very small compared with that of the solution originally present, the actual quantity of solvent which flows before osmosis ceases is so small that there is effectively a negligible change in the composition of the original solution. Thus we have converted a situation in which solution and solvent, at the same

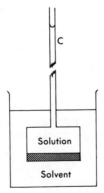

Fig. 9-6

total pressure, have different solvent fugacities to one in which they have the same fugacities because the solution is under a higher total pressure. This condition of equal solvent fugacities implies equal chemical potential through Eq. (7-2) even though, because of the difference in P, solution and solvent are not in *mechanical* equilibrium. If the vapor of the solvent behaves ideally fugacity in the above account can be replaced by partial pressure in the equilibrium vapor. The additional pressure which must be exerted on the solution to raise p_A up to $p_A^{\bullet}$ is called the **osmotic pressure** of the solution. We shall give this quantity the symbol π.

To relate π to p_A and $p_A^{\bullet}$ we proceed as follows. Before the increased pressure was exerted we had:

$$\mu_A^{\bullet} - \mu_A = RT \ln (p_A^{\bullet}/p_A) \qquad (7\text{-}7)$$

where μ_A and $\mu_A^{\bullet}$ refer to the solvent in the solution and in pure solvent, respectively, assuming the vapor to be ideal. But $\mu_A^{\bullet} - \mu_A$ is the amount by which μ_A is increased when the total pressure on the solution is increased from p_A to $p_A + \pi$. This quantity is calculated by integration of Eq. (4-28) applied to components in solution as follows:

$$\mu_A^{\bullet} - \mu_A = \int_{p_A}^{p_A + \pi} \overline{\overline{V}}_A \, dP$$

where $\overline{\overline{V}}_A$ is the partial molar volume of the solvent in the solution. But $\overline{\overline{V}}_A$ is almost independent of P for substances in liquid solution, so it may be moved to the left of the integration sign. Furthermore, $\overline{\overline{V}}_A = \overline{V}_A$, the molar volume of pure A(l), if the solution is dilute. With these approximations in mind we obtain:

$$\mu_A^{\bullet} - \mu_A = \overline{V}_A \, \pi$$

Equating these two expressions for $\mu_A^{\bullet} - \mu_A$ gives:

$$\pi = (RT/\overline{V}_A) \ln (p_A^{\bullet}/p_A) \qquad (9\text{-}29)$$

It will be seen that this relation is valid only for solutions dilute enough for $\overline{\overline{V}}_A$ to be given by $\overline{V}_A$ and whose vapor can be considered ideal. If $\overline{V}_A$ is in liters per mole R must be in liter-atmospheres per mole per deg if π is to be in atmospheres.

Example 9-9 Find the osmotic pressure of the aqueous solution referred to in Example 9-3 at 20° given that the density of water is 0.998 g ml^{-1}. *Ans.* $\overline{V}_{H_2O} = 18.0/0.998 = 18.0$ ml^3 mole^{-1} or 0.0180 liter mole^{-1}. Substitution in Eq. (9-29) gives:

$$\pi = [0.0821(293)/0.0180] \ln (17.535/17.474) = 4.68 \text{ atm.}$$

Note The osmotic pressure must not be confused with the vapor pressure lowering. In this example $\pi = 4.68$ atm whereas the vapor pressure lowering is $17.535 - 17.474 = 0.061$ mm.

Further approximations may be made in Eq. (9-29). If Raoult's law applies $p_A{}^\bullet/p_A$ may be replaced by $1/X_A$ or $\pi = -(RT/\overline{V}_A) \ln X_A = -(RT/\overline{V}_A) \ln (1 - X_B)$. But, as shown above, $\ln (1 - X_B) \cong -X_B$ if $X_B \ll 1$ so we have:

$$\pi \cong (RT/\overline{V}_A)X_B \tag{9-30}$$

Thus π is proportional to the mole fraction of solute. Moreover, replacing X_B by $n_B/(n_A + n_B) \cong n_B/n_A$ we have $\pi \cong (n_B/n_A\overline{V}_A)RT$. Since $n_A\overline{V}_A$ is the volume of all the solvent that has n_B moles of solute in it this becomes:

$$\pi \cong (n_B/V_{solvent})RT \tag{9-31}$$

(cf. the ideal gas law, $P = (n/V)RT$). Finally, since in dilute solution the volume of all the solvent is practically equal to the volume of all the solution, $n_B/V_{solvent}$ becomes $n_B/V_{solution}$ which is the same as the molarity c of the solution. We may then write:

$$\pi \cong cRT \tag{9-32}$$

which is **van't Hoff's law of osmotic pressure**. Of the relations given by Eqs. (9-29), (9-30), (9-31) and (9-32) the first is the most accurate, but all become identical and correct at infinite dilution. All four show that π is proportional to T. Eq. (9-31) is sometimes called the **Morse equation**.

Example 9-10 Calculate the osmotic pressure of a $3.00m$ aqueous sucrose solution at $30.0°$ by Eqs. (9-29) to (9-32). The vapor pressure of the solution is 29.675 mm and that of water 31.824 mm at this temperature. Take the density of $H_2O(l)$ and of the solution to be 0.9957 and 1.230 g cm^{-3}, respectively. $M_{sucrose} = 342$ and $M_{H_2O} = 18.016$.

Ans. $\overline{V}_{H_2O} = 18.016/0.9957 = 18.09$ cm^3 mole^{-1} so Eq. (9-29) gives:

$$\pi = [0.08206(303.2)/0.01809] \ln (31.824/29.675) = 96.2 \text{ atm}$$

$X_{sucrose} = 3.00/[3.00 + (1000/18.02)] = 0.0513$ so Eq. (9-30) gives:

$$\pi = [0.0821(303.2)/0.01809](0.0513) = 70.6 \text{ atm}$$

If we consider as much solution as contains 1000 g of H_2O, $V_{solvent}$ becomes $1000/0.9957 = 1004.4$ cm^3 and Eq. (9-31) yields:

$$\pi = (3.00/1.0044)[0.0821(303.2)] = 74.4 \text{ atm}$$

Since 3.00 moles or $3(342) = 1026$ g of sucrose are dissolved in 1000 g of water the solution will weigh $1026 + 1000 = 2026$ g and occupy a volume of $2026/1.230 = 1647$ ml.   The molarity is therefore $3.00/1.647 = 1.822$. Substitution in Eq. (9-32) gives:

$$\pi = 1.822(0.0821)(303.2) = 45.4 \text{ atm}$$

Note The experimental osmotic pressure is 95.2 atm. Clearly, Eq. (9-29) gives the best result but requires a knowledge of vapor pressures.

Eqs. (9-17), (9-21), (9-24) and (9-30) show that the four properties of dilute solutions, relative vapor pressure lowering, boiling point elevation, freezing point depression and osmotic pressure, are all proportional to the mole fraction of the solute. This point of similarity has resulted in their being called the **colligative properties of solutions.**

CHEMICAL EQUILIBRIA IN DILUTE SOLUTION

Consider the following equilibria in dilute solution:

$$C_6H_{10} + I_2 \;\rightleftharpoons\; C_6H_{10}I_2 \quad \text{(all in } CCl_4)$$
$$CH_3COOC_2H_5 + H_2O \rightleftharpoons CH_3COOH + C_2H_5OH \quad \text{(all in } H_2O)$$

In the first example it is assumed that the reactants and products are all present in small concentrations in the solvent, CCl_4. In the   second example the ester, acid and alcohol are assumed to be present in small concentration in the solvent, water, which is also a reactant and present at high concentration, i.e., $X_{solvent} \cong 1$.   Under these conditions it is permissible to assume that Henry's law holds for all the substances except the solvent, and that where the solvent is also a reactant or product Raoult's law may be applied to it. Thus, in the general reaction:

$$aA + bB + \ldots = dD + eE + \ldots \quad \text{(all dissolved in A)}$$

we may apply Eq. (9-12) to B, D and E, and Eq. (9-11) to A. Following the treatment used in arriving at Eq. (7-22):

$$K_X = \frac{(X_D)^d (X_E)^e \ldots}{(X_B)^b \ldots} \tag{9-33}$$

where the mole fractions are those at equilibrium and K_X is an equilibrium constant. It is to be observed that (1) the solvent does not appear in this equilibrium expression and that (2) although K_X is here an equilibrium constant it is not so for homogeneous gas reactions unless $\Delta n = 0$ (cf. Eq. (7-28)).

Because of the direct proportionality existing between mole fraction and molarity (c) at high dilution we may also write:

$$K_c = \frac{(c_D)^d (c_E)^e \ldots}{(c_B)^b \ldots} \tag{9-34}$$

Molalities may also be used to form still another equilibrium constant.

Both K_X and K_c can be shown to be related to $\Delta G°$ by expressions analogous to Eq. (7-23), viz.

$$\Delta G°_{(X)} = -RT \ln K_X \qquad (9\text{-}35)$$

and

$$\Delta G°_{(c)} = -RT \ln K_c \qquad (9\text{-}36)$$

but these two $\Delta G°$'s refer to different standard states.

Example 9-11 (a) for $N_2O_4(CCl_4) \rightleftharpoons 2NO_2(CCl_4)$, K_X is $6.0(10^{-5})$ at $25°$. The density of $CCl_4(l)$ is 1.59 g cm^{-3} and its molecular weight 154. If the mole fraction of NO_2 in a certain solution at equilibrium is $7.5(10^{-5})$ at this temperature find $X_{N_2O_4}$. (b) Find the degree of dissociation of the N_2O_4 under these conditions. (c) Compute K_c.

Ans. (a) At equilibrium $X_{NO_2}{}^2/X_{N_2O_4} = [7.5(10^{-5})]^2/X_{N_2O_4} = 6.0(10^{-5})$, or $X_{N_2O_4} = 9.4(10^{-5})$.

(b) One mole of equilibrium solution contains $9.4(10^{-5})$ moles of N_2O_4 and $7.5(10^{-5})$ moles of NO_2. This much NO_2 must have arisen from $0.5(7.5)(10^{-5}) = 3.8(10^{-5})$ moles of N_2O_4 to give a total of $(3.8 + 9.4) \times (10^{-5}) = 13.2(10^{-5})$ moles of N_2O_4 if no dissociation had occurred. The degree of dissociation is therefore $3.8(10^{-5})/13.2(10^{-5}) = 0.29$ or 29%.

(c) One mole of solution, consisting almost entirely of CCl_4, will occupy $154/1.59 = 96.9$ cm^3 or 0.0969 liter. But this volume contains $9.4(10^{-5})$ moles of N_2O_4 and $7.5(10^{-5})$ moles of NO_2, so $c_{N_2O_4} = 9.4(10^{-5})/0.0969 = 9.7(10^{-4})$ mole liter^{-1}. Similarly $c_{NO_2} = 7.8(10^{-4})$ moles liter^{-1}. Then $K_c = [7.8(10^{-4})]^2/9.7(10^{-4}) = 6.3(10^{-4})$.

Since we are dealing with condensed systems the influence of total pressure change on the position of equilibria such as those under discussion is negligible. The variation of K_X with temperature is found from Eq. (9-35) as was done in developing Eq. (7-41). We find, that

$$\text{d} \ln K_X/\text{d}T = \Delta H°_{(X)}/RT^2 \qquad (9\text{-}37)$$

Similarly, starting with Eq. (9-36), we find:

$$\text{d} \ln K_c/\text{d}T = \Delta H°_{(c)}/RT^2 \qquad (9\text{-}38)$$

where $\Delta H°_{(X)}$ and $\Delta H°_{(c)}$ are the enthalpy changes for the reactants and products in their respective hypothetical standard states, analogous to $\Delta G°_{(X)}$ and $\Delta G°_{(c)}$. The difference between Eqs. (9-38) and (7-45) is noteworthy.

THE DISTRIBUTION LAW

When a solute is distributed between two immiscible solvents a simple relation exists between its concentrations in the two phases *if* both are *dilute* solutions. In this event Eq. (9-12) applies to the distributed substance in both phases thus:

$$\mu_B = \mu_B^o + RT \ln X_B \qquad \text{in one phase}$$

and

$$\mu_B' = \mu_B^{o'} + RT \ln X_B' \qquad \text{in the other phase}$$

At equilibrium, however, $\mu_B = \mu_B'$, so the two right-hand sides are equal. Therefore we have:

$$\mu_B^o - \mu_B^{o'} = RT \ln (X_B'/X_B)$$

Since μ_B^o and $\mu_B^{o'}$ are both constant at a given temperature this becomes:

$$X_B/X_B' = K \qquad\qquad (9\text{-}39)$$

where K is a constant at a given temperature, known as the **partition coefficient** or **distribution coefficient**. Eq. (9-39) is called the **distribution law**. Any concentration unit which is proportional to X_B in dilute solution may be substituted for either or both X_B or X_B' without upsetting the constancy of K, but such a change will alter its numerical value. If, e.g., molality is used in one solvent and mole fraction in another the resulting expression is:

$$m_B/X_B' = \text{constant} \qquad\qquad (9\text{-}40)$$

Clearly, any statement of a value of coefficient must be accompanied by a statement of the concentration units used (if different for the two phases) and the solvents to which numerator and denominator refer. Alternatively, we may think of K as an equilibrium constant for B (in solvent 1) $\rightleftharpoons$ B (in solvent 2) and treat this as in the preceding section with the same result.

Example 9-12 When a small amount of iodine is shaken with 10 ml of CS_2(l) and 20 ml of H_2O(l) at 18° the CS_2 phase is found to contain 1.29 g of I_2 and the H_2O phase 0.0064 g of I_2. (a) Find the distribution coefficient for I_2 (aqueous layer in denominator). (b) If 2.20 g of I_2 had been used altogether what weight of I_2 would have been found in the aqueous layer?

Ans. Concentration of I_2 in H_2O layer = 0.0064(1000/20) = 0.32 g liter^{-1} and concentration of I_2 in CS_2 layer = 1.29(1000/10) = 129 g liter^{-1}. Therefore K = 129/0.32 = 400.
(b) Let x be the weight of I_2 found in the aqueous layer. Then 400 = [(2.20 − x)(1000)/10]/[(x)(1000)/20], the solution of which is x = 0.0109 g.

It is important to realize that the equality of chemical potentials of B in both phases, assumed in obtaining Eq. (9-39), implies that B is *the same species in both phases*. When we say that B in one phase is in equilibrium with B in the other we are implying that its fugacity is the same in both phases, and this indicates equilibrium only when the fugacities of the same molecular species are equal in both phases.

Example 9-13 The distribution coefficient for I_2 distributed between $CS_2(l)$ and $0.125M$ KI is 625 at $14°$ when the numerator refers to the CS_2 layer. In the aqueous KI phase some of the iodine forms triiodide ion I_3^-. When 2.00 liter of $0.125M$ KI is shaken with 3.00 liter of CS_2 and 6.00 moles of I_2 the aqueous layer is found to contain 0.06584 moles of iodine altogether (not counting free I^-). How many moles of the I_2 in the aqueous layer are in the form of triiodide ion?

Ans. The distribution law should refer to that species common to both layers, viz. I_2. Let x be the number of moles of I_2 (as such) in the aqueous layer. Then the number in the CS_2 layer will be $6.00 - x$. The respective concentrations will be $x/2.00$ and $(6.00 - x)/3.00$ mole liter^{-1}, so we use:

$$[(6.00 - x)/3.00]/(x/2) = 625$$

the solution of which is $x = 0.00639$ moles of I_2. But there are 0.06584 moles, including the iodine present as I_3^-. Therefore $0.06584 - 0.00639 = 0.05945$ moles of I_2 are present as triiodide ion.

PROBLEMS

1. The partial pressures of C_2H_5OH(A) and CCl_4(B) over C_2H_5OH-CCl_4 solutions at $45.0°$ at several concentrations were found by J. A. Barker, I. Brown and F. Smith (*Discussions Faraday Soc.*, 15, 142 (1953)) to be as follows:

X_B	0	0.0212	0.0356	0.1016	0.1638	1.0000
p_A(mm)	173.09	169.41	167.34	158.45	150.97	0
p_B(mm)	0	23.32	38.31	95.32	135.56	258.84

(a) Does this system show positive or negative deviations from ideality?

(b) Show the approach to (i) Raoult's law for A and (ii) Henry's law for B as X_B approaches zero.

(c) Assuming a Henry's law constant for B of 1135 mm and ideal behavior in the vapor phase what is the fugacity of B in the hypothetical standard state?

(d) *Assuming Henry's law to hold for* $X_B < 0.025$ find

(i) $\Delta G_{318.2}$ for B $(X_B = 0.1016) \longrightarrow$ B $(X_B = 0.0356)$

(ii) $\Delta G_{318.2}$ for B $(X_B = 0.0212) \longrightarrow$ B (hypothetical standard state)

(iii) $\Delta H_{318.2}$ and $\Delta S_{318.2}$ for the transfer in (ii)

(iv) $\Delta H_{318.2}$ for B (hypothetical standard state) $\longrightarrow$ B $(X_B = 0)$.

(e) Find $\Delta G_{318.2}$ for the transfer in (d) (i) if Henry's law were valid up to $X_B = 0.1016$.

2. Show, by the use of the Gibbs-Duhem equation, Eq. (6-12), that for a binary solution Henry's law *must* hold over the range of concentration for which Raoult's law holds.

3. In Chapter 6, Table 6-5, it was stated that μ and $\overline{\overline{S}}$ fall in the Type 2 category insofar as their behavior at high dilution is concerned. In Fig. 6-2, however, two possible categories are shown for Type 2. In which of these categories does (a) μ and (b) $\overline{\overline{S}}$ fall?

4. The normal boiling point of dilute solutions are often *lower* than those of the pure solvent so $\Delta T_b < 0$. Reconcile this with Eq. (9-21) which predicts $T > T_A{}^\circ$.

5. The Henry's law constants for $H_2(g)$ in $H_2O(l)$ are $6.85(10^4)$ and $7.63(10^4)$ at 20° and 40°, respectively, when pressures are in atmospheres and concentrations in mole fraction. By adapting Eq. (9-28) to this situation find the average heat of solution of $H_2(g)$ in $H_2O(l)$ at infinite dilution over this temperature range for small pressures of H_2.

6. The solubility of ice (A) in glycerol (B) at -0.0300° is $X_A = 0.99971$. The heat of vaporization of $H_2O(l)$ at its normal boiling point is 9.72 kcal mole^{-1}. Glycerol may be considered involatile.
   (a) What is the freezing point depression of a solution of B in A in which $X_B = 0.00029$?
   (b) Find the normal boiling point of the solution in (a).
   (c) Find the lowering of the vapor pressure of A by B in the solution in (a) at 100°.
   (d) Find the osmotic pressure of the solution in (a) at 100° if the molar volume of $H_2O(l)$ at this temperature is 18.80 ml mole^{-1}.

7. A certain aqueous solution has an osmotic pressure of 20 atm at 25°. What would be the effect of exerting a pressure of more than 20 atm on it at this temperature if it were placed in an osmotic cell?

8. The melting point of white phosphorus (B) is 44° and its heat of fusion is 600 cal mole^{-1}.
   (a) Find its *ideal* solubility at 25°.
   (b) The heat of solution of B in n-heptane (A) at infinite dilution at 25° is $\Delta H = 4.1$ kcal mole^{-1}. Estimate the solubility of B in A at 40° if the actual solubility at 25° is $X_B = 0.0124$.

9. In the $0.125M$ KI layer of Ex. 9-13 the equilibrium $I_2 + I^- \rightleftharpoons I_3{}^-$ exists. Assuming that Henry's law applies to each of these three species find K_c for this equilibrium at 14° using the results given in the answer.

10. When benzoic acid (HB) is distributed between water (W) and benzene (bz) at 10° it dissociates in part in the water and associates in part in the benzene. The following concentrations were found present at equilibrium in four runs.[***] $c_{(W)}$ is the concentration *of the species* HB

[***]From Taylor and Glasstone's *Treatise on Physical Chemistry*, Vol. I, Copyright 1942, D. Van Nostrand Company, Inc., Princeton, N. J.

in the aqueous phase and $c_{(bz)}$ the *total* concentration of HB in the benzene phase, both expressed in moles of HB per liter of solution. The concentration of $(HB)_2$ in the benzene phase in moles of $(HB)_2$ per liter of solution is indicated by $c''_{(bz)}$.

(a) Show that $c_{(w)}/c_{(bz)}$ is not constant. Why?

(b) Find $c'_{(bz)}$, the concentration of the species HB in the benzene layer in moles of HB per liter, for each run.

(c) Show that $c_{(w)}/c'_{(bz)}$ is constant. Why is this to be expected?

(d) Show that $c_{(w)}/c''_{(bz)}$ is not constant. Why?

(e) Show that $c_{(w)}/(c''_{(bz)})^{1/2}$ is constant. Why is this to be expected?

Run	$c_{(W)}$	$c_{(bz)}$	$c''_{(bz)}$
1	0.0357	0.1449	0.0470
2	0.1007	0.8843	0.3702
3	0.1626	2.1777	0.9727
4	0.2249	4.0544	1.8666

10

Non-ideal systems—activity

We have considered the behavior of ideal solutions (Chapter 7) and of dilute real solutions (Chapter 9). There remain those systems which are neither ideal nor dilute. It is in this latter category that most systems fall. The theory is an extension of previously developed concepts.

GAS MIXTURES

For pure gases at low pressure and/or high temperature we have seen:

$$\mu_i = RT \ln p_i + \mathbf{B}_i \tag{7-6}$$

where $\mathbf{B}_i$ depends only on T and on the gas to which reference is made. If the gas is not ideal the following applies:

$$\mu_i = RT \ln f_i + \mathbf{B}_i \tag{7-2}$$

under all conditions.

For ideal gas mixtures Eq. (7-6) may still be used and for non-ideal behavior we must use Eq. (7-2). In the latter event, however, we are faced with finding f_i in the mixture. The method is similar to that used for finding it for pure gases (Chapter 5). By defining b_i as the difference between the ideal partial molar volume of the ith gas in the mixture (cf. Ex. 6-2) and the actual partial molar volume, viz.:

$$b_i = \overline{\overline{V}}_i - (RT/P) \tag{10-1}$$

combining this with Eq. (5-11) written as:

$$RT \; d \ln f_i = \overline{\overline{V}}_i dP \qquad (10\text{-}2)$$

integrating from a very small total pressure P^*, to the given total pressure P, and replacing f_i^* by $X_i P^*$ and $X_i P$ by p_i we find:

$$\ln (f_i/p_i) = (1/RT) \int_0^P b_i dP \qquad (10\text{-}3)$$

analogous to Eq. (5-13). Thus, to find f_i, measurements of b_i, and therefore of $\overline{\overline{V}}_i$, are required at the given temperature for a range of total pressures up to P.

Example 10-1 Find f_{N_2} in a N_2-H_2 mixture at $0.00°$ and 200 atm in which $X_{N_2} = 0.400$, given the following data from A. R. Merz and C. W. Whittaker (*J. Am. Chem. Soc.*, **50**, 1522 (1928):

$\overline{\overline{P}}$ (atm)	50.0	100	200
$\overline{V}_{N_2}$ (cm³ mole⁻¹)	447.5	226.7	120.3

Ans. $b_{N_2} = \overline{\overline{V}}_{N_2} - R(273.15)/P = 447.5 - 22414/50.0 = -0.8$ cm³ mole⁻¹ at 50.0 atm. Similarly $b_{N_2} = 2.6$ and 8.2 cm³ mole⁻¹ at 100 and 200 atm. A plot of these values vs. P gives a curve the area under which, from $P = 0$ to $P = 200$ atm is about 340 cm³ atm mole⁻¹. Moreover, $p_{N_2} = X_{N_2}P = 0.400(200) = 80.0$ atm. Therefore, using Eq. (10-3), we have ln $(f_{N_2}/80.0) = (1/22414)(340)$ or $f_{N_2} = 81.2$ atm.

Note The ideal value is $0.400(200) = 80.0$ atm.

The reader is reminded that the activity coefficient of the gas, γ_i (cf. Chapter 5), is given by

$$\gamma_i = f_i/p_i \qquad (10\text{-}4)$$

where $p_i = X_i P$. In Example 10-1, e.g., $\gamma_{N_2} = 81.2/80.0 = 1.015$.

Eq. (10-3) becomes simpler if it happens that $\overline{\overline{V}}_i = \overline{V}_i$ at the same total pressure and temperature (cf. Eq. (7-14) for ideal solutions). In this case b_i in Eq. (10-3) and b in Eq. (5-13) become identical so f/P for the pure gas, which we shall write $f_i^{\bullet}/P$, equals f_i/p_i for the same gas in the mixture at the *total* pressure P and the same temperature. Since $f_i^{\bullet}/P = f_i/p_i$ and $p_i = X_i P$, we have:

$$f_i = f_i^{\bullet}{}' X_i \qquad (10\text{-}5)$$

where $f_i^{\bullet}{}'$ is the fugacity of the ith gas when it is pure and at the same pressure as the *total* pressure of the mixture. This is known as the **Lewis and Randall rule**. It is only an approximation and it rests on the equality of $\overline{\overline{V}}_i$ and $\overline{V}_i$.

The extensive series of experiments needed to evaluate f_i by Eq. (10-3) and the comparative simplicity of finding $f_i^{\bullet}$ by the methods given in Chapter 5 have led to the frequent use of Eq. (10-5) in spite of its uncertainty.   One common method consists of finding $f_i^{\bullet'}$ from generalized fugacity charts followed by application of the Lewis and Randall rule.

Example 10-2 A certain gas mixture containing ammonia, for which X_{NH_3} = 0.500, is held at 450° and a total pressure of 300 atm. Estimate the fugacity of the NH_3(g) using Fig. 5-6 and the Lewis and Randall rule given that, for NH_3, T_c = 406°K and P_c = 111.5 atm.

Ans. Under these conditions θ = 723/400 = 1.78 and π = 300/111.5 = 2.69.   For these values we find from Fig. 5-6 that $f_{NH_3}^{\bullet'}/300 \cong 0.90$ so $f_{NH_3}^{\bullet'} \cong 270$ atm, which is the estimated fugacity of *pure* NH_3 at 450° and 300 atm.   By the Lewis and Randall rule f_{NH_3} in the mixture $\cong$ 270(0.500) = 135 atm.

We are now in a position to relate fugacities of gases in gas mixtures to other thermodynamic quantities through Eq. (7-2).   Thus for the isothermal transfer of one mole of gas i from a state where its fugacity is f_i to another in which it is f_i' is given immediately by:

$$\Delta G = RT \ln (f_i'/f_i) \tag{10-6}$$

Example 10-3 (a) Find ΔG_{273} for the transfer of 2 moles of N_2(g) from pure nitrogen at 200 atm and 273°K to a N_2-H_2 mixture at a total pressure of 200 atm and 273°K containing NH_3 in which X_{N_2} = 0.400, using the data and results of Examples 5-6 and 10-1.   (b) Find ΔG_{273} for the same transfer assuming completely ideal behavior.

Ans. (a) f_{N_2} in initial state = 195 atm, f_{N_2} in final state = 81.2 atm so, by Eq. (10-6), ΔG_{273} = 2(1.987)(273) ln (81.2/195) = – 951 cal.
(b) p_{N_2} in initial state = 200 atm, p_{N_2} in final state = 80.0 atm so, by Eq. (7-7), ΔG_{273} = 2(1.987)(273) ln (80.0/200) = – 994 cal.

The need to use Eq. (7-2) in place of Eq. (7-6) for gases in non-ideal gas mixtures has many consequences, but a review of Eq. (7-6) and the many results it leads to will show that the only essential change is *the replacement of* p_i *by* f_i *wherever it occurs*.   Among the more important consequences is the conversion of Eq. (7-23) for $aA(g) + bB(g) + \ldots \rightleftharpoons cC(g) + dD(g) + \ldots$ into

$$\Delta G° = -RT \ln K_f \tag{10-7}$$

where $\Delta G°$ is the value of ΔG when each gas is at unit *fugacity* and where

$$K_f = (f_C)^c(f_D)^d \ldots/(f_A)^a(f_B)^b \ldots \tag{10-8}$$

f_A, f_B, f_C, f_D, etc. being the fugacities *at equilibrium*. K_f is, of course, a true constant. Using Eq. (10-4) we may write Eq. (10-8) as:

$$K_f = \frac{(\gamma_C)^c (\gamma_D)^d \cdots}{(\gamma_A)^a (\gamma_B)^b \cdots} K_p$$

where γ_A, γ_B, γ_C, γ_D, etc. are the respective activity coefficients. This shows that K_p for non-ideal equilibrium mixtures must be multiplied by a factor involving activity coefficients in order to make it a true constant.

Example 10-4 An equilibrium gas mixture of N_2, H_2 and NH_3 at 450° and 300 atm has the following composition: $X_{N_2} = 0.161$, $X_{H_2} = 0.483$.

(a) Find K_X and K_p for $\frac{1}{2}N_2(g) + \frac{3}{2}H_2(g) \rightleftharpoons NH_3(g)$
(b) Find γ_{NH_3} in the equilibrium mixture using the Lewis and Randall rule and Fig. 5-6.
(c) Taking γ_{N_2} and γ_{H_2} to be 1.20 and 1.12, respectively, in the mixture find K_f at 450°.
(d) Find ΔG_{723} for $N_2(g, f = 1 \text{ atm}) + 3H_2(g, f = 1 \text{ atm}) \rightleftharpoons 2NH_3(g, f = 1 \text{ atm})$.

Ans. (a) $X_{NH_3} = 1 - (0.161 + 0.483) = 0.356$ so, by Eq. (7-29), $K_X = 0.356/(0.161)^{1/2}(0.483)^{3/2} = 2.64$.   By Eq. (7-28) $K_p = 2.64(300)^{-1} = 0.0088$ (atm).
(b) As shown in Example 10-2, $f_{NH_3} \cong 270(0.356)$ atm so $\gamma_{NH_3} \cong 270(0.356)/(0.356)(300) = 0.90$.
(c) By Eq. (10-8) $K_f = [0.90/(1.20)^{1/2}(1.12)^{3/2}]0.0088 = 0.0062$ (atm).
(d) The required ΔG_{723} is the standard free energy change, $\Delta G°$, for $N_2(g) + 3H_2(g) \longrightarrow 2NH_3(g)$ which is twice that for the reaction as written in (a).   Therefore $\Delta G_{723}° = 2(-RT \ln K_f) = -2(1.987)(723) \ln 0.0062 = 14,600$ cal.

Note The K_f and the $\Delta G°$ found in (c) and (d) are still only approximate because of the use of Eq. (10-5), but the constancy of K_f calculated in this way is much better than that of K_p.

LIQUID SOLUTIONS

In relating chemical potential to concentration we have thus far developed and used the following expressions:

$$\mu_i = \mu_i^\bullet + RT \ln X_i \tag{7-5}$$

for components of ideal solutions, and:

$$\mu_A = \mu_A^\bullet + RT \ln X_A \tag{9-7}$$

and

$$\mu_B = \mu_B^\circ + RT \ln X_B \tag{9-12}$$

for dilute solutions of B in A, as discussed in the previous chapter. Clearly, these are all reducible to the form:

$$\mu_i = \mu_i^\circ + RT \ln X_i \qquad (10\text{-}9)$$

provided μ_i° be given the appropriate meaning in each case. Most solutions, however, are not ideal and not even dilute. How are *they* to be handled?

One might consider measuring fugacities of the dissolved components and then relating these to free energy changes by Eq. (10-6), which is valid for all solutions, but many solutes have immeasurably small fugacities. A better idea was proposed by G. N. Lewis who suggested that X_i in Eq. (10-9) be replaced by a_i, where a_i is called the activity of i, and defined in the following way:

$$\mu_i = \mu_i^\circ + RT \ln a_i$$

This amounts to the use of a_i as a "corrected" X_i—corrected in the sense that a_i gives the true relationship to $\mu_i - \mu_i^\circ$ even though X_i does not. Let us approach this relation in a more fundamental manner.

Consider the component i in a solution. Whether or not its fugacity can be measured, the following applies:

$$\mu_i = RT \ln f_i + \mathbf{B}_i \qquad (7\text{-}2)$$

In some state of the component at the same temperature, which we may choose arbitrarily and designate as its **standard state**, Eq. (7-2) will still be valid so we have:

$$\mu_i^\circ = RT \ln f_i^\circ + \mathbf{B}_i$$

where μ_i° and f_i° are the values of μ_i and f_i in this standard state. Subtraction of one equation from the other yields:

$$\mu_i = \mu_i^\circ + RT \ln (f_i/f_i^\circ) \qquad (10\text{-}10)$$

We now define the activity, a_i, by:

$$a_i = f_i/f_i^\circ \qquad (10\text{-}11)$$

so Eq. (10-10) becomes:

$$\mu_i = \mu_i^\circ + RT \ln a_i \qquad (10\text{-}12)$$

as before. It is evident that a_i in the standard state is unity since there $f_i = f_i^\circ$ in Eq. (10-11), or:

$$a_i^\circ = 1 \qquad (10\text{-}13)$$

It is important to realize that (1) a_i has no dimensions for it is a ratio of fugacities, and (2) the numerical value of a_i for a given component in a given solution at a given temperature *will depend upon what state is chosen to be the standard state.* Even if the choice of standard state is described clearly one may wonder how a_i could have any meaning if the choice depends on the whim of the experimenter. The answer to this is that (1) as long as the experimenter is consistent the arbitrariness of his choice will disappear by cancellation when his data are used to calculate quantities like ΔG and (2) convention dictates the use of a certain choice as being the most convenient in a given situation. The conventional choices are described later.

It is possible that at this point the reader will wonder what merit the activity concept has for non-volatile solutes. If one cannot measure their fugacity in *any* state how can one hope to find $f/f°$? We shall defer answering this until later in the chapter. Suffice to say here that solute activities can be calculated if solvent activities have been measured and vice versa.

Suppose that a_i has been determined for i in two different states (e.g. two different solutions of i in a solvent) at the same temperature, and we wish to find ΔG for the transfer of one mole of i from one to the other. If a_i' is the activity of i in the initial and a_i that in the final state we can apply Eq. (10-12) to both to give:

$$\mu_i' = \mu_i^° + RT \ln a_i'$$

and

$$\mu_i = \mu_i^° + RT \ln a_i$$

the difference between which is:

$$\Delta G = \mu_i - \mu_i' = RT \ln (a_i/a_i') \qquad (10\text{-}14)$$

which may be compared with Eqs. (5-19) and (7-4). Notice that $\mu_i^°$ does not appear in Eq. (10-14), so the element of arbitrariness has vanished. In other words ΔG is completely defined and independent of choice of standard state *as long as the choice is the same for both the initial and final states.*

The term activity coefficient of a gas was defined by Eq. (10-4). The **activity coefficient**, γ_i, of component i in a liquid solution is defined, similarly, by:

$$\gamma_i = a_i/X_i \qquad (10\text{-}15)$$

When solute activities are being considered and when their concentration is expressed in molality, m_i, it is convenient to define the **activity coefficient** of i by:

$$\gamma_i = a_i/m_i \qquad (10\text{-}16)$$

More will be said about this later.

Eqs. (10-12) and (10-14) apply equally well to components of gas mixtures for they are based on Eq. (7-2) which also holds for gases. The use of the term "activity" in connection with gases is unnecessary, however, for by *choosing the standard state for gas i as that state in which* $f_i = 1$ *atm*, $f_i^°$ becomes unity and $a_i = f_i$.

CHOICE OF STANDARD STATE FOR SOLVENT AND ITS CONSEQUENCES

As shown in Chapter 9 *the standard state for the solvent*, which we shall call A, *is* conventionally *the pure solvent at the given temperature and a total pressure of 1 atm*. (The stipulation of a pressure of 1 atm is usually not important.) The pure liquid is thus assigned an activity of unity. Since the fugacity of the solvent in any solution (at the same temperature and pressure) must always be less than that of the pure solvent, $a_A < a_A^\circ = 1$. By Eq. (10-15) $\gamma_A = a_A/X_A$. For *ideal* solutions both Eqs. (10-12) and (10-9) are valid and, since μ_A° in both refers to the pure liquid, $X_A = a_A$. This is, in fact, the purpose behind the conventional choice, for then activity and mole fraction of solvent become identical in ideal solution and γ_A is unity at all concentrations. The extent by which γ_A differs from unity is thus an indication of the extent of deviation from Raoult's law for the solvent. When A shows positive deviations $a_A > X_A$ and $\gamma_A > 1$; when A shows negative deviations $a_A < X_A$ and $\gamma_A < 1$. Since sufficiently dilute real solutions obey Raoult's law, γ_A approaches unity as X_A approaches unity. For this reason the pure solvent is also called the **reference state** for the solvent:

$$\lim_{X_A \to 1} a_A/X_A = 1 \tag{10-17}$$

Such a reference state is always needed as a basis for assignment of numerical values of activity, whether it be to solvent or solute. (Cf. the comments in Chapter 5 on reference state for a gas.)

CHOICE OF STANDARD STATE FOR SOLUTES (NONELECTROLYTES) AND ITS CONSEQUENCES

The following choices of standard state, introduced in Chapter 9, are in common use:

(1) If the pure liquid solute has a stable existence at the temperature of study then its **standard state** *can* be analogous to that for solvent, viz. *the pure liquid solute at the given temperature (and a pressure of 1 atm)*. On this basis, letting B stand for the solute, $a_B < a_B^\circ = 1$ and $\gamma_B = a_B/X_B$ is a measure of deviation from Raoult's law for B. Furthermore, the following is true:

$$\lim_{X_B \to 1} a_B/X_B = 1 \tag{10-18}$$

and the **reference state** for B is also the pure solute.

But what about solutes which cannot be obtained in the pure *liquid* state at the temperature of study? If we cannot realize the reference state experimentally we cannot apply Eq. (10-18) to assign numerical values so are forced in such situations to abandon the basis just suggested. Moreover, the particular study may be confined to dilute solutions, and we may be more interested in deviations from Henry's law than in deviations from Raoult's law. A more suitable choice is then one of the following.

(2) **The standard state** *for the solute is the hypothetical pure liquid solute at the given temperature and a total pressure of 1 atm, with a fugacity equal to that predicted by Henry's law* $(f_B = k_B X_B)$ *if the law were still valid.* As a consequence f_B° may be greater or less than $f_B^\bullet$ (if $f_B^\bullet$ is realizable), depending on the nature of the deviations from Raoult's law, and a_B can be < or > than 1. The activity coefficient indicates the nature of the deviations from *Henry's* law in the form $f_B = k_B X_B$: positive deviations yield $\gamma_B > 1$, negative deviations yield $\gamma_B < 1$. As infinite dilution is approached Henry's law becomes more and more valid and we have:

$$\lim_{X_B \to 0} a_B/X_B = 1 \qquad (10\text{-}19)$$

the **reference state** for the solute being the infinitely dilute solution. (It is incorrect to say that the standard state is the infinitely dilute solution for there the value of μ_B is minus infinity, not unity.) This standard state will be illustrated below.

(3) When the solute concentration unit is molality rather than mole fraction **the standard state** *is the hypothetical one-molal solution, at the given temperature and a total pressure of 1 atm, with a fugacity equal to that predicted by Henry's law* $(f_B = k'_B m)$ *if the law were still valid.* Note that the Henry's law constant is k'_B, not k_B as in (2). (Cf. Eqs. (9-5) and (9-14).) Again, a_B can be < or > 1, and the activity coefficient, defined by Eq. (10-16), indicates the nature of the deviations from *Henry's* law in the form just given: positive deviations yield $\gamma_B > 1$, negative deviations yield $\gamma_B < 1$. Furthermore

$$\lim_{m \to 0} a_B/m = 1 \qquad (10\text{-}20)$$

the **reference state** for the solute again being the infinitely dilute solution.

The similarities and differences in (1) and (2) are illustrated by the data in Table 10-1 for a (fictitious) system A-B at 25°. The values in the first two columns are shown graphically in Fig. 10-1 (cf. Fig. 9-1 (a)). Basis (1) is the same as that for solvents so the latter need not be illustrated separately. All the data are found from the experimental mole fractions and fugacities. The value of 150 mm for f_B° in basis (2) may be found by extrapolation. Observe the approach of γ_B to unity at large values of X_B in column 4 and at small values of X_B in column 6. Most of the activity coefficients in column 4 are greater than unity indicating positive deviations from Raoult's law; most of those in column 6 are less than unity indicating negative deviations from Henry's law. Fig. 10-1 should be self-explanatory.

Table 10-1

X_B	f_B (mm)	Basis (1) $\lim_{X_B \to 1} a_B/X_B = 1$ $f_B^\circ = 100.0$ mm		Basis (2) $\lim_{X_B \to 0} a_B/X_B = 1$ $f_B^\circ = 150$ mm	
		a_B	γ_B	a_B	γ_B
0	0	0	(1.500)	0	(1.000)
0.0200	3.00	0.0300	1.500	0.0200	1.000
0.0500	7.50	0.0750	1.500	0.0500	1.000
0.1000	14.00	0.1400	1.400	0.0933	0.933
0.200	26.00	0.2600	1.300	0.175	0.875
0.600	64.0	0.640	1.067	0.427	0.712
0.850	86.0	0.860	1.012	0.573	0.674
0.900	90.0	0.900	1.000	0.600	0.667
0.950	95.0	0.950	1.000	0.633	0.667
1.000	100.0	1.000	1.000	0.667	0.667

The mole fractions of Table 10-1 have been converted to molalities in Table 10-2 assuming, for the purpose of illustration, that the solvent has a molecular weight of 50.0. Concentrations have not been listed up to $X_B = 1$ since molality is unsuitable for large concentrations of solute. The activities and activity coefficients have been calculated in terms of basis (3). The value of 7.50 mm for f_B° for the hypothetical one-molal solution is an extrapolated one. Activities can be either greater or less than unity. The approach of γ_B to unity as concentration is diminished

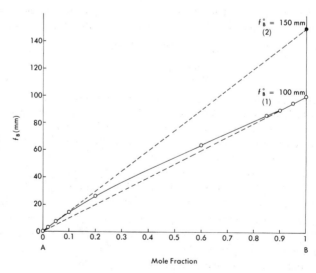

Fig. 10-1

Table 10-2

X_B	Basis (3): $\lim\limits_{m \to 0} a_B/m = 1$		f°_B – 7.50 mm	
	m	f_B (mm)	a_B	γ_B
0	0.	0	0	(1.000)
0.0200	0.408	3.00	0.400	0.980
0.0500	1.053	7.50	1.000	0.952
0.1000	2.222	14.00	1.866	0.841
0.200	5.00	26.00	3.467	0.693
0.600	30.00	64.0	8.53	0.284

conforms to the approach to Henry's law, but with a different constant from that for basis (2) $(150 \neq 7.50)$. The experimental data are plotted in Fig. 10-2 (cf. Fig. 9-2 (a)). It will be seen that the solution for which $m = 1.053$ happens to have unit activity for B, but B is not in its standard state in that solution for Henry's law does not hold for it.

Finally, the reader is reminded of the statement made in connection with Eq. (9-15): the enthalpy of the solute in its standard state is identical to that in the infinitely dilute solution.

Example 10-5 Find ΔG_{298} for $B(X_B = 0.600) \rightarrow B(X_B = 0.100)$ for the system shown in Tables 10-1 and 10-2, using the data obtained on the basis of (a) pure liquid B for the standard state (b) hypothetical pure B (Henry's law extrapolation) for the standard state (c) hypothetical one-molal solution (Henry's law extrapolation) for the standard state.

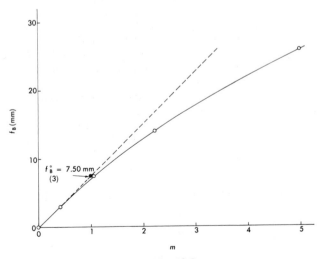

Fig. 10-2

Ans. (a) When $X_B = 0.600$, $a_B = 0.640$; when $X_B = 0.100$, $a_B = 0.1400$. Therefore, by Eq. (10-14), $\Delta G_{298} = 1.987(298.2) \ln (0.1400/0.640) = -901$ cal.

(b) When $X_B = 0.600$, $a_B = 0.427$; when $X_B = 0.100$, $a_B = 0.0933$. Therefore, by Eq. (10-14), $\Delta G_{298} = 1.987(298.2) \ln (0.0933/0.427) = -901$ cal.

(c) When $X_B = 0.600$, $a_B = 8.53$; when $X_B = 0.100$, $a_B = 1.866$. Therefore, by Eq. (10-14), $\Delta G_{298} = 1.987(298.2) \ln (1.866/8.53) = -901$ cal.

DETERMINATION OF ACTIVITY

The most obvious method for evaluating activities is by measurement of fugacity and application of the method just illustrated, provided, of course, that the component in question has a measurable vapor pressure. It may usually be assumed that the vapor which is in equilibrium with the various solutions is ideal enough for f_i to be replaceable by p_i so we have:

$$a_i = p_i/p_i^\circ \qquad (10\text{-}21)$$

Experimentally, then, p_i is measured as a function of composition at a given temperature. The range of composition *must include the reference state*, whichever one is chosen. If, e.g., pure i is the reference state we must know the vapor pressure of pure liquid i. If the infinitely dilute solution is the reference state we must make a series of careful measurements at high dilution in order to obtain an accurate Henry's law extrapolation. In addition to the conventional static methods for measuring p_i mention should be made of the **isopiestic technique** originated by W. R. Bousfield *(Trans. Faraday Soc.*, **13**, 401 (1918)) and subsequently refined by D. A. Sinclair *(J. Phys. Chem.*, **37**, 495 (1933)) and others. A fuller description of it will be found in Chapter 11. It is suitable when the other component of a solution is involatile. If not only i is volatile but also any other component(s), analysis of the equilibrium vapor is desirable in order to find p_i from $X_i P$, but methods are available for finding partial pressures from total pressures without direct vapor analysis (see e.g., J. A. Barker, *Australian J. Chem.*, **6**, 207 (1953)).

Activities can also be determined experimentally from freezing point measurements, from distribution studies, and by other methods such as emf determination for components of metallic solutions. Further attention will be given to emf methods in Chapter 11.

DISTRIBUTION LAW

If a solute, B, is distributed between two immiscible solvents, A and A′ we have, by Eq. (10-12),

$$\mu_B = \mu_B^\circ + RT \ln a_B \qquad \text{in A}$$

and

$$\mu_B' = \mu_B^{\circ'} + RT \ln a_B' \qquad \text{in A}'$$

But $\mu_B = \mu'_B$ at equilibrium so $\mu_B^{\circ} + RT \ln a_B = \mu_B^{\circ'} + RT \ln a'_B$ or $RT \ln (a_B/a'_B) = \mu_B^{\circ'} - \mu_B^{\circ}$ = constant at a given temperature. Therefore

$$a_B/a'_B = \text{constant} \tag{10-22}$$

which is a more general form of the distribution law, originally given as Eq. (9-39). If we happen to choose the same reference state for B in both phases then $\mu_B^{\circ} = \mu_B^{\circ'}$ so

$$a_B = a'_B \tag{10-23}$$

and, knowing a_B in one phase gives a'_B for the solute in the other solution.

INTERCONVERSION OF ACTIVITIES OF SOLVENT AND SOLUTE

Rather than conduct a separate series of activity measurements for solvent and solute it is possible to find the activity of one component at any concentration if that of the other component is known over a suitable range of composition. This procedure is not only convenient, it is sometimes necessary. The feasibility and details of the method depend on the choice of reference state. Suppose, e.g., for solutions of B in A we know the values of a_A at all concentrations and that they are expressed in terms of pure A(l) for the reference state (basis (1) above). We wish, let us say, to find a_B at a given concentration, X'_B in terms of pure B(l) for the reference state. Now a_A and a_B are related through Eq. (6-12):

$$X_A d\mu_A + X_B d\mu_B = 0$$

But, by differentiation of Eq. (10-12) at constant T and P, we obtain:

$$d\mu_A = RT \, d \ln a_A \tag{10-24}$$

and

$$d\mu_B = RT \, d \ln a_B \tag{10-25}$$

so

$$X_A RT \, d \ln a_A + X_B RT \, d \ln a_B = 0$$

or

$$d \ln a_B = -(X_A/X_B) d \ln a_A \tag{10-26}$$

since $RT \neq 0$. However, for a binary solution $X_A + X_B = 1$ so $dX_A = -dX_B$. Multiplying the left-hand side of this equality by X_A/X_A and the right-hand side by X_B/X_B gives $X_A d \ln X_A = -X_B d \ln X_B$ or:

$$d \ln X_B = -(X_A/X_B) d \ln X_A \tag{10-27}$$

Subtraction of this from Eq. (10-26) yields:

$$d \ln \gamma_B = -(X_A/X_B) d \ln \gamma_A \tag{10-28}$$

This is valid whenever concentrations and activities are on a *mole fraction* basis. Integrating Eq. (10-28) between $X_B = 1$ and $X_B = X'_B$ and changing to common logarithms gives:

$$\int_{X_B=1}^{X_B=X_B'} d \log \gamma_B = \log \gamma_B' = \int_{X_B=1}^{X_B=X_B'} (X_A/X_B) d \log \gamma_A \quad (10\text{-}29)$$

where γ_B' is the activity coefficient at $X_B = X_B'$ from which the activity can be found. The lower limit on the left disappears since $\gamma_B = 1$ at $X_B = 1$. The right side can be evaluated graphically from the area under the curve for a plot of X_A/X_B vs. $\log \gamma_A$ from pure B to the given concentration (X_A'/X_B').

The general type of graph obtained in such a procedure is shown schematically in Fig. 10-3 (a) and (b), depending on whether γ_A is greater or less than unity, respectively. In comparatively rare instances one activ-

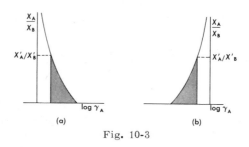

(a)   (b)

Fig. 10-3

ity coefficient is greater than unity while the other is less, over a range of composition (see M. L. McGlashan, *J. Chem. Educ.*, **40**, 516 (1963)). The areas to be measured are shaded.

If, however, one wishes to find a_B on basis (2) (hypothetical pure B(l) for reference state) from values of a_A on basis (1) (real pure A(l) for reference state) difficulty is encountered. If we proceed as before and write:

$$\int_{X_B=0}^{X_B=X_B'} d \log \gamma_B = -\int_{X_B=0}^{X_B=X_B'} (X_A/X_B) d \log \gamma_A$$

to give:

$$\log \gamma_B' = -\int_{X_B=0}^{X_B=X_B'} (X_A/X_B) d \log \gamma_A \quad (10\text{-}30)$$

with γ_B here being unity at *infinite dilution* instead of at $X_B = 1$, we are faced with measuring an area that extends to infinity, since $(X_A/X_B) = \infty$ when $X_B = 0$. The importance of accurate data at high dilution (large values of X_A/X_B) is at once apparent. Various devices for improving the accuracy of this extrapolation have been used but they will not be discussed.

Interconversion of activities involving the molality basis (3) is less straightforward. Since $X_A/X_B = n_A/n_B = (1000/M_A)/m$, where M_A is the molecular weight of the solvent, Eq. (10-26) can be expressed as:

$$d \ln a_B = -(1000/mM_A) d \ln a_A \qquad (10-31)$$

the integration of which is accomplished with the aid of special techniques, e.g. the introduction of the **practical osmotic coefficient**, ϕ, defined by:

$$\phi = -(1000 \ln a_A)/mM_A \qquad (10-32)$$

but we shall defer consideration of this function to the next chapter.

Example 10-6 The following data for the system H_2O (A)—n-C_3H_7OH (B) at 25° are taken from a paper by J. A. V. Butler and co-workers, *J. Chem. Soc.*, 674 (1933). The reference state for B is pure B(l).

X_B	0	0.0100	0.0200	0.0500	0.1000	0.2000
γ_B	12.5	12.3	11.6	9.92	6.05	3.12

(a) Find γ_A in the solution for which $X_B = 0.1000$ assuming the reference state for A to be also the pure liquid.
(b) What value of γ_A is approached as X_A approaches unity? Why?
(c) What can be said about the limit of γ_A as X_B approaches unity?

Ans. (a) A plot of log γ_B vs. X_B/X_A according to Eq. (10-29) with the subscripts interchanged gives a line resembling Fig. 10-3 (a). The data converted into the form needed for plotting are:

X_B/X_A	0	0.0101	0.0204	0.0526	0.1111	0.2500
log γ_B	1.097	1.090	1.065	0.997	0.782	0.494

The area between $X_B/X_A = 0$ and $X_B/X_A = 0.1111$ is found to be -0.0211 units (negative since d log γ_B is negative and X_B/X_A is positive). (The upper limit of integration is $X_B/X_A = 0.1111$ since this corresponds to $X_B = 0.1000$.) Therefore log $\gamma_A = -(-0.0211) = 0.0211$, so $\gamma_A = 1.05$.
(b) γ_A approaches unity as X_A approaches unity since pure A(l) is the reference state for A.
(c) As X_B approaches unity γ_A approaches a finite non-zero value.

VARIATION OF ACTIVITY WITH PRESSURE AND TEMPERATURE

We have seen how fugacity varies with P and T in Chapter 5, Eqs. (5-21) and (5-22). For fugacity of components in solution these become, respectively:

$$(\partial \ln f_i/\partial P)_{T,X} = \bar{\bar{V}}_i/RT \qquad (10-33)$$

and

$$(\partial \ln f_i/\partial T)_{P,X} = \overline{H_i^*} - \bar{\bar{H}}_i/RT^2 \qquad (10-34)$$

These may be used to find the analogous expressions for a_i. By taking logarithms of Eq. (10-11) we obtain:

$$\ln a_i = \ln f_i - \ln f_i^\circ \qquad (10\text{-}35)$$

Differentiation with respect to P at constant T and composition, yields, with the help of Eq. (10-33):

$$(\partial \ln a_i / \partial P)_{T,X} = \overline{\overline{V}}_i / RT \qquad (10\text{-}36)$$

since f_i° is independent of P. Similarly, differentiation of Eq. (10-35) with respect to T at constant P and composition yields, with the help of Eq. (10-34),

$$(\partial \ln a_i / \partial T)_{P,X} = (\overline{\overline{H}}_i^\circ - \overline{\overline{H}}_i)/RT^2$$

But $\overline{\overline{H}}_i^\circ - \overline{\overline{H}}_i = -\overline{\overline{L}}_i$ as in Eq. (6-17) so we have:

$$(\partial \ln a_i / \partial T)_{P,X} = -\overline{\overline{L}}_i / RT^2 \qquad (10\text{-}37)$$

A corollary of Eq. (10-37) is obtained by taking the logarithm of Eq. (10-15) and differentiating with respect to T at constant P and composition to give:

$$(\partial \ln \gamma_i / \partial T)_{P,X} = (\partial \ln a_i / \partial T)_{P,X} - (\partial \ln X_i / \partial T)_{P,X}$$

The last term on the right is zero, however, so from Eq. (10-37) we have:

$$(\partial \ln \gamma_i / \partial T)_{P,X} = -\overline{\overline{L}}_i / RT^2 \qquad (10\text{-}38)$$

The same result is obtained if Eq. (10-16) is used instead of Eq. (10-17).

Example 10-7 The activities of mercury (A) and thallium (B) in liquid thallium amalgams were determined from emf measurements (see T. W. Richards and F. Daniels, *J. Am. Chem. Soc.*, 41, 1732 (1919) and G. N. Lewis and M. Randall, ibid., 43, 233 (1921)). It was found that when $X_B = 0.2000$, $a_A = 0.693$ and $a_B = 0.996$ at 20°, the reference state for A being pure A(l) and that for B being the infinitely dilute solution of B in A on a mole fraction basis. It was also reported that in the neighborhood of 30° $\overline{\overline{L}}_A = -112$ cal mole^{-1} and $\overline{\overline{C}}_P$ for A = 6.85 cal deg^{-1} mole^{-1}. The heat capacity of A(l) is 6.70 cal deg^{-1} mole^{-1}. Taking these heat capacities to be independent of T find a_A at 80° for the same concentration.

Ans. Eq. (10-37) applied to A cannot be integrated unless $\overline{\overline{L}}_A$ is known as a function of T. This is found as follows: For A(l) $\longrightarrow$ A(amalgam, $X_B = 0.2000$), $\Delta H = \overline{\overline{H}}_A - \overline{H}_A^\circ = \overline{\overline{L}}_A = -112$ cal mole^{-1} (cf. Eq. (6-17)) and, by Eq. (1-18), $(\partial \Delta H / \partial T)_P = (\partial \overline{\overline{L}}_A / \partial T)_P = \Delta C_P = 6.85 - 6.70 = 0.15$ cal deg^{-1} so $d\overline{\overline{L}}_A = 0.15\, dT$. Integrating between $T = 303°K$ and $T°K$ gives $\overline{\overline{L}}_A(\text{at } T°) - (-112) = 0.15(T - 303)$ or $\overline{\overline{L}}_A(\text{at } T°) = 0.15T - 157$ (cf. Eq. (1-22)). Substituting in Eq. (10-37) and integrating gives:

$$\int_{T=293}^{T=353} d \ln a_A = -\int_{293}^{353} \frac{0.15T - 157}{RT^2} dT$$

and substituting $a_A = 0.693$ at $293°K$ gives $a_A = 0.715$ at $353°K$.

ACTIVITY AND CHEMICAL EQUILIBRIUM

We have seen that the use of fugacity in place of partial pressure in free energy expressions for gases leads to Eqs. (10-6) and (10-7) for the representation of the behavior of non-ideal gas mixtures undergoing chemical changes. Analogously, the need to use Eq. (10-12) for real liquid solutions rather than Eqs. (9-11) or (9-12) has been shown to lead to Eq. (10-14):

$$\Delta G = RT \ln (a_i/a_i') \qquad (10\text{-}14)$$

for the isothermal transfer of one mole of i from one solution to another. It follows by analogy that the standard free energy change for:

$$aA + bB + \ldots \rightleftharpoons cC + dD + \ldots$$

where any or all of the substances are in solution is given by:

$$\Delta G° = -RT \ln K_a \qquad (10\text{-}39)$$

$\Delta G°$ being the value of ΔG when each species is in its own standard state and K_a being a true **equilibrium constant** given by:

$$K_a = \frac{(a_C)^c (a_D)^d \ldots}{(a_A)^a (a_B)^b \ldots} \qquad (10\text{-}40)$$

analogous to Eq. (10-8) and independent of pressure. In Eq. (10-40) the a's are the activities *at equilibrium*. We have, in addition:

$$\Delta G = \Delta G° + RT \ln Q_a \qquad (10\text{-}41)$$

which is analogous to Eq. (7-20), where Q_a is of the same form as K_a but where the a's are the activities in the *given* initial and final states. Finally, the variation of K_a with temperature at constant pressure is found by dividing Eq. (10-39) by T, differentiating with respect to T at constant P and using the Gibbs-Helmholtz relation, Eq. (4-35), to give:

$$(\partial \ln K_a/\partial T)_P = \Delta H°/RT^2 \qquad (10\text{-}42)$$

We will defer illustrating these expressions to the next chapter.

THERMODYNAMICS OF MIXING.
EXCESS THERMODYNAMIC FUNCTIONS

The activity coefficient may be thought of as a measure of deviation from the norm, provided one recognizes that the norm is not always Raoult's law. In Eq. (10-16), e.g., the norm is the extrapolated Henry's law behavior as given by Eq. (9-14). An alternative description of deviation from ideality lies in the **excess thermodynamic functions**.

In Chapter 7 expressions for free energy, entropy and enthalpy of mixing were found for ideal systems, Eqs. (7-12), (7-15) and (7-16), respectively. These expressions are not valid, in general, for non-ideal systems. The *difference* between the observed values of ΔG^M, ΔS^M and ΔH^M and the ideal values which we shall designate ΔG_{id}^M, ΔS_{id}^M and ΔH_{id}^M, are called the excess quantities, ΔG^E, ΔS^E and ΔH^E. Consider the mixing process:

$$X_A A(l) + X_B B(l) \longrightarrow \text{One mole of non-ideal solution}$$

In this change each mole of A suffers a free energy change given by Eq. (10-14), viz. $RT \ln (a_A/a_A')$, which in this case becomes $RT \ln a_A$ if we choose pure A(l) as the standard state of A, a_A being the activity of A in the final solution. The free energy change of X_A moles will be $X_A RT \ln a_A$. Similarly the free energy change for B will be $X_B RT \ln a_B$ if pure B(l) is the standard state for B. The actual free energy of mixing per mole of solution is therefore:

$$\Delta G^M = RT (X_A \ln a_A + X_B \ln a_B) \tag{10-43}$$

Since $a_A = \gamma_A X_A$ and $a_B = \gamma_B X_B$, the **excess free energy of mixing** will be $\Delta G^E = \Delta G^M - \Delta G_{id}^M = RT (X_A \ln \gamma_A + X_A \ln X_A + X_B \ln \gamma_B + X_B \ln X_B) - RT (X_A \ln X_A + X_B \ln X_B) = RT (X_A \ln \gamma_A + X_B \ln \gamma_B)$. In general, then, we have:

$$\Delta G^E = RT \sum_i X_i \ln \gamma_i \tag{10-44}$$

Similarly, the **excess entropy of mixing** will be given by:

$$\Delta S^E = \Delta S^M + R (X_A \ln X_A + X_B \ln X_B) \tag{10-45}$$

or, in general:

$$\Delta S^E = \Delta S^M + R \sum_i X_i \ln X_i \tag{10-46}$$

Since $\Delta H_{id}^M = 0$ the **excess enthalpy of mixing** is:

$$\Delta H^E = \Delta H^M \tag{10-47}$$

The following will also be seen:

$$\Delta G^E = \Delta H^E - T \Delta S^E \tag{10-48}$$

Example 10-8 In Example 10-6, referring to a solution of $n\text{-}C_3H_7OH$ (B) in $H_2O(l)$ (A) at 25° in which $X_B = 0.100$, γ_B was given as 6.05 and γ_A was found to be 1.05. Find the excess free energy of mixing per mole of solution at this concentration.

Ans. By Eq. (10-44) $\Delta G^E = 1.987(298)(0.900 \ln 1.05 + 0.100 \ln 6.05) =$ 133 cal per mole of solution.

REGULAR SOLUTIONS

For a considerable number of systems $\Delta S^E \cong 0$ even though $\Delta G^E \cong \Delta H^E \neq 0$ (cf. Eq. (10-48). Such solutions are said to be **regular**. This means that the entropy of mixing for a regular solution is that of an ideal system even though the solution is not ideal. Statistically the regular solution has a random distribution, although not ideal by Raoult's law standards. For these solutions heat will be absorbed on mixing the components if they show positive deviations from Raoult's law since γ_i is then greater than unity and $\Delta G^E = \Delta H^E > 0$ by Eq. (10-44). For negative deviations heat will be evolved on mixing.

PROBLEMS

1. If the critical pressure and temperature of N_2 are 33.5 atm and 126.1°K estimate the fugacity of N_2 in a gas mixture of N_2 and H_2 at 0.0° and a total pressure of 200 atm in which $X_{N_2} = 0.400$. Use Eq. (5-18) and the Lewis and Randall rule.

2. G. Scatchard and C. L. Raymond (*J. Am. Chem. Soc.*, **60**, 1278 (1938)), in a study of the vapor-liquid equilibria in the system chloroform (A)-ethanol (B), obtained the following results at 55°:

X_B	0	0.0443	0.4595	0.8740	0.9288
P (mm)	433.54	448.49	425.28	249.92	214.44
Y_B	0	0.0681	0.2297	0.6026	0.7533

X_B	0.9524	0.9811	0.9843	1
P (mm)	199.62	182.63	180.96	172.76
Y_B	0.8283	0.9284	0.9400	1

X_B and Y_B are the mole fractions of B in the liquid and vapor phases, respectively, and P is the total pressure.

(a) Does this system show positive or negative deviations from ideality?

(b) Find γ_A for each solution when the standard state for A is pure A(l).

(c) Find γ_B for the solution for which $X_B = 0.9288$ when the standard state for B is pure B(l).

(d) Find γ_A for the solution for which $X_B = 0.9288$ when the standard state for A is the hypothetical pure A(l) (Henry's law extrapolation).

(e) Estimate γ_B for the $X_B = 0.9288$ solution *using the γ's found in (b)*, and compare with the result in (c).

3. Referring to Example 10-6, find ΔG_{298} for the transfer of 2.00 moles of $n\text{-}C_3H_7OH$ from an aqueous solution in which the alcohol mole fraction is 0.200 to one in which it is 0.0100.

4. The activity coefficients for solid solutions of $p\text{-}C_6H_4Cl_2$ (A) in

p-C_6H_4BrCl (B) at $50°$ were measured by P. N. Walsh and N. O. Smith (*J. Phys. Chem.*, **65**, 718 (1961)) with the following results:

X_A	0.056	0.312	0.409	0.660	0.841	0.949
γ_A	0.87	0.98	1.01	1.04	1.02	1.00
γ_B	1.00	0.97	0.95	0.93	1.01	1.14

Pure A(s) and B(s) were taken as the standard states for A and B, respectively.

(a) If $p_A^{\bullet}$ and $p_B^{\bullet}$ are 7.48 and 2.36 mm, respectively, at this temperature find the total pressure of the vapor in equilibrium with the solution for which $X_A = 0.660$.

(b) What unusual feature does this system exhibit?

5. Since mole fraction of solute, X_B, and molality, m, are related through the molecular weight of the solute, M_A, by $X_B = mM_A/1000$ at infinite dilution, there is also a simple relation between solute activities obtained on the hypothetical pure B basis (Henry's law extrapolation), which we shall denote $(a_B)_X$, and those on the hypothetical one-molal basis, which we shall denote $(a_B)_m$.

(a) Find this relation. (*Hint*: The ratio of the activity of B in any given solution to that at infinite dilution must be the same regardless of which basis is used.)

(b) In Table 10-1 $(a_B)_X = 0.427$ when $X_B = 0.600$. Find $(a_B)_m$ for this solution when $M_A = 50.0$ and compare with the value given in Table 10-2.

6. What value does ϕ, the osmotic coefficient, approach at high dilution?

7. Find (a) the free energy of mixing and (b) the excess free energy of mixing for one mole of solution of H_2O (A) in n-C_3H_7OH (B) at $25°$ for which X_B is 0.1000, using the data of Example 10-6.

8. The system benzene (A)-carbon tetrachloride (B) is regular at $25°$ but not ideal: the enthalpy of mixing for a solution containing equimolar quantities of A and B is $\Delta H^M = 26$ cal per mole of solution.

(a) Find the excess free energy of mixing for this solution.

(b) Suggest how the excess entropy of mixing could be determined without measuring ΔH^M.

9. In $2m$ sucrose (B) solution in water (A) at $25°$, $\gamma_B = 1.435$ and $\bar{\bar{L}}_B = 453$ cal mole^{-1}. Find γ_B in this solution at $35°$ assuming $\bar{\bar{L}}_B$ to be independent of T over this range.

Aqueous solutions of electrolytes

ELECTROLYTES AND HENRY'S LAW

In Figs. 9-1 and 9-2 we saw that the limits of f_B/X_B and f_B/m, as infinite dilution is approached, are finite and non-zero. When the solute is an electrolyte, however, both of these limits are zero, as shown schematically for f_B vs. m in Fig. 11-1. This "anomalous" behavior of electrolytes is manifested in many well known ways such as values of freezing point depression which are considerably larger than the corresponding quantities for nonelectrolytes. Suppose the electrolyte is HCl in solution. In contrast to Fig. 11-1, if for this electrolyte m^2 instead of m be plotted, as in Fig. 11-2 (schematic), the limiting slope is once again finite and non-zero. In general, when one "molecule" of electrolyte yields ν ions on complete dissociation it is found that

$$\lim_{m \to 0} f_B/m^\nu = \text{constant} \tag{11-1}$$

Furthermore, since f_B is proportional to a_B, we also have:

$$\lim_{m \to 0} a_B/m^\nu = \text{constant}' \tag{11-2}$$

The numerical value of this latter constant depends, of course, on what standard state is chosen. This will be discussed later. Suffice to say here that, perhaps unexpectedly, it is conventionally *not* such as to make

213

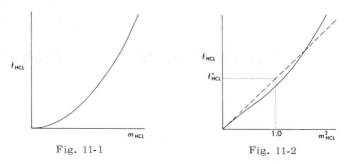

Fig. 11-1   Fig. 11-2

the constant generally unity as in the analogous Eq. (10-20) for nonelectrolytes. The need for the exponent ν is shown in the data in Table 11-1 for HCl at 25° by the approach to constancy in column (4) but not in column (3).

The consequences of introducing ν into Eqs. (11-1) and (11-2) are farreaching. Much of the remainder of this chapter will be concerned with how various concepts developed in the preceding chapter are modified for application to electrolytes, and with the role played by ν.

MOLALITY, ACTIVITY AND ACTIVITY COEFFICIENT

The implication of the preceding section is that the various ionic species (at least two) must be considered individually, even though in solutions of a single electrolyte their concentrations cannot be varied independently of one another. With + and − signs as subscripts to denote cation and anion, respectively, m_+ and m_- will represent their **ion molalities**, a_+, a_- their **ion activities** and γ_+, γ_- their **ion activity coefficients**. Thus we have:

$$\gamma_+ = a_+/m_+ \qquad \text{and} \qquad \gamma_- = a_-/m_- \qquad (11\text{-}3)$$

The reference state of an ion *is chosen as the ion in infinitely dilute solution* so the following is true:

$$\lim_{m \to 0} (a_+/m_+) = \lim_{m \to 0} (a_-/m_-) = 1 \qquad (11\text{-}4)$$

We shall return to this.

Table 11-1

HCl at 25°

m (1)	a_{HCl} (2)	a_{HCl}/m (3)	a_{HCl}/m^2 (4)
0.0001	$9.76 \ (10^{-9})$	$9.76 \ (10^{-5})$	0.976
0.0005	$2.38 \ (10^{-7})$	$4.76 \ (10^{-4})$	0.952
0.001	$9.31 \ (10^{-7})$	$9.31 \ (10^{-4})$	0.931
0.002	$3.63 \ (10^{-6})$	$1.82 \ (10^{-3})$	0.908
0.005	$2.15 \ (10^{-5})$	$4.30 \ (10^{-3})$	0.860

It has been stated that $f_B \propto m^{\nu}$ at high dilution. If we consider each ion separately this suggests that $f_B \propto m_+^{\nu_+} m_-^{\nu_-}$, where each "molecule" of electrolyte yields on complete dissociation ν_+ cations and ν_- anions and where $\nu_+ + \nu_- = \nu$. On the basis of our choice of ion reference state as given by Eq. (11-4), however, $m_+^{\nu_+} m_-^{\nu_-} = a_+^{\nu_+} a_-^{\nu_-}$ at high dilution so $f_B \propto a_+^{\nu_+} a_-^{\nu_-}$. Now $f_B = f_B^{o} a_B$ by Eq. (10-11) so $f_B^{o} a_B \propto a_+^{\nu_+} a_-^{\nu_-}$ or $a_B = (\text{constant}) a_+^{\nu_+} a_-^{\nu_-}$ at high dilution. Now we can make the numerical value of a_B anything we please merely by appropriate choice of standard state for B. Accordingly, that **standard state of the electrolyte** (as a whole) *is chosen which will make the proportionality constant in the above relation unity.* On this basis $a_B = a_+^{\nu_+} a_-^{\nu_-}$ at high dilution. However, the electrolyte can be taken to be in equilibrium with its ions at all concentrations according to:

$$B \rightleftharpoons \nu_+ \text{ cations} + \nu_- \text{ anions}$$

so we obtain:

$$\frac{a_+^{\nu_+} a_-^{\nu_-}}{a_B} = K_a \tag{11-5}$$

This can still be said even though the undissociated electrolyte as a species in solution may not be detectable. Now if $a_B = a_+^{\nu_+} a_-^{\nu_-}$ at high dilution K_a must be unity and so we have:

$$a_B = a_+^{\nu_+} a_-^{\nu_-} \tag{11-6}$$

at *all* concentrations. Moreover ΔG° for the dissociation must be zero by Eq. (10-39) so this gives:

$$\mu_B^{o} = \nu_+ \mu_+^{o} + \nu_- \mu_-^{o} \tag{11-7}$$

in addition to

$$\mu_B = \nu_+ \mu_+ + \nu_- \mu_- \tag{11-8}$$

It may be noted that subtraction of Eq. (11-7) from Eq. (11-8) gives:

$$\mu_B - \mu_B^{o} = \nu_+ (\mu_+ - \mu_+^{o}) + \nu_- (\mu_- - \mu_-^{o}) \tag{11-9}$$

Furthermore, by application of Eq. (10-12) to the cation and anion, we obtain:

$$\mu_+ = \mu_+^{o} + RT \ln a_+ \quad \text{and} \quad \mu_- = \mu_-^{o} + RT \ln a_- \tag{11-10}$$

The standard state of an electrolyte for which $\nu = 2$, chosen as just described, is equivalent to the hypothetical one-molal solution (where f_B is still proportional to m^2). In Fig. 11-2 the fugacity for HCl in the standard state is indicated by f_{HCl}^{o}. In general the value of f_B^{o} is the fugacity in the hypothetical one-molal solution (where f_B is still proportional to m^{ν}) *divided by* $\nu_+^{\nu_+} \nu_-^{\nu_-}$.

In connection with Eq. (11-4), it must be admitted that neither a_+ nor a_- can be evaluated, since positive and negative ions cannot be isolated from each other in solution.   We therefore introduce one more activity function, the **mean ion activity** $a_\pm$, which *can* be measured, and which is defined by:

$$a_\pm = (a_+{}^{\nu_+} a_-{}^{\nu_-})^{1/\nu} \tag{11-11}$$

Introducing Eqs. (11-3) gives:

$$a_\pm = [(\gamma_+ m_+)^{\nu_+} (\gamma_- m_-)^{\nu_-}]^{1/\nu} = (\gamma_+{}^{\nu_+} \gamma_-{}^{\nu_-})^{1/\nu} (m_+{}^{\nu_+} m_-{}^{\nu_-})^{1/\nu} \tag{11-12}$$

Moreover, if we assume:

$$m_+ = m\nu_+ \qquad \text{and} \qquad m_- = m\nu_-$$

Eq. (11-12) becomes:

$$a_\pm = (\gamma_+{}^{\nu_+} \gamma_-{}^{\nu_-})^{1/\nu} m (\nu_+{}^{\nu_+} \nu_-{}^{\nu_-})^{1/\nu} \tag{11-13}$$

The factor involving the γ's is called the **mean ion activity coefficient**, $\gamma_\pm$, the remaining factors the **mean ion molality**, $m_\pm$ so, by definition, they are expressed as:

$$\gamma_\pm = (\gamma_+{}^{\nu_+} \gamma_-{}^{\nu_-})^{1/\nu} \tag{11-14}$$

and

$$m_\pm = m (\nu_+{}^{\nu_+} \nu_-{}^{\nu_-})^{1/\nu} \tag{11-15}$$

and

$$a_\pm = \gamma_\pm m_\pm \tag{11-16}$$

Observe that since γ_+ and γ_- approach unity as m approaches zero (cf. Eq. (11-4)) so also must $\gamma_\pm$:

$$\lim_{m \to 0} (a_\pm/m_\pm) = 1 \tag{11-17}$$

Finally, combination of Eqs. (11-6) and (11-11) gives:

$$a_B = a_\pm^\nu \tag{11-18}$$

which leads to:

$$a_B = (\gamma_\pm m_\pm)^\nu \tag{11-19}$$

Note A common student error is to write $a_B = \gamma_\pm m$, by analogy with non-electrolytes. The fact that $\gamma_\pm$ *is often written as* γ makes this pitfall all the more likely.

Example 11-1 Show that the value of the constant in Eq. (11-2) is $\nu_+{}^{\nu_+} \nu_-{}^{\nu_-}$.

Ans.

$$\text{Constant} = \lim_{m \to 0} a_B/m^\nu = \lim_{m \to 0} \frac{(\gamma_\pm m_\pm)^\nu}{m^\nu}$$

$$= \lim_{m \to 0} \frac{\gamma_\pm^\nu [m (\nu_+^{\nu_+} \nu_-^{\nu_-})^{1/\nu}]^\nu}{m^\nu} = \lim_{m \to 0} \gamma_\pm^\nu \nu_+^{\nu_+} \nu_-^{\nu_-} = \nu_+^{\nu_+} \nu_-^{\nu_-}$$

since $\lim_{m \to 0} \gamma_\pm = 1.$

Example 11-2 Given that $\gamma_\pm$ for $In_2(SO_4)_3$ in $0.100m$ solution is 0.025 at $25°$ find $m_\pm$, $a_\pm$ and $a_{In_2(SO_4)_3}$.

Ans. For $In_2(SO_4)_3$, $\nu_+ = 2$, $\nu_- = 3$ and $\nu = 5$ so, by Eq. (11-15), $m_\pm = 0.100(2^2 3^3)^{1/5} = 0.255$. By Eq. (11-16) $a_\pm = 0.025(0.255) = 0.0064$. By Eq. (11-18) $a_{In_2(SO_4)_3} = (0.0064)^5 = 1.07(10^{-11})$.

Note Although the concentration is only $0.100m$, $\gamma_\pm$ is far from unity for this electrolyte because it is polyvalent. Extremely high dilution is required to bring $\gamma_\pm$ close to unity.

As a result of the preceding material the student should not be surprised to find activities of an unusual magnitude in concentrated solution. In $16m$ HCl, e.g., where $\gamma_\pm = 42.4$, $a_\pm = 678$ and $a_{HCl} = 460,000!$

The previous considerations, particularly Eqs. (11-13) and (11-15) and their consequences, have been concerned primarily with strong electrolytes because m_+ was replaced by $m\nu_+$ and m_- by $m\nu_-$. It is not essential, however, that dissociation be complete for this treatment to apply. Even when it is not we can still *define* m_+ by $m\nu_+$ and m_- by $m\nu_-$, *define* $m_\pm$ by Eq. (11-15) and *define* $\gamma_\pm$ by $a_\pm/m_\pm$ (Eq. (11-16)). Whether dissociation is complete or not $\gamma_\pm$ on this basis is called the **stoichiometric activity coefficient** to distinguish it from the **true coefficient** when the two differ, as they do for weak electrolytes. The latter will be considered in a later section.

Example 11-3 Find $a_{H_2SO_4}$ in $0.1000m$ solution at $25°$ if $\gamma_\pm = 0.265$.

Ans. $m_\pm = 0.1000(2^2 1^1)^{1/3} = 0.1587$ so, by Eq. (11-19), $a_{H_2SO_4} = [0.265(0.1587)]^3 = 7.44(10^{-5})$.

Note H_2SO_4 is far from being completely dissociated but, since $\gamma_\pm$ is the *stoichiometric* activity coefficient, its value makes allowance for this.

ELECTROMOTIVE FORCE AND FREE ENERGY CHANGE

It was mentioned briefly in Chapter 4 that emf measurements can be used to obtain values of ΔG. This topic has been postponed until now because electrolytes are involved in this method. In the study of electrochemistry one learns that it is often possible to harness a chemical reaction in such a way that the "chemical energy" of the reactants is converted into electrical energy. A few examples are given in Table 11-2 accompanied by the corresponding galvanic cells, represented in the conventional manner. Usually two, but sometimes four, electrodes are involved. The cells in the right-hand column of the table are written so that the *negative electrode*, where *oxidation* occurs, is on the left and the *positive electrode*, where *reduction* occurs, is on the right. In this context the negative electrode is the **anode** and the positive the **cathode**. (In electrolytic cells the reverse is true.) It is most important to realize that only *reversible* galvanic cells can be used to measure ΔG, even though many cells which are not reversible can still be employed as a source of electrical energy. When a cell is operating reversibly it is exerting the maximum emf under the given conditions of temperature, pressure and concentration and, as seen in Chapter 1, it must be opposed by an emf only infinitesimally smaller than its own emf. As a result, it discharges at an infinitesimally small rate. An infinitesimal increase in the opposing emf will cause all the processes occurring in the cell to reverse. Since under these conditions the emf is a maximum, the maximum work will be accomplished.

If we let $\mathcal{E}$ be the reversible emf in volts and allow $\mathcal{Q}$ coulombs of electricity to flow under its action (this will require infinite time!) the electrical work done will be $\mathcal{E}\mathcal{Q}$ joules. Since both P and T are supposed constant and $P = p_{ex}$, and since the only work done other than P-V work, is electrical we can equate $\mathcal{E}\mathcal{Q}$ to $-\Delta G$ by Eq. (4-16), or:

$$\Delta G = -\mathcal{E}\mathcal{Q} \qquad (11\text{-}20)$$

Now for every **faraday** of electricity (96,487 coulombs) which is allowed to flow, one equivalent of chemical reaction must occur. Letting $\mathcal{F}$ stand for the faraday and n for the number of equivalents of reaction occurring as a result of the passage of $\mathcal{Q}$ coulombs, we have:

$$n\mathcal{F} = \mathcal{Q} \qquad (11\text{-}21)$$

which leads to:

$$\Delta G = -n\mathcal{E}\mathcal{F} \qquad (11\text{-}22)$$

When the participating substances are in their standard states the value of $\mathcal{E}$ becomes $\mathcal{E}°$, the standard emf of the cell. Since, then, $\Delta G = \Delta G°$, we obtain:

$$\Delta G° = -n\mathcal{E}°\mathcal{F} \qquad (11\text{-}23)$$

The value of $\mathcal{F}$ given above, 96,487 coulomb equiv^{-1}, will yield ΔG in joules when used in Eqs. (11-22) and (11-23). To express ΔG in calories $\mathcal{F}$ must be expressed in calories per volt per equivalent. Since 1 cal = 4.1840 joules, $\mathcal{F}$ = 96,487/4.1840 = 23,061 cal volt^{-1} equiv^{-1}.

Combination of Eqs. (11-23) and (10-39) leads immediately to:

$$\ln K_a = n\mathcal{E}°\mathcal{F}/RT \qquad (11\text{-}24)$$

Table 11-2

Cell No.		
1	$\frac{1}{2}H_2(g) + \frac{1}{2}Cl_2(g) \longrightarrow HCl(aq)$	$\ominus H_2(Pt)\,\vert\,HCl(aq)\,\vert\,(Pt)H_2^{\oplus}$
2	$\frac{1}{2}H_2(g) + AgCl(s) \longrightarrow HCl(aq) + Ag(s)$	$\ominus H_2(Pt)\,\vert\,HCl(aq)\,\vert\,AgCl\,\vert\,Ag^{\oplus}$
3	Tl in $Hg \longrightarrow Tl$ in Hg $(X_{Tl} = X')\quad (X_{Tl} = X)$	$\ominus Tl$ in $Hg\,\vert\,TlNO_3(aq)\,\vert\,Tl$ in $Hg^{\oplus}$ $(X_{Tl} = X')\qquad (X_{Tl} = X)$
4	$Zn(s) + Hg_2SO_4(s) \longrightarrow ZnSO_4(aq) + Hg(l)$	$\ominus Zn\,\vert\,ZnSO_4(aq)\,\vert\,Hg_2SO_4(s)\,\vert\,Hg^{\oplus}$
5	$HBr(aq) \longrightarrow HBr(aq)$ $(a_{HBr} = a')\quad (a_{HBr} = a)$	$\ominus Ag\,\vert\,AgBr\,\vert\,HBr(aq)\,\vert\,(Pt)H_2(Pt)\,\vert\,HBr(aq)\,\vert\,AgBr\,\vert\,Ag^{\oplus}$ $(a = a')\qquad (a = a)$

Example 11-4 For the second cell listed in Table 11-2 $\mathcal{E} = 0.3420$ volt when the HCl is $0.1238m$, the temperature $298.15°K$ and the pressure 1 atm. Find $\Delta G_{298.15}$ for $H_2(g, 1 \text{ atm}) + 2AgCl(s) \longrightarrow 2HCl(0.1238m) + 2Ag(s)$.

Ans. In Eq. (11-22) $\mathcal{E} = 0.3420$ volt, $\mathcal{F} = 23{,}061$ cal volt^{-1} equiv^{-1} and $n = 2$ so $\Delta G_{298.15} = -2(0.3420)(23{,}061) = -15{,}774$ cal.

Example 11-5 When all the substances in the cell of Example 11-4 are in their standard states the emf at 25° is 0.222 volt. Find K_a for $H_2(g) + 2AgCl(s) \rightleftharpoons 2HCl(aq) + 2Ag(s)$ at this temperature.

Ans. $\mathcal{E}° = 0.222$ volt so, by Eq. (11-24), $\ln K_a = 2(0.222)(23{,}061)/1.987(298.2)$ or $K_a = 3.2(10^7)$.

A word is in order here concerning the sign of $\mathcal{E}$. When the cell reaction as written corresponds to the direction of the change as it occurs when the cell does electrical work $\mathcal{E}$ is positive; when written for the reverse change $\mathcal{E}$ is negative. Thus, referring to Example 11-4, we could say that for $HCl(0.1238m) + Ag(s) \longrightarrow \frac{1}{2}H_2(g) + AgCl(s)$, $\mathcal{E}_{298} = -0.3420$ volt. Moreover, the magnitude of $\mathcal{E}$ is independent, of course, of the *quantity* of reaction being considered. The latter determines n and ΔG, but not $\mathcal{E}$.

Eq. (11-23) permits the **Gibbs-Helmholtz** relation to be cast into still another form. Substitution of $\Delta G = -n\mathcal{E}\mathcal{F}$ into Eq. (4-34) gives

$$[\partial(-n\mathcal{E}\mathcal{F})/\partial T]_P = (-n\mathcal{E}\mathcal{F} - \Delta H)/T$$

or

$$\Delta H = n\mathcal{F}[T(\partial \mathcal{E}/\partial T)_P - \mathcal{E}] \tag{11-25}$$

Thus instead of measuring enthalpy change for a reaction calorimetrically we need merely to set up the corresponding reversible galvanic cell and measure its emf over a range of temperature, provided that such a cell is possible.

Example 11-6 For the cell $Pb \mid PbSO_4, H_2SO_4(0.1m), PbSO_4 \mid PbO_2 \mid Pt$ H. S. Harned and W. J. Hamer (*J. Am. Chem. Soc.*, **57**, 33 (1935)) found that the emf varies with the temperature $t(°C)$ according to $\mathcal{E} = 1.80207 - 265(10^{-6})t + 129(10^{-8})t^2$. The cell reaction is $Pb(s) + PbO_2(s) + 2H_2SO_4(0.1m) \longrightarrow 2PbSO_4(s) + 2H_2O(0.1m \ H_2SO_4)$. Find $\Delta H_{298.15}$ and $\Delta S_{298.15}$ for this change.

Ans. $\mathcal{E}_{298.15} = 1.80207 - 265(10^{-6})25.00 + 129(10^{-8})25.00^2 = 1.79625$ volt. Furthermore $n = 2$ and $(\partial \mathcal{E}/\partial T)_P = -265(10^{-6}) + 258(10^{-8})t = -0.000200$ volt deg^{-1} when $t = 25.00°$. Therefore, by Eq. (11-25), $\Delta H_{298.15} = 2(23{,}061)[298.15(-0.000200) - 1.79625] = -85{,}597$ cal. To find ΔS we may first find ΔG and then use $\Delta G = \Delta H - T\Delta S$: $\Delta G_{298.15} = -2(1.79625)(23{,}061) = -82{,}846$ cal, so $\Delta S_{298.15} = [-85{,}597 - (-82{,}846)]/298.15 = -9.227$ eu.

Note Alternatively we may replace ΔG in Eq. (4-33) by $-n\mathcal{E}\mathcal{F}$ to give
$$\Delta S = n\mathcal{F}(\partial \mathcal{E}/\partial T)_P = 2(23{,}061)(-0.000200) = -9.22 \text{ eu.}$$

$\mathcal{E}$ and $\mathcal{E}^\circ$ can readily be related through Eqs. (11-22), (11-23) and the reaction isotherm, Eq. (10-41), to give:
$$-n\mathcal{E}\mathcal{F} = -n\mathcal{E}^\circ\mathcal{F} + RT \ln Q_a$$

or
$$\mathcal{E} = \mathcal{E}^\circ - (RT/n\mathcal{F}) \ln Q_a \qquad (11\text{-}26)$$

This permits $\mathcal{E}$ to be calculated at a given temperature when $\mathcal{E}^\circ$ and the activities of the participating species are known. At 25°, where most calculations are made, Eq. (11-26) becomes:
$$\mathcal{E} = \mathcal{E}^\circ - 2.3026(1.9873)(298.150/23{,}061n) \log Q_a$$

or
$$\mathcal{E} = \mathcal{E}^\circ - (0.05916/n) \log Q_a \qquad \text{at } 25° \qquad (11\text{-}27)$$

Example 11-7 If $\mathcal{E}^\circ$ for the cell given in Example 11-6 is 2.0402 volts at 25° find $\mathcal{E}$ when the electrolyte is $1m$ H_2SO_4 for which $\gamma_\pm$ is 0.131. Assume $a_{H_2O} = 1$.

Ans. We must first find Q_a for $Pb(s) + PbO_2(s) + 2H_2SO_4(1m) \longrightarrow 2PbSO_4(s) + 2H_2O(1m \; H_2SO_4)$. All these species have unit activity except H_2SO_4. By Eq. (11-15) $m_\pm = 1(2^2 1^1)^{1/3} = 1.587$. Substitution in Eq. (11-19) gives $a_{H_2SO_4} = [(0.131)(1.587)]^3 = 0.524$ so $Q_a = (a_{PbSO_4})^2 \times (a_{H_2O})^2/(a_{Pb})(a_{PbO_2})(a_{H_2SO_4})^2 = (1)^2(1)^2/(1)(1)(0.524)^2 = 3.64$. Therefore $\mathcal{E} = 2.0402 - (0.05916/2) \log 3.64 = 2.0236$ volt.

DETERMINATION OF ACTIVITY OF STRONG ELECTROLYTES

We have thus far described the meaning and, to some extent, the use of, electrolyte activities without showing how they are obtained. The methods used for nonelectrolytes, referred to in the preceding chapter, are all applicable in principle, provided the quantity ν is introduced. How this is done will be shown later. Measurement of partial pressure of electrolyte over its solution is not generally feasible since most electrolytes are involatile. Determinations of the emf of appropriate galvanic cells can be a good source of activity data and will now be described.

Consider the strong electrolyte HBr, whose activity at 25° at a number of molalities is to be determined. By setting up the cell
$$^\ominus H_2(g, 1 \text{ atm})(Pt) \mid HBr(m), AgBr \mid Ag^\oplus$$

analogous to Cell No. 2 in Table 11-2, the measured $\mathcal{E}$ will be related to the activity of the HBr by Eq. (11-27), viz.
$$\mathcal{E} = \mathcal{E}^\circ - 0.05916 \log a_{HBr}$$

since the cell reaction is $\frac{1}{2}H_2(g) + AgBr(s) \longrightarrow HBr(m) + Ag(s)$. Now by Eq. (11-19) $a_{HBr} = (\gamma_\pm m_\pm)^2$ where $\gamma_\pm$ and $m_\pm$ refer to the HBr. Furthermore, by Eq. (11-15) $m_{\pm} = m$ so $a_{HBr} = (\gamma_{\pm}m)^2$ and we have:

$$\mathcal{E} = \mathcal{E}° - 0.05916 \log(\gamma_{\pm}m)^2 = \mathcal{E}° - 0.11832 \log m - 0.11832 \log \gamma_{\pm}$$

or

$$\mathcal{E} + 0.11832 \log m = \mathcal{E}° - 0.11832 \log \gamma_{\pm} \qquad (11\text{-}28)$$

Since the reference state of HBr is the infinitely dilute solution measurements of $\mathcal{E}$ must extend to high dilution. (Emf methods are particularly well suited to this.) We therefore measure $\mathcal{E}$ over a wide range of concentration which includes high dilution, m being known for each concentration, and plot $\mathcal{E} + 0.11832 \log m$ vs. $m^{1/2}$. The type of result obtained is shown schematically in Fig. 11-3. The use of $m^{1/2}$ rather than m for

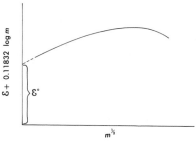

Fig. 11-3

abscissa permits a more accurate extrapolation to $m = 0$ since the graph is then linear at high dilution. Now by Eq. (11-28) we have:

$$\lim_{m \to 0} (\mathcal{E} + 0.11832 \log m) = \lim_{m \to 0} (\mathcal{E}° + 0.11832 \log \gamma_{\pm}) = \mathcal{E}°$$

since $\gamma_{\pm} = 1$ at infinite dilution. In this way $\mathcal{E}°$, the intercept on the vertical axis, is found to be 0.07103 volt. Having determined $\mathcal{E}°$ we may then find $\gamma_{\pm}$ for any concentration for which $\mathcal{E}$ has been measured using Eq. (11-28). For example, when $m = 0.02000$ $\mathcal{E}$ was found to be 0.27855 so $0.27855 + 0.11832 \log 0.02000 = 0.07103 - 0.11832 \log \gamma_{\pm}$, from which $\gamma_{\pm} = 0.881$ and $a_{HBr} = [(0.881)(0.02000)]^2 = 3.52(10^{-4})$. (Cf. A. S. Keston, *J. Am. Chem. Soc.*, **57**, 1671 (1935) and H. S. Harned, A. S. Keston and J. G. Donelson, ibid., **58**, 989 (1936).)

The remaining important methods for finding strong electrolyte activities involve determination of solvent activities first.

IONIC STRENGTH

A useful quantity, originally obtained empirically and later shown to have a theoretical basis, is the **ionic strength**, μ, defined by:

$$\mu = \frac{1}{2} \sum m_i z_i^2 \qquad (11\text{-}29)$$

where m_i is the molality of the ith kind of ion, z_i is its charge, and the summation is over all kinds of ions present. It applies to solutions containing any number of electrolytes. For *dilute aqueous* solutions, since $m_i \cong c_i$, the ion molarity, $\mu \cong \frac{1}{2} \Sigma\ c_i z_i^2$.

Example 11-8 A certain solution is $0.2m$ with respect to $CaCl_2$ and $0.1m$ with respect to NaCl. Find its ionic strength.

Ans. Since $m_{Ca^{+2}} = 0.2$, $m_{Na^+} = 0.1$ and $m_{Cl^-} = 2(0.2) + 0.1 = 0.5$, $\mu = \frac{1}{2}[0.2(2)^2 + 0.1(1)^2 + 0.5(1)^2] = 0.7$.

Note Strictly, one should include the molality of H^+ and OH^- in the summation but their concentrations are negligibly small.

ACTIVITY OF DIFFICULTLY SOLUBLE ELECTROLYTES

If we represent sparingly soluble electrolytes by $M_{\nu_+} N_{\nu_-}$ the following equilibria obtain in saturated solution:

$$M_{\nu_+} N_{\nu_-}(s) \rightleftharpoons M_{\nu_+} N_{\nu_-}(\text{dissolved}) \rightleftharpoons \nu_+ M^{z+} + \nu_- N^{z-}$$

and

$$a_+^{\nu+} a_-^{\nu-} / a_{B(s)} = \text{constant}$$

by Eqs. (10-22) and (11-6), where z stands for ion charge and the subscripts $+$ and $-$ refer to the M and N ions. However, following the usual choice of standard state for solids, $a_{B(s)} = 1$ so we have:

$$a_+^{\nu+} a_-^{\nu-} = K_{sp} \tag{11-30}$$

where K_{sp} is a constant called the **thermodynamic solubility product** of B. Observe that so far the argument applies to all saturated salt solutions, whether concentrated or not, as long as the solid phase is not a solvate. Eq. (11-30) may be rewritten:

$$(\gamma_\pm m_\pm)^\nu = K_{sp} \tag{11-31}$$

as usual. Suppose now that the solubility of B be measured not only in pure water at the given temperature but also in water containing soluble salts. (We shall assume for simplicity that the latter have no ions in common with B.) If B is slightly soluble its solubility will be found to increase, at least initially, as the concentration of added salt increases, for reasons to be given later. If s be the solubility of B in terms of molality then $m_\pm = s(\nu_+^{\nu+} \nu_-^{\nu-})^{1/\nu}$. For each solution μ is calculated. If, now, $m_\pm$ be plotted vs. $\mu^{1/2}$ a curve resembling Fig. 11-4 (schematic) results. It is extrapolated to $\mu^{1/2} = 0$. It is necessary to work with a difficultly soluble salt in order to reduce the length and therefore the uncertainty of the extrapolation, as is evident here. The use of ionic strength for abscissa improves the accuracy by reducing the curvature; other devices in plotting are also used. Now Eq. (11-31) applies to all points on the curve but, since the reference state for the *dissolved* B and its ions

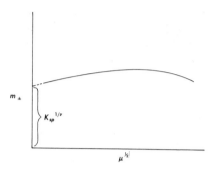

Fig. 11-4

is the infinitely dilute solution, $\gamma_{\pm}$ approaches unity as $\mu^{1/2}$ approaches zero. Thus we have:

$$\lim_{\mu \to 0} = (\gamma_{\pm} m_{\pm})^{\nu} = \lim_{\mu \to 0} m_{\pm}^{\nu} = K_{sp}$$

so the intercept of the curve on the $m_{\pm}$ axis gives $K_{sp}^{1/\nu}$. We can now, by means of Eq. (11-31), find $\gamma_{\pm}$ at any value of μ on the curve. In this way activity coefficients (and therefore activities) of B are obtained in its saturated solutions whether other salts are present or not.

Example 11-9 I. M. Kolthoff and J. J. Lingane, *J. Phys. Chem.*, **42**, 133 (1938), measure the solubility of $AgIO_3(s)$ in water and in solutions of KNO_3 at 25°. A solution 0.0705m in KNO_3, e.g., when saturated with $AgIO_3$ was found to be 0.0002301m in $AgIO_3$. When no KNO_3 was present the saturated solution was 0.0001770m in $AgIO_3$. Extrapolation of a number of such results, as in Fig. 11-4, was found to give an intercept of $m_{\pm} = 0.0001744$. Find (a) K_{sp} for $AgIO_3$ (b) $\gamma_{\pm}$ for $AgIO_3$ in saturated aqueous solution (c) a_{AgIO_3} in saturated aqueous solution.

Ans. (a) For $AgIO_3$ $m_{\pm} = m$ so the given solubilities are identical to $m_{\pm}$ and $K_{sp}^{1/\nu} = \lim_{\mu \to 0} m = \lim_{\mu \to 0} m_{\pm} = 0.0001744$. Therefore $K_{sp} = 0.0001744^2 = 3.04(10^{-8})$.
(b) By Eq. (11-31), $[\gamma_{\pm}(0.0001770)]^2 = 3.04(10^{-8})$ or $\gamma_{\pm} = 0.985$.
(c) $a_{AgIO_3} = [0.985(0.0001770)]^2 = 3.04(10^{-8})$ (in all the saturated solutions).

Note The activity of the $AgIO_3$ in all the saturated solutions is the same since they are all in equilibrium with $AgIO_3(s)$, the activity of which is constant. By Eq. (10-22) $a_{AgIO_3(dissolved)}/a_{AgIO_3(s)}$ = constant, but this constant is not unity since the standard states of $AgIO_3$ are different in the two phases.

ELECTROLYTE ACTIVITIES FROM SOLVENT ACTIVITIES

Apart from the emf method the most widely used techniques for determining electrolyte activities (a_B) involve finding solvent activity (a_A) by isopiestic or freezing point measurements and from these computing a_B through the Gibbs-Duhem relation. In this connection the **practical osmotic coefficient**, ϕ, was mentioned briefly in reference to Eq. (10-31). As applied to a solution of an *electrolyte*, however, this quantity is defined by:

$$\phi = -(1000/\nu m M_A) \ln a_A \qquad (11\text{-}32)$$

which, for aqueous solutions, since $M_A = 18.016$, becomes

$$\phi = -(55.51/\nu m) \ln a_A \qquad (11\text{-}33)$$

At high dilution $\ln a_A \cong \ln X_A \cong \ln (1 - X_B) \cong -X_B$. But when m is very small $X_B = \nu m/(\nu m + 55.51) \cong \nu m/55.51$, so $\phi \cong (\nu 55.51 m/55.51)/\nu m$ and we have:

$$\lim_{m \to 0} \phi = 1 \qquad (11\text{-}34)$$

As m increases from zero upward a_A decreases and the effect of these two trends is to cause ϕ to decrease at first and then increase. For KCl solutions at $25°$, e.g., ϕ passes through a minimum of 0.899 at about $m = 0.75$.

Let us suppose that a_A has been found at a given temperature for the water in the given electrolyte solution over a range of concentration including dilute solution, and that ϕ for each solution has been calculated therefrom by Eq. (11-33). We wish to convert these values of ϕ into values of $\gamma_\pm$ from which a_B can then be found. Now $a_B = (\gamma_\pm m_\pm)^\nu$ by Eq. (11-19) so d ln $a_B = \nu$ d ln $\gamma_\pm + \nu$ d ln $m_\pm$. But, by Eq. (11-15), d ln $m_\pm$ = d ln m so we have:

$$\text{d ln } a_B = \nu \text{ d ln } \gamma_\pm + \nu \text{ d ln } m$$

Combining this with Eq. (10-31) and recalling that $1000/M_A = 55.51$ for water yields:

$$\text{d ln } \gamma_\pm + \text{d ln } m = -(55.51/\nu m) \text{ d ln } a_A$$

or

$$\text{d ln } a_A = -(\nu m/55.51)(\text{d ln } \gamma_\pm + \text{d ln } m) \qquad (11\text{-}35)$$

We now introduce ϕ by rewriting Eq. (11-33) as:

$$\ln a = -(\nu/55.51) m \phi \qquad (11\text{-}36)$$

and differentiating (noting that both m and ϕ are variables) to give:

$$\text{d ln } a_A = -(\nu/55.51)(m \text{ d}\phi + \phi \text{ d}m) \qquad (11\text{-}37)$$

The left-hand sides of Eqs. (11-35) and (11-37) are identical so we obtain:

$$m(\text{d ln } \gamma_\pm + \text{d ln } m) = m \text{ d}\phi + \phi \text{ d}m$$

or

$$\text{d ln } \gamma_\pm = \text{d}\phi - (1 - \phi) \text{d ln } m \qquad (11\text{-}38)$$

which may be integrated between $m = 0$ where $\gamma_{\pm} = 1$ and $\phi = 1$ to the given concentration where $m = m$, $\gamma_{\pm} = \gamma_{\pm}$ and $\phi = \phi$ to give:

$$\ln \gamma_{\pm} = -(1 - \phi) - \int_0^m \frac{1 - \phi}{m}\, dm \qquad (11\text{-}39)$$

which is written in this way because ϕ is usually less than unity. The integral is evaluated graphically as the area under a curve. The accuracy with which this area can be found depends on the method used for finding ϕ. Clearly, the more dilute the solutions for which ϕ has been measured the better the result. The extrapolation is improved if dm is replaced by $2m^{1/2}\,dm^{1/2}$ to give:

$$\ln \gamma_{\pm} = -(1 - \phi) - 2 \int_0^{m^{1/2}} \frac{(1 - \phi)}{m^{1/2}}\, dm^{1/2} \qquad (11\text{-}40)$$

It is further facilitated by the use of Debye-Hückel theory, to be mentioned later, in much the same way as theory aids the extrapolation in finding third law entropies from heat capacities (Chapter 3).

In the isopiestic technique (see Chapter 10) the required values of ϕ are found by bringing a solution of B, the electrolyte being studied, to isopiestic equilibrium with a solution of some reference electrolyte R (usually KCl) for which values of ϕ have already been established by some other method. This means that the solutions of B and R have identical solvent vapor pressures at the given temperature. In their final states, then, a_A will be the same for both solutions and so, by Eq. (11-33), we have:

$$-\nu_R m_R \phi_R / 55.51 = -\nu m \phi / 55.51$$

or

$$\phi = \nu_R m_R \phi_R / \nu m \qquad (11\text{-}41)$$

where ν_R is the value of ν for the reference electrolyte ($= 2$ for KCl).

Example 11-10 If $2.077m$ $CaCl_2$ and $3.937m$ NaCl are in isopiestic equilibrium at $25°$, and if the osmotic coefficient for the latter solution is 1.111, find ϕ for $2.077m$ $CaCl_2$ and the activity of water in these solutions.

Ans. By Eq. (11.41) $\phi = 2(3.937)(1.111)/3(2.077) = 1.404$. By Eq. (11-33), $1.404 = -[(55.51/3(2.077)] \ln a_{H_2O}$ or $a_{H_2O} = 0.854$.

Note The same result could have been obtained, of course, by applying Eq. (11-33) to the NaCl solution: $1.111 = -[(55.51/2(3.937)] \ln a_{H_2O}$.

Unfortunately, the isopiestic method is not feasible for finding ϕ at concentrations below about $0.1m$ so that, in using Eq. (11-40), problems arise in the evaluation of the integral. Consider, e.g., the osmotic coefficients for KBr found at $25°$ by this method and given in Table 11-3. A plot of

Table 11-3

KBr at 25°

m	$m^{1/2}$	ϕ	$(1 - \phi)\,m^{1/2}$
0.1	0.3162	0.928	0.2277
0.2	0.4472	0.916	0.1878
0.3	0.5477	0.910	0.1643
0.5	0.7071	0.904	0.1358
0.8	0.8944	0.905	0.1062
1.0	1.0000	0.907	0.093

$(1 - \phi)/m^{1/2}$ vs. $m^{1/2}$ using these data, represented in Fig. 11-5 by the circled points, is clearly inadequate for accurate extrapolation to $m^{1/2} = 0$. With the help of Debye-Hückel theory in its simplest form, e.g., it can be shown that at 25°, the following is true:

$$1 - \phi \cong (2.303/3)(0.511) \mid z_+ z_- \mid \mu^{1/2} \qquad (11\text{-}42)$$

at high dilution, z_+ and z_- being the charges on the cation and anion, respectively, so $1 - \phi$ may be predicted, at least for very small molalities. When $m = 10^{-4}$ for KBr, $\mu = 10^{-4}$ and $\mu^{1/2} = 10^{-2}$ so $1 - \phi = (2.303/3) \times (0.511)(1)(1)(10^{-2}) = 0.00392$ and $(1 - \phi)/m^{1/2} = 0.392$. This point is shown in Fig. 11-5 as a square. Its location removes much of the doubt about the course of the curve at high dilution. Additional points may be obtained by use of more extended forms of Eq. (11-42). Even with only the points shown we may attempt to find γ_+ in $1m$ solution. The area under the curve from $m^{1/2} = 0$ to $m^{1/2} = 1^{1/2} = 1$ is found to be 0.192 units and the table gives $\phi = 0.907$ at this concentration. Substitution of these figures into Eq. (11-40) gives $\ln \gamma_+ = -(1 - 0.907) - 2(0.192)$ or $\gamma_+ = 0.621$. Since $m_+ = m$ for KBr, $a_{\text{KBr}} = [1(0.621)]^2 = 0.386$. (The literature value for a_{HBr} is 0.381.)

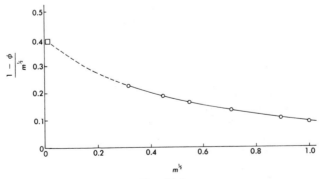

Fig. 11-5

The lack of data at high dilution may also be obviated by measuring activity coefficients for the most dilute solutions by other methods more suitable at high dilution.

In our attention to methods of finding a_B we must not lose sight of the most important use of such information, viz. the evaluation of free energy changes involving electrolytes in solution.

Example 11-11 Find ΔG_{298} for $Na_2SO_4(0.5m) \longrightarrow Na_2SO_4(0.1m)$ if $\gamma_{\pm}$ in 0.5 and $0.1m$ solution is 0.27 and 0.45, respectively.

Ans. $a_{Na_2SO_4}$ (in $0.1m$)/$a_{Na_2SO_4}$ (in $0.5m$) = $[\gamma_{\pm}m_{\pm}$ (in $0.1m$)/$\gamma_{\pm}m_{\pm}$ (in $0.5m$)]^3 = $[(0.45/0.27)(0.1/0.5)]^3$ = 0.037 using Eqs. (11-15) and (11-19). Therefore ΔG_{298} = 1.99(298) ln 0.037 = -1950 cal.

TRENDS IN ACTIVITY COEFFICIENT VALUES

Typical activity coefficients for 25°, determined by the foregoing methods for various types of electrolytes, are shown in Table 11-4. When values

Table 11-4

Mean Ion Activity Coefficients at 25°

m	HCl	KBr	$MgBr_2$	$FeCl_2$	$ZnSO_4$	$NiSO_4$	$LaCl_3$	$Al_2(SO_4)_3$
0.001	0.965				0.700		0.788	
0.01	0.904				0.387		0.559	
0.1	0.796	0.771	0.582	0.525	0.150	0.150	0.336	0.0350
0.5	0.757	0.657	0.579	0.460	0.0626	0.0628	0.285	0.0115
0.7	0.772	0.637	0.635	0.475	0.0520	0.0516	0.305	0.0133
1.0	0.809	0.617	0.764	0.519	0.0434	0.0426	0.366	0.0176
1.5	0.900	0.601	1.123	0.637	0.0368	0.0360	0.554	
2.0	1.009	0.596		0.817	0.0350	0.0343		
2.5	1.158	0.596			0.0360	0.0357		
3.0	1.316	0.600						

such as these are plotted against molality a distinct pattern emerges. In the first place they all show a minimum with decrease in concentration and then rise to the limiting value of unity for infinite dilution because that is the reference state. (As already stated ϕ also passes through a minimum but at a different concentration.) In the second place electrolytes of the same valence type approach identical values with dilution but these values are different for different **valence types**, except at infinite dilution. A few examples are presented in Fig. 11-6. By valence type is meant the particular pair of values of z_+ and z_-. Thus KCl and HBr are described as belonging to the 1-1 type, $ZnSO_4$ and $MgCO_3$ to the 2-2 type, $BaCl_2$ to the 2-1, K_2CrO_4 to the 1-2, etc. In the third place, when log $\gamma_{\pm}$ vs. $\mu^{1/2}$ is plotted instead of $\gamma_{\pm}$ vs. m, the curves approach a finite limiting slope which is dependent on the product $|z_+ z_-|$ and therefore only on the valence type. A fundamental significance is therefore attached to μ and to valence type.

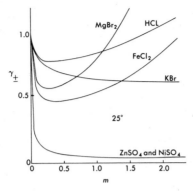

Fig. 11-6

Example 11-12 If, at $25°$, $\gamma_\pm$ in individual $0.1m$ solutions of $NaBrO_3$, $ZnCl_2$, $Al_2(SO_4)_3$ and Na_2SO_4 is 0.76, 0.58, 0.04 and 0.45, respectively, *estimate* $\gamma_\pm$ for each of the following at the same concentration: $BaBr_2$, K_2CrO_4, $TlClO_4$ and $Cr_2(SO_4)_3$.

Ans. In the examples given $\gamma_\pm$ for 1-1, 2-1, 3-2 and 1-2 types are 0.76, 0.58, 0.04 and 0.45. Since $BaBr_2$, K_2CrO_4, $TlClO_4$ and $Cr_2(SO_4)_3$ belong to types 2-1, 1-2, 1-1 and 3-2, respectively, we would estimate their $\gamma_\pm$'s to be 0.58, 0.45, 0.76 and 0.04.

Note The literature values are 0.51, 0.46, 0.73 and 0.05. Observe the similarity of the 1-2 and 2-1 types for both of which $|z_+ z_-|$ is 2. At very high dilution $ZnCl_2$, Na_2SO_4, $BaBr_2$ and K_2CrO_4 should have identical $\gamma_\pm$'s.

DEBYE-HÜCKEL THEORY

Although classical thermodynamics takes activity coefficients simply as an experimental result it is necessary to mention the immense contribution made in the interpretation and correlation of the results by the well known **Debye-Hückel theory of electrolytes**. We shall give here only the predictions of the theory for infinite dilution. Caution must be exercised in applying these relations at finite concentrations, but they are useful in obtaining approximate values. The **Debye-Hückel limiting law**, which becomes more and more valid as concentration is diminished, is:

$$\log \gamma_\pm = -A\,|\,z_+ z_-\,|\,\mu^{1/2} \qquad (11\text{-}43)$$

where $\gamma_\pm$ is the mean ion activity coefficient of the electrolyte to which z_+ and z_- refer, μ is the ionic strength of the solution (which may include ions other than those to which z_+ and z_- refer), and A is a constant for a given solvent at a given temperature the value of which is given by:

$$A = \frac{1}{2.303}\left(\frac{e^2}{DkT}\right)^{3/2}\left(\frac{2\pi N_o d}{1000}\right)^{1/2} \qquad (11\text{-}44)$$

where e is the charge on the electron, D and d the dielectric constant and density of the solvent, k the Boltzmann constant, T the absolute temperature and N_0 the Avogadro number. For aqueous solutions $A = 0.492$ at $0°$ and 0.511 at $25°$. When any electrolytes are present which are not completely dissociated this must be taken into account in calculating μ, i.e., the m_i's in Eq. (11-29) must be the true ion molalities, not the stoichiometric ones. The activity coefficient found is the true activity coefficient (see later) which, for strong electrolytes, is identical to the stoichiometric one.

An analogous expression for osmotic coefficient, valid at infinite dilution, can also be obtained from theory:

$$1 - \phi = (2.303/3)A \mid z_+ z_- \mid \mu^{1/2} \tag{11-45}$$

Eqs. (11-43) and (11-45) and extended forms of them serve a useful purpose in predicting values of $\gamma_\pm$ and ϕ at high dilution where the experimental errors are too great for satisfactory results. The use of Eq. (11-45) has already been mentioned in connection with Fig. 11-5. Eq. (11-43) permits an estimate of $\gamma_\pm$ for an electrolyte either in the presence or absence of other electrolytes.

Example 11-13 (a) Find $\gamma_\pm$ for KCl in 0.0100m solution at $25°$ by the limiting law and compare with the experimental value of 0.902. (b) Find $\gamma_\pm$ for BaCl$_2$ in 0.0100m solution at $25°$ by the limiting law and compare with the experimental value of 0.723.

Ans. (a) KCl is a 1-1 electrolyte so $\mu = 0.0100$ and, by Eq. (11-43), $\log \gamma_\pm = -0.511(1)(1)0.0100^{1/2} = -0.0511$ or $\gamma_\pm = 0.889$. (b) $\mu = \frac{1}{2}[0.0100(2^2) + 0.0200(1^2)] = 0.0300$ so $\log \gamma_\pm = -0.511(2)(1)0.0300^{1/2} = -0.177$ or $\gamma_\pm = 0.665$. The agreement for KCl is good, and better than that for BaCl$_2$, a higher valence type, as expected. In neither does Eq. (11-43) reproduce the experimental result exactly, for it is valid only at infinite dilution.

Example 11-14 A certain solution is 0.00100m in HBr and 0.00100m in BaBr$_2$. Find (a) $\gamma_\pm$ for HBr and (b) $\gamma_\pm$ for BaBr$_2$ in this solution at $25°$ using the limiting law.

Ans. (a) $\mu = \frac{1}{2}[0.00100(1^2) + 0.00100(2^2) + 0.00300(1^2)] = 0.00400$ so $\log \gamma_{\pm(HBr)} = -0.511(1)(1)0.00400^{1/2} = -0.0323$ or $\gamma_{\pm(HBr)} = 0.928$.
(b) $\log \gamma_{\pm(BaBr_2)} = -0.511(2)(1)0.00400^{1/2} = -0.0646$ or $\gamma_{\pm(BaBr_2)} = 0.862$.

SOLUBILITY OF SPARINGLY SOLUBLE SALTS IN SOLUTIONS OF OTHER SALTS

The general variation of $\gamma_\pm$ with μ, as illustrated in Fig. 11-6, can be used to predict the effect on the solubility of a difficultly soluble salt, AB, of the presence of another salt. Because AB is sparingly soluble the ionic strength of its saturated solution will lie to the left of the minimum on the curve. When the added (soluble) salt has no ion in common with AB the increase in μ, resulting from the addition, will cause $\gamma_{\pm}$ to decrease at first and therefore, through Eq. (11-31), cause $m_{\pm}$ and thus the solubility of AB to increase. This is called the **salt effect**. Still further addition of soluble salt will eventually cause the solubility of AB to decrease again when the minimum has been passed. The initial increase is exemplified by the data of Example 11-9: the solubility of $AgIO_3$ in water at 25° is only $0.0001770m$ whereas in $0.0705m$ KNO_3 it is $0.0002301m$. These measurements were not carried far enough to show the eventual decrease.

If, on the other hand, the added salt has an ion in common with the given salt the phenomenon is a little more complex. Let us designate the sparingly soluble salt by $A_{\nu_+}B_{\nu_-}$ and let the A ion be common to both salts. For $A_{\nu_+}B_{\nu_-}$, $m_{\pm} = (m_A^{\nu_+} m_B^{\nu_-})^{1/\nu}$ and s, the solubility of $A_{\nu_+}B_{\nu_-}$ (in molality) will be related to m_B by $m_B = \nu_- s$. Eq. (11-31) will then become:

$$(m_A)^{\nu_+}(\nu_- s)^{\nu_-}(\gamma_{\pm})^{\nu} = K_{sp} \qquad (11\text{-}46)$$

As more soluble salt is added, $\gamma_{\pm}$ will decrease as before but m_A will increase (because the added salt also provides A ion), K_{sp} remaining constant. Since m_A increases and $\gamma_{\pm}$ decreases, will s increase or decrease? Actually the effect of the increase in m_A is larger than that of the decrease in $\gamma_{\pm}$ so the net effect is a decrease in s. This is the well known **common ion effect**. When the minimum in Fig. 11-6 has been passed both factors operate to decrease s.

When the added salt has an *anion* in common with the saturating salt, Eq. (11-46) is replaced by:

$$(\nu_+ s)^{\nu_+}(m_B)^{\nu_-}(\gamma_{\pm})^{\nu} = K_{sp} \qquad (11\text{-}47)$$

If one were to ignore the fact that $\gamma_{\pm}$ is not unity, as if often done in elementary calculation, the conclusion drawn from Eqs. (11-46) or (11-47) would be that s would decrease even more with addition of soluble salt.

These arguments assume no specific chemical interaction between AB and the added salt. If such interaction is present, as when complex ions are formed, the effect of addition of salt is always to increase s.

Example 11-15 The solubility of PbI_2 in water at 20° is $1.37(10^{-3})m$ and the value of A in the limiting law, Eq. (11-43), is 0.507 at that temperature. (a) Find the solubility product assuming that $\gamma_{\pm}$ is unity. (b) Estimate $\gamma_{\pm}$ by means of the limiting law and find the thermodynamic solubility product. (c) Find the solubility of PbI_2 in $0.030m$ KI assuming all the $\gamma_{\pm}$'s to be unity. (d) Find the solubility of PbI_2 in $0.030m$ KI by estimating $\gamma_{\pm}$.

Ans. (a) $K_{sp} = [1.37(10^{-3})][2(1.37)(10^{-3})]^2 = 1.03(10^{-8})$.
(b) In a saturated solution of PbI_2 in water $\mu = \frac{1}{2}[1.37(10^{-3})(2^2) + 2.74(10^{-3})(1^2)] = 4.11(10^{-3})$. By the limiting law $\log \gamma_{\pm} \cong -0.507(2)(1) \times [4.11(10^{-3})]^{1/2} = -0.0650$ or $\gamma_{\pm} \cong 0.861$. Furthermore, by Eq. (11-15)

$m_{\pm} = 1.37(10^{-3})(1^1 2^2)^{1/3} = 2.17(10^{-3})$, so, by Eq. (11-31), the true (thermodynamic) $K_{sp} \cong [0.861(2.17)(10^{-3})]^3 = 6.52(10^{-9})$.

(c) If all the $\gamma_{\pm}$'s are unity and if we ignore the iodide contributed by the dissolved PbI_2 $s^1(0.030)^2 = 1.03(10^{-8})$ or $s = 1.15(10^{-5})m$.

(d) $\mu = \frac{1}{2}[0.030(1^2) + 0.030(1^2) + $ negligible   contribution   from $PbI_2] = 0.030$ so, by the limiting law, $\log \gamma_{\pm} \cong -0.507(2)(1)(0.030)^{1/2} = -0.175$ or $\gamma_{\pm} \cong 0.668$. Using Eq. (11-47), since the two salts have an *anion* in common, we have by substitution $(1s)^1(0.030 + $ negligible amount   from $PbI_2)^2(0.668)^3 = 6.52(10^{-9})$ or $s \cong 2.43(10^{-5})m$.

WEAK ELECTROLYTES

For the ions of electrolytes which are only partly dissociated it is preferable to use the true activity coefficient $(f_{\pm})$ rather than the stoichiometric one $(\gamma_{\pm})$. The former is defined by:

$$f_{\pm} = (f_{+}^{\nu_+} f_{-}^{\nu_-})^{1/\nu} \tag{11-48}$$

where

$$f_{+} = a_{+}/m_{+}, \quad \text{and} \quad f_{-} = a_{-}/m_{-} \tag{11-49}$$

m_{+} and m_{-} being the *true* ion molalities which, for a 1-1 electrolyte, are given by:

$$m_{+} = \alpha m_{t} \quad \text{and} \quad m_{-} = \alpha m_{t} \tag{11-50}$$

where m_t is the total molality and α is the degree of dissociation. Clearly, $f_{\pm}$ and $\gamma_{\pm}$ are identical only when α is unity. When this situation arises, as with strong electrolytes, the symbol $\gamma_{\pm}$ is used.

For the undissociated species (B) the activity coefficient will be designated by f_B. Since the ion activities, a_{+} and a_{-}, are true activities whether we use $\gamma_{\pm}$'s or $f_{\pm}$'s, we have:

$$a_{+} = \gamma_{+} m_{t} \quad \text{and} \quad a_{-} = \gamma_{-} m_{t} \tag{11-51}$$

for 1-1 electrolytes. Use of Eqs. (11-49) gives:

$$\gamma_{+} m_{t} = f_{+} m_{+} \quad \text{and} \quad \gamma_{-} m_{t} = f_{-} m_{-} \tag{11-52}$$

With the help of Eqs. (11-50) this gives:

$$\gamma_{+} = \alpha f_{+} \quad \text{and} \quad \gamma_{-} = \alpha f_{-} \tag{11-53}$$

As implied already, $\gamma_i = f_i$ when $\alpha = 1$, as for weak electrolytes at infinite dilution, or for strong electrolytes. Finally, multiplying the two Eqs. (11-53) together gives $\gamma_{+}\gamma_{-} = \alpha^2 f_{+} f_{-}$ which, from Eqs. (11-14) and (11-48) is seen to yield:

$$\gamma_{\pm} = \alpha f_{\pm} \tag{11-54}$$

for 1-1 electrolytes.

Example 11-16 The degree of dissociation of acetic acid (HAc) is 0.1238 in $0.001028m$ solution at $25°$. Find (a) μ, (b) $f_{\pm}$ and (c) $\gamma_{\pm}$ with the help of the limiting law.

Ans. (a) The true ion concentrations are $m_{H^+} = m_{Ac^-} = \mu =$ 0.001028(0.1238) = 0.0001273.

(b) By the limiting law $\log f_{\pm} = -0.511(1)(1)(0.0001273)^{1/2} = -0.00576$ or $f_{\pm} = 0.987$.

(c) By Eq. (11-54) $\gamma_{\pm} = 0.1238(0.987) = 0.1222$.

Note This calculation ignores any possible effect the undissociated acid may have on the solvent and therefore on the constant 0.511.

For weak electrolytes, since the undissociated species is a very real one it is possible to determine its concentration from the degree of dissociation. If we consider, again, a 1-1 electrolyte, HA, dissociating according to:

$$HA \rightleftharpoons H^+ + A^-$$

we may apply Eq. (10-40) to give:

$$K_a = a_{H^+}a_{A^-}/a_{HA} = f_{H^+}m_{H^+}f_{A^-}m_{A^-}/f_{HA}m_{HA}$$

If α is the degree of dissociation and m_t the total molality of HA, we have:

$$K_a = \frac{f_{H^+}f_{A^-}}{f_{HA}} \frac{\alpha^2 m_t^2}{(1-\alpha)m_t} = \frac{f_{\pm}^2}{f_{HA}} \frac{\alpha^2 m_t}{(1-\alpha)}$$

where the f's are true activity coefficients (not fugacities!). Now f_{HA} is taken to be virtually unity (since HA is an uncharged species in a solution of very small ionic strength) so we have, to a very close approximation:

$$K_a = f_{\pm}^2 \frac{\alpha^2 m_t}{1-\alpha} \tag{11-55}$$

(When α is sufficiently small we may replace $1 - \alpha$ by 1 in the denominator.) This result may be used to find an approximate value for K_a, the thermodynamic dissociation constant of HA, by estimating $f_{\pm}$ from the limiting law, provided α is known. Knowing K_a we may then find $\Delta G°$ for the dissociation process and so obtain free energy changes involving this electrolyte.

The determination of accurate values of dissociation constants of weak electrolytes will not be described. The method used by H. S. Harned and R. W. Ehlers, *J. Am. Chem. Soc.*, 54, 1350 (1932), is typical.

Example 11-17 (a) Estimate K_a for acetic acid (HAc) from the information given and found in Ex. 11-16. (b) Find $\Delta G_{298}°$ for HAc(aq) $\longrightarrow$ H^+(aq) + Ac^-(aq).

Ans. (a) By Eq. (11-55) $K_a = 0.987^2(0.1238)^2(0.001028)/(1 - 0.1238) = 1.752(10^{-5})$.

(b) By Eq. (10-39) $\Delta G_{298}° = -1.987(298) \ln 1.752(10^{-5}) = 6489$ cal.

Example 11-18 Predict whether the dissociation of a weak acid at high dilution is increased or decreased by the addition of a small quantity of a soluble salt with which it has no ion in common.

Ans. At high dilution $f_\pm$ is to the left of the minimum of Fig. 11-6 so addition of salt would increase μ, decrease $f_\pm$ and, through Eq. (11-55), cause α to increase.

Example 11-19 For 0.200m acetic acid α is 0.95% at 25°. Find $f_\pm$ given that $K_a = 1.754(10^{-5})$.

Ans. By Eq. (11-55) $1.754(10^{-5}) = f_\pm^2(0.0095)^2(0.200)/(1 - 0.0095)$ or $f_\pm = 0.981$.

EMF OF HALF-CELLS. ION ACTIVITIES. pH

When requiring emfs in our discussions thus far we have used only whole cell values and made no attempt to break up the measured $\mathcal{E}$ into the contributions of the individual electrodes or half-cells which comprise the whole. In the first cell of Table 11-2, e.g., we have not concerned ourselves with how much of the overall $\mathcal{E}$ is caused by the hydrogen and how much by the chlorine electrode. We have so far not needed to know this, but even if we had, there is no way of finding this information! Any attempt to measure such half-cell emfs requires the unwanted introduction of another electrode. Nevertheless, since presumably one half-cell emf is independent of the other, we can imagine that it has a value ever though it cannot be measured. Suppose, e.g., that we designate the above half-cell emfs by $\mathcal{E}_{H_2}$ and $\mathcal{E}_{Cl_2}$, respectively, where, in both cases, the corresponding cell reaction is for the *oxidation* reaction. These would then correspond to the half-cell reactions:

$$\frac{1}{2}H_2(g) \longrightarrow H^+(aq) + e \qquad \mathcal{E} = \mathcal{E}_{H_2}$$
$$Cl^-(aq) \longrightarrow \frac{1}{2}Cl_2(g) + e \qquad \mathcal{E} = \mathcal{E}_{Cl_2}$$

and the difference between these would give the overall cell reaction:

$$\frac{1}{2}H_2(g) + \frac{1}{2}Cl_2(g) \longrightarrow HCl(aq) \qquad \mathcal{E} = \mathcal{E}_{H_2} - \mathcal{E}_{Cl_2}$$

(We pause to point out that usage is not uniform here. Electrode potentials are often tabulated so as to correspond to half-cell reactions for *reduction*. Still another convention, increasing in popularity and adopted by the I.U.P.A.C., is the designation of single electrode potentials by the symbol $\mho$, which does not depend on whether the cell reaction is for oxidation or reduction.* Each system has its merits and gives the same result if used consistently. We shall think of $\mathcal{E}$ values for half-cells as associated with oxidation reactions and call them **oxidation potentials**.)

*For an excellent description of the differences in convention see T. S. Licht and A. J. deBethune, *J. Chem. Educ.*, **34**, 433 (1957).

Now when, in the above-mentioned cell, all the species are at unit activity ($a_{H_2} = a_{Cl_2} = a_{HCl} = a_{H^+} = a_{Cl^-} = 1$) we write:

$$\mathcal{E}^\circ_{cell} = \mathcal{E}^\circ_{H_2} - \mathcal{E}^\circ_{Cl_2}$$

Although $\mathcal{E}^\circ_{cell}$ can be measured—it has the value 1.3595 volt at 25°—we do not know either $\mathcal{E}^\circ_{H_2}$ or $\mathcal{E}^\circ_{Cl_2}$ so, in order to obtain at least a set of relative values, $\mathcal{E}^\circ_{H_2}$ *is arbitrarily called zero at all temperatures*. On this basis we have for the other electrode:

$$Cl^-(aq) \longrightarrow \tfrac{1}{2}Cl_2(g) + e \qquad \mathcal{E}^\circ_{Cl_2} = -1.3595 \text{ volt}$$

By replacing the chlorine electrode by any other one, $\mathcal{E}^\circ$ values for the latter are obtained similarly. In this way the familiar tabulations of the emfs of half-cells are obtained, but *they are all only relative to* $\mathcal{E}^\circ_{H_2} = 0$.

Not only is it impossible to measure $\mathcal{E}$ for a half-cell, it is also impossible to measure $\mathcal{E} - \mathcal{E}^\circ$. If we were to try to measure it by setting up the cell:

$$H_2(Pt) \mid H^+(a = a) \mid H^+(a = 1) \mid (Pt)H_2$$

the emf we measure would include an undetermined **liquid junction potential** at the boundary between the two solutions. It follows, therefore, that if we write Eq. (11-26) for the hydrogen electrode, viz.

$$\mathcal{E}_{H_2} - \mathcal{E}^\circ_{H_2} = -(RT/\mathcal{F}) \ln (a_{H^+}/a_{H_2}^{1/2})$$

we have no way of finding a_{H^+}, even though we can find a_{H_2}. The same difficulty arises for any other electrode. The conclusion is, therefore, that *ion activities cannot be measured*.

Our ignorance of ion activities is sometimes unimportant and sometimes a serious drawback. In the cell:

$$H_2(Pt) \mid HCl(aq) \mid AgCl \mid Ag$$

for instance, the half-cell reactions given earlier lead to:

$$\tfrac{1}{2}H_2(g) + \tfrac{1}{2}Cl_2(g) \longrightarrow H^+(aq) + Cl^-(aq)$$

and

$$Q_a = a_{H^+}a_{Cl^-}/a_{H_2}^{1/2}a_{Cl_2}^{1/2}$$

However, $a_{H^+}a_{Cl^-}$ is identical with a_{HCl} since the H^+ and Cl^- are provided *by a single solution of HCl*, so the question of ion activities and the difficulties associated with them does not arise. Contrast this with the following cell:

$$Zn \mid Zn^{2+} \mid Cu^{2+} \mid Cu$$

where the half-cell reactions are:

$$Zn \longrightarrow Zn^{2+} + 2e$$

and

$$Cu \longrightarrow Cu^{2+} + 2e$$

Here Q_a will involve $a_{Zn^{2+}}$ and $a_{Cu^{2+}}$ and the measured $\mathcal{E}$ will be comprised of the half-cell emfs of the zinc and copper electrodes *as well as* a liquid junction potential arising from the juxtaposition of the zinc and copper salt solutions. This leads to the dilemma that ion activities cannot be found because liquid junction potentials cannot be found, and vice versa. It is for reasons of this kind that *chemical* cells with transport are avoided in strict thermodynamic treatments.

Example 11-20 (a) Write the half-cell and whole cell reactions for each of the following cells:
(i) $^{\ominus}$Cd | CdSO$_4$(aq), Hg$_2$SO$_4$(s) | Hg$^{\oplus}$
(ii) $^{\ominus}$Ag | AgCl(s) | FeCl$_2$(aq), FeCl$_3$(aq) | Pt$^{\oplus}$
(b) Show that in (i) ion activities are not needed in evaluating $\mathcal{E} - \mathcal{E}^\circ$ for the whole cell and in (ii) they are needed.

Ans. (a) (i)

$$Cd(s) \longrightarrow Cd^{2+}(aq) + 2e$$
$$SO_4^{2-}(aq) + 2Hg(l) \longrightarrow Hg_2SO_4(s) + 2e$$

Subtraction gives: $Cd(s) + Hg_2SO_4(s) \longrightarrow Cd^{2+}(aq) + SO_4^{2-}(aq) + 2Hg(l)$
(ii)

$$Cl^-(aq) + Ag(s) \longrightarrow AgCl(s) + e$$
$$Fe^{2+}(aq) \longrightarrow Fe^{3+}(aq) + e$$

Subtraction gives: $Cl^-(aq) + Ag(s) + Fe^{3+}(aq) \longrightarrow AgCl(s) + Fe^{2+}(aq)$
(b) For (i) $\mathcal{E} = \mathcal{E}^\circ - (RT/2\mathcal{F}) \ln (a_{Cd^{2+}} a_{SO_4^{2-}}) = \mathcal{E}^\circ - (RT/2\mathcal{F}) \ln (a_{CdSO_4})$, so ion activities are not required. For (ii) $\mathcal{E} = \mathcal{E}^\circ - (RT/\mathcal{F}) \ln (a_{Fe^{2+}}/a_{Fe^{3+}})(a_{Cl^-})$, so ion activities are required.

Note Although (ii) is not a chemical cell with transport it is still unsuitable for exact thermodynamic treatment.

The adoption of the convention that $\mathcal{E}^\circ_{H_2} = 0$ at all temperatures means that for:

$$\tfrac{1}{2}H_2(g) \longrightarrow H^+(aq) + e$$

$\Delta G^\circ = 0$ at all temperatures too. For:

$$Cl^-(aq) \longrightarrow \tfrac{1}{2}Cl_2(g) + e$$

$\Delta G^\circ_{298} = -1(-1.359)(23,060) = 31,350$ cal by Eq. (11-23), and similarly for all other half-cell reactions. Reversing this equation gives:

$$\tfrac{1}{2}Cl_2(g) + e \longrightarrow Cl^-(aq)$$

and $\Delta G_{298}^{\circ} = -31{,}350$ cal. In this way **standard free energies of formation of ions** are obtained. That for H^{+}(aq) is, of course, zero. Such quantities can then be combined to give ΔG° for other changes. For example, since the standard free energies of formation of Cl^{-}(aq) and Br^{-}(aq) are $-31{,}350$ and $-24{,}560$ cal mole^{-1}, respectively, ΔG° for:

$$Br^{-}(aq) + \tfrac{1}{2}Cl_2(g) \longrightarrow Cl^{-}(aq) + \tfrac{1}{2}Br_2(l)$$

is given by $[-31{,}350 + \tfrac{1}{2}(0)] - [-24{,}560 + \tfrac{1}{2}(0)] = -6790$ cal.

Example 11-21 Determine whether Hg_2^{2+}(aq) will oxidize Fe^{2+}(aq) to Fe^{3+}(aq) at $25°$ when all species are in their standard states, if the oxidation potentials are as follows:

$$Fe^{2+}(aq) \longrightarrow Fe^{3+}(aq) + e \qquad \mathcal{E}^{\circ} = -0.771 \text{ volt}$$
$$2Hg(l) \longrightarrow Hg_2^{2+}(aq) + 2e \qquad \mathcal{E}^{\circ} = -0.789 \text{ volt}$$

Ans. Subtraction of the half-cell reactions, after doubling the first one (but not the $\mathcal{E}^{\circ}$ value!) gives:

$$2Fe^{2+}(aq) + Hg_2^{2+}(aq) \longrightarrow 2Hg(l) + 2Fe^{3+}(aq),$$
$$\mathcal{E}^{\circ} = -0.771 - (-0.789) = 0.018 \text{ volt.}$$

Since this is positive the reaction is possible in the standard state.

Example 11-22 If $\mathcal{E}^{\circ}$ for $Ag(s) \longrightarrow Ag^{+}$ (aq) $+ e$ is -0.799 volt and $\mathcal{E}^{\circ}$ for $Ag(s) + Cl^{-}$(aq) $\longrightarrow AgCl(s) + e$ is -0.222 volt at $25°$ find the thermodynamic solubility product for AgCl at this temperature.

Ans. Subtraction of the second half-cell reaction from the first gives:

$$AgCl(s) \longrightarrow Ag^{+}(aq) + Cl^{-}(aq)$$
$$\mathcal{E}^{\circ} = -0.799 - (-0.222) = -0.577 \text{ volt.}$$

Hence, by Eq. (11-24), $\ln K_a = \ln K_{sp} = 1(-0.577)(23{,}060)/1.987(298.2)$ or $K_{sp} = 1.8(10^{-10})$.

The arbitrariness of the convention $\mathcal{E}_{H_2}^{\circ} = 0$ disappears when ΔG values for whole cells are obtained from the differences between the individual ΔG's for the half-cells, and it is usually the whole cells that are of ultimate interest. Any subsequent change in the convention would alter all the half-cell values by the same amount and not affect the difference between these for any given pair of electrodes.

There is one particular ion activity however, viz. a_{H^+}, which is of paramount interest because of its relation to acidity and alkalinity and described by the term pH. Originally this was defined by:

$$pH = -\log c_{H^+} \qquad (11\text{-}56)$$

where c is molarity; it is now defined by:

$$pH = -\log a_{H^+} \tag{11-57}$$

There is a curious incongruity here, for c_{H^+} can be measured but a_{H^+} can only be approximated. Since a_{H^+} cannot be found with certainty neither can pH by the latter definition! Nevertheless, the convenience of electrical measurements and the dependence of emf on ion activities rather than on ion concentrations have led to the adoption of Eq. (11-57) as a definition. Now it will be seen that a cell designed to find pH and therefore a_{H^+}, such as:

$$H_2(Pt) \,|\, H^+(\text{given solution}) \,|\, \text{Reference electrode}$$

will involve a liquid-liquid junction, so that the emf will depend not only upon a_{H^+} but also upon the electrolytes, etc. in juxtaposition. Depending on what reference electrode is used slightly different pH values will be obtained for the same solution. Obviously, then, pH will have meaning only for the particular cell arrangement used. In practice a combination of glass electrode and calomel electrode is used thus:

$$Ag \,|\, AgCl \,|\, HCl(0.1N) \;\}\; H^+(\text{given solution}) \,|\, \text{Calomel}$$

the emf of which at 25° varies with a_{H^+} in the given solution according to:

$$\mathcal{E} = \text{constant} - 0.05916 \log a_{H^+} = \text{constant} + 0.05916\, pH$$

or

$$pH = (\mathcal{E} - \text{constant})/0.05916 \tag{11-58}$$

Thus pH is found by measuring $\mathcal{E}$. The constant is determined by replacing the given solution with a buffer the pH of which is estimated as accurately as possible from thermodynamic ionization constants and procedures designed to minimize uncertainties concerning ion activities.

In this connection it may be pointed out that ion activities are often *estimated* by using $\gamma_{\pm}$ in place of γ_i. If, for instance, we wish to estimate a_{Cl^-} in $0.1m$ HCl, for which $\gamma_{\pm} = 0.796$, we may say that $\gamma_{Cl^-} \cong 0.796$, and so $a_{Cl^-} \cong 0.796(0.1)$ since $m_{Cl^-} = 0.1$. This approximation is all the better the more dilute the solution.

Example 11-23 When the cell with the glass electrode contained a buffer solution of pH = 4.00 its emf was 0.1122 volt. Find the pH of a solution which gives an emf of 0.2471 volt.

Ans. From Eq. (11-58) $4.00 = (0.1122 - \text{constant})/0.05916$ so the constant is $0.1122 - 4.00(0.05916) = -0.1244$. Hence, for the second solution pH = $[0.2471 - (-0.1244)]/0.05916 = 6.28$.

The hydrogen ion activity is related quantitatively to that of the hydroxyl ion since the equilibrium:

$$H_2O(l) \rightleftharpoons H^+(aq) + OH^-(aq)$$

occurs, for which $K_a \doteq a_{H^+} a_{OH^-} / a_{H_2O}$. This relation will be true not only in pure water but in any aqueous solution. In pure water $a_{H_2O} = 1$ and, in dilute aqueous solution, $a_{H_2O} \cong 1$, so in the latter $a_{H^+} a_{OH^-} \cong K_a(1)$ which is given the symbol K_w, so we have:

$$a_{H^+} a_{OH^-} \cong K_w \tag{11-59}$$

which becomes more exact as solute concentration is reduced. At $25°$ $K_w = 1.002(10^{-14})$.

ION ENTROPIES AND ENTHALPIES

The inability to find ion activities has its analogue in the inability to find ion entropies so, again, an arbitrary standard is required. For this purpose the standard partial molar entropy of $H^+(aq)$ is called zero, or we use:

$$\overline{\overline{S}}{}^{\circ}_{H^+} = 0 \tag{11-60}$$

(This convention is most commonly applied at $25°$.) The question may be raised as to the effect of this choice on the standard entropy of formation of $H^+(aq)$, i.e. the effect on $\Delta S°$ for:

$$\tfrac{1}{2} H_2(g) \longrightarrow H^+(aq) + e$$

since $\overline{\overline{S}}_{H_2(g)} = 31.21$ eu mole^{-1}. If $\overline{\overline{S}}_{H^+} = 0$ the molar entropy of electrons would have to be $31.21/2 = 15.61$ eu for consistency. Since this value will always cancel in whole cell reactions it has no particular significance.

Having established Eq. (11-60) as a basis we may now proceed to evaluate other ion entropies. This can be done by finding ΔS values from ΔG and ΔH through $\Delta G = \Delta H - T \Delta S$ for solution processes. To find $\overline{\overline{S}}{}^{\circ}_{Cl^-}$, e.g., consider:

$$HCl(g) \longrightarrow H^+(aq) + Cl^-(aq)$$

for which $\Delta G°_{298.2} = -8606$ cal and $\Delta H°_{298.2} = -17,960$ cal (cf. Problem 15 at the end of this chapter). We also know that the standard entropy of $HCl(g)$ at $25°$ is 44.62 eu mole^{-1}. $\Delta S°_{298.2}$ will then be $(-17,960 + 8606)/298.2 = -31.37$ eu which equals $\overline{\overline{S}}{}^{\circ}_{H^+} + \overline{\overline{S}}{}^{\circ}_{Cl^-} - \overline{\overline{S}}{}^{\circ}_{HCl(g)} = 0 + \overline{\overline{S}}{}^{\circ}_{Cl^-} - 44.62$. It follows that $\overline{\overline{S}}{}^{\circ}_{Cl^-} = -31.37 + 44.62 = 13.25$ eu mole^{-1}. We may say also that the standard partial molar entropy of $HCl(aq)$, $\overline{\overline{S}}{}^{\circ}_{HCl(aq)} = 13.25$ eu mole^{-1} because when an electrolyte is in its standard state its ions are also in their standard states and $\Delta G° = \Delta S° = \Delta H° = 0$ for $HCl(aq) \longrightarrow H^+(aq) + Cl^-(aq)$ (cf. Eq. (11-7)). By methods of this nature ion entropies are obtained.

Example 11-24 The standard entropies of $NaCl(s)$ and $Na_2CO_3(s)$ at $25°$ are 17.3 and 32.5 eu mole^{-1}, respectively. If $\Delta S°_{298}$ for $NaCl(s) \longrightarrow Na^+(aq) + Cl^-(aq)$ is 10.4 eu and if $\Delta S°_{298}$ for $Na_2CO_3(s) \longrightarrow 2Na^+(aq) + CO_3{}^{2-}(aq)$ is -16.4 eu find the standard partial molar entropies of $Na^+(aq)$ and $CO_3{}^{2-}(aq)$ at $25°$. Use $\overline{\overline{S}}{}^{\circ}_{298}$ for $Cl^-(aq)$ given above.

Ans. From the first equation $\overline{\overline{S}}^\circ_{Na^+} + 13.25 - 17.3 = 10.4$ so $\overline{\overline{S}}^\circ_{Na^+} = 14.4$ eu mole^{-1}. From the second equation $2(14.4) + \overline{\overline{S}}^\circ_{CO_3^{-2}} - 32.5 = -16.4$ so $\overline{\overline{S}}^\circ_{CO_3^{-2}} = -12.7$ eu mole^{-1}.

Note Ion entropies are not always positive.

Standard enthalpies of formation of ions are based on a convention analogous to that employed for free energies: the standard enthalpy of formation of H^+(aq) is taken as zero so, for:

$$\frac{1}{2}H_2(g) \longrightarrow H^+(aq) + e$$

$\Delta H° = 0$ at all temperatures (but usually 25°). This subject was discussed and illustrated in Chapter 1 in the section entitled "Heats of Ionic Reactions."

PROBLEMS

1. Show from the following data for $CaCl_2$ at 25° that Eq. (11-2) applies better for $\nu = 3$ than for any smaller integer.

m	0.0001	0.0005	0.001	0.005
a_{CaCl_2}	$3.56(10^{-12})$	$3.86(10^{-10})$	$2.79(10^{-9})$	$2.40(10^{-7})$

2. If $\mathcal{E}°$ for the cell $H_2(Pt)\,|\,HCl(aq)\,|\,AgCl\,|\,Ag$ at 25° is 0.222 volt find the emf when the pressure of the hydrogen is 0.500 atm and the HCl is 0.500m, where its mean ion activity coefficient is 0.757. Assume the hydrogen to be ideal.

3. Describe a method by which the standard oxidation potential of the zinc-zinc ion electrode at 25° could be accurately determined.

4. Suppose that the following cell, similar to Cell No. 5 of Table 11-2 be set up:

$$Ag\,|\,AgCl\,|\,FeCl_2(1.5m)\,|\,Fe\,|\,FeCl_2(0.5m)\,|\,AgCl\,|\,Ag$$

Find the emf at 25° with the help of the data in Table 11-4.

5. (a) Suppose it were possible to build a reversible galvanic cell:

$$^\ominus C(graphite)\,|\,CO_2(g)\,|\,O_2(g)^\oplus$$

for which the cell reaction would be $C(graphite) + O_2(g) \longrightarrow CO_2(g)$. $\Delta G°_{298}$ for this is $-94,260$ cal. What is the maximum electrical work which such a cell could perform at 25° and 1 atm per mole of $CO_2(g)$ formed?

(b) Suppose, on the other hand, a mole of $CO_2(g)$ were formed by the combustion of graphite at 25° and 1 atm, and the heat used to run a reversible heat engine operating between 250°K and 800°K. The engine, in turn, is used to run an electric generator with no energy losses. If $\Delta H°_{298}$ for $C(graphite) + O_2(g) \longrightarrow CO_2(g)$ is $-94,052$ cal how much electrical work would be done?

(c) Which of (a) or (b) represents the most efficient production of electrical work from the same chemical change?

6. The reversible oxygen electrode, $O_2(g)$ in equilibrium with $OH^-(aq)$ for which the half-cell reaction is:

$$2OH^-(aq) \longrightarrow \tfrac{1}{2}O_2(g) + H_2O(l) + 2e$$

is not realizable experimentally, but its potential can be calculated indirectly. Find the hypothetical oxidation potential at $25°$ with the help of the following data for this temperature:

$$\Delta G_f^\circ \text{ for } H_2O(l) = -56.690 \text{ kcal mole}^{-1}$$

$$K_a \text{ for } H_2O(l) \rightleftharpoons H^+(aq) + OH^-(aq) = 1.002(10^{-14})$$

7. (a) Write the cell reaction for the cell:

$$^\ominus Zn \mid ZnI_2(aq) \mid AgI \mid Ag^\oplus$$

for which $\mathcal{E}^\circ$ is 0.610 volt at $25°$.

(b) Find ΔS° for the reaction at $25°$ if, at this temperature, the standard entropies of $Ag(s)$, $Zn(s)$, $AgI(s)$, $I^-(aq)$ and $Zn^{2+}(aq)$ are 10.21, 9.95, 27.6, 26.14 and -25.45 eu mole^{-1}, respectively.

(c) Find a general expression for $(\partial \mathcal{E}^\circ / \partial T)_P$ in terms of entropy and evaluate $(\partial \mathcal{E}^\circ / \partial T)_P$ for the cell in part (a).

(d) Find ΔH°_{298} for the cell reaction.

8. Find the ionic strength of a solution which is $0.0500m$ in acetic acid (HAc) and $0.01000m$ in $CaBr_2$, if the former is 1.88% dissociated.

9. If $0.565m$ $Cr_2(SO_4)_3$ is isopiestic with $0.796m$ KCl at $25°$ where the osmotic coefficient of the latter is 0.897, find ϕ for the other solution.

10. Osmotic coefficients cannot be obtained by isopiestic methods for concentrations below $0.1m$, so activity coefficients cannot be determined without assistance from theory in the extrapolation to $m = 0$. Nevertheless the ratio $\gamma_\pm / \gamma_\pm'$, where $\gamma_\pm$ is the mean ion activity coefficient at $m = m$ and $\gamma_\pm'$ that at $m = 0.1$, can be found.

(a) Integrate Eq. (11-38) between the limits of $m = 0.1$ and $m = m$ to find an expression for $\ln (\gamma_\pm / \gamma_\pm')$, and then change the variable from m to $m^{1/2}$.

(b) Use this expression and the following values of ϕ for $Cr(NO_3)_3$ solutions at $25°$ (N. O. Smith, *J. Am. Chem. Soc.*, 69, 91 (1947)) to find $\gamma_\pm / \gamma_\pm'$ graphically, where $\gamma_\pm$ refers to $1.2m$.

m	0.1	0.2	0.3	0.4	0.5	0.7	1.0	1.2	1.4
ϕ	0.793	0.816	0.859	0.905	0.955	1.057	1.231	1.349	1.469

11. (a) Eq. (10-37) is just as true for electrolytes as for nonelectrolytes. Is Eq. (10-38) also true for electrolytes when γ is the mean ion activity coefficient?

(b) If the relative partial molar enthalpy of NaCl in $1.00m$ solution is -186 cal mole^{-1} in the neighborhood of room temperature and $\gamma_\pm$ is 0.656 at $25°$, find $\gamma_\pm$ at $35°$.

12. Mean ion activity coefficients pass through a minimum as the concentration increases. Do the activities also pass through a minimum? Why?

13. Use the Debye-Hückel limiting law to predict $\gamma_{\pm}$ for $ZnSO_4$ in $0.0100m$ solution at $25°$ and compare with the value given in Table 11-4.

14. Given that the aqueous solubility of $TlCl(s)$ is $1.41(10^{-2})m$ at $25°$ find (a) its thermodynamic solubility product and (b) its solubility in $0.0500m$ $NaNO_3$ with the help of the Debye-Hückel limiting law. (Hint: In finding $\gamma_{\pm}$ in (b) ignore the salt effect to find an approximate solubility; then use the latter to find an improved $\gamma_{\pm}$. Proceed by iteration.)

15. At $25°$ the partial pressure of HCl over $5m$ solution is $6.974(10^{-5})$ atm, the mean ion activity coefficient at this concentration is 2.38 and the heat of solution of $HCl(g)$ at infinite dilution is $\Delta H = -17.960$ kcal mole^{-1}. Find $\Delta S_{298.2}^{\circ}$ for:

$$HCl(g) \longrightarrow H^+(aq) + Cl^-(aq)$$

16. (a) If the standard oxidation potentials for the ferrous-ferric and stannous-stannic electrodes are $\mathcal{E}° = -0.77$ and -0.14 volt, respectively at $25°$, find K_a for:

$$2Fe^{3+}(aq) + Sn^{2+}(aq) \rightleftharpoons 2Fe^{2+}(aq) + Sn^{4+}(aq)$$

(b) If the standard free energies of formation of $Fe^{3+}(aq)$, $Sn^{2+}(aq)$, $Fe^{2+}(aq)$ and $Sn^{4+}(aq)$ at $25°$ are -2.53, -6.27, -20.30 and $+0.7$ kcal mole^{-1}, respectively, find K_a from these data and compare with that found in part (a).

17. A saturated aqueous solution of $KBr(s)$ at $25°$ is $5.75m$. In this solution $\gamma_{\pm}$ is 0.645. When a mole of $KBr(s)$ is dissolved in a very large amount of water at this temperature 4.79 kcal of heat are absorbed.
(a) Find ΔG_{298}° and ΔS_{298}° for $KBr(s) \longrightarrow KBr(aq)$.
(b) If the standard entropy of $KBr(s)$ is 23.05 eu mole^{-1} and the standard entropy of $K^+(aq)$ is $\bar{\bar{S}}_{K^+}^{\circ} = 24.5$ eu mole^{-1} find $\bar{\bar{S}}_{Br^-}^{\circ}$.

18. (a) The true pH of $0.100m$ HCl, as nearly as possible in accordance with Eq. (11-57), is found to be 1.085 at $25°$. Find γ_{H^+} and a_{OH^-} in the HCl solution.
(b) What is the pH as defined by Eq. (11-56), assuming molality equals molarity?

Appendix:
Physical constants and numerical relations

R, the gas constant = 0.082058 liter-atm deg^{-1} mole^{-1}
$\phantom{R, \text{the gas constant}}$ = 82.058 cm^3 atm deg^{-1} mole^{-1}
$\phantom{R, \text{the gas constant}}$ = 8.3143 joule deg^{-1} mole^{-1}
$\phantom{R, \text{the gas constant}}$ = 1.9872 cal deg^{-1} mole^{-1}
N_o, the Avogadro number = 6.0225(10^{23}) mole^{-1}
k, the Boltzmann constant = 1.3805(10^{-16}) erg deg^{-1}
$\mathcal{F}$, the faraday = 96,487 coulomb equiv^{-1}
$\phantom{\mathcal{F}, \text{the faraday}}$ = 96,487 joule volt^{-1} equiv^{-1}
$\phantom{\mathcal{F}, \text{the faraday}}$ = 23,061 cal volt^{-1} equiv^{-1}
h, Planck's constant = 6.6256(10^{-27}) erg sec

1 cal = 4.1840 joule = 4.1840(10^7) erg = 0.041293 cm^3 atm
1 cm^3 atm = 24.217 cal
1 joule = 0.23901 cal

$\ln x = 2.3026 \log x$
$R \ln x = 4.5757 \log x$ when R is in cal deg^{-1} mole^{-1}
$R\,(298.15) \ln x = 1364.2$ when R is in cal deg^{-1} mole^{-1}
$\dfrac{R\,(298.15)}{\mathcal{F}} \ln x = 0.05916 \log x$

Answers to problems

CHAPTER 1

1. (a) $\Delta E = 3(4.97)(50) = 750$ cal; $\Delta H = 3(6.96)(50) = 1040$ cal.
   (b) w is not defined since no details of the process are given.

2. (a) $V_1 = 3(0.0821)(273)/10.0 = 6.72$ liters. Using $V_1 T_1{}^{\overline{C}_V/R} = V_2 T_2{}^{\overline{C}_V/R}$, $V_2 = 4.42$ liters, so $P_2 = nRT_2/V_2 = 18.1$ atm. $q = 0$. $w = -\Delta E = -3(4.97)(50) = -750$ cal. $\Delta H = 3(6.96)(50) = 1040$ cal.
   (b) $V_1 = 4.42$ liters and $V_2 = P_1 V_1/P_2 = 18.1(4.42)/2 = 40.0$ liters. $\Delta E = \Delta H = 0$. $q = w = RT_2 \ln (V_2/V_1) = 3(1.987)(323)(2.303) \log (40.0/4.42) = 4240$ cal. Overall values: $\Delta E = 750$ cal, $\Delta H = 1040$ cal, $w = 3490$, $q = 4240$ cal. The values of ΔE and ΔH are the same as for Problem 1 because the same change of state is involved.

3. (a) $q = 0$ so $n\overline{C}_V \Delta T = -p_{ex} \Delta V$, i.e. $3(4.97)(50) = -18.1(V_2 - 6.72)(24.2)$ cal, when V_2 is in liters. Solving gives $V_2 = 5.0$ liters and $P_2 = nRT_2/V_2 = 15.9$ atm. $\Delta E = 3(4.97)(50) = 750$ cal. $\Delta H = 3(6.96)(50) = 1040$ cal. $w = -750$ cal.
   (b) $\Delta E = \Delta H = 0$. $q = w = p_{ex}\Delta V = 2.0(40.0 - 5.0)24.2 = 1690$ cal. Overall values: $\Delta E = 750$ cal, $\Delta H = 1040$ cal, $w = 940$ cal, $q = 1690$ cal. The values of ΔE and ΔH for the overall change are the same as those found in Problem 2 because the same change of state is involved. *Note* The change in Problem 2(a) is a different change from that in Problem 3(a), for the gas occupies a final volume of 4.42 liters at a pressure of 18.1 atm in 2(a), but a final volume of 5.0 liters at a pressure of 15.9 atm in 3(a). $q \neq \Delta H$ in 3(a) for, even though p_{ex} is constant, $P \neq p_{ex}$.

4. (a) $P_A = nRT_A/V_A = 1(0.0821)(300)/2.40 = 10.26$ atm.
   (b) By Eq. (1-14), $P_A V_A{}^\gamma = P_B V_B{}^\gamma$ where $\gamma = [(5/2)R]/[(3/2)R] = 1.40$,

244

so $10.26(2.40)^{1.40} = P_B(5.00)^{1.40}$ or $P_B = 3.67$ atm.

(c) $T_B = P_B V_B / nR = 3.67(5.00)/0.0821 = 224°K$.

(d) $w = -C_V \Delta T = -(5/2)(1.987)(224 - 300) = 378$ cal.

(e) For A $\longrightarrow$ C, $w = P\Delta V = 10.26(5.00 - 2.40)$ liter-atm = 646 cal. For C $\longrightarrow$ B, $w = 0$ since volume is constant. Hence w for the two-stage process = $646 + 0 = 646$ cal. Both w's thus calculated, viz. 378 and 646 cal are for reversible processes and refer to the same change, A $\longrightarrow$ B. More work is done in the two-stage process than in the one-stage. They are not necessarily equal because A $\longrightarrow$ B is not isothermal. Neither quantity can be described as w_{max} for the given change.

5. (a) $q_P = \int_{200}^{300} [6.000 + 2.500(10^{-3})T]\,dT = 6(300 - 200) + 0.002500 \times$

(90,000 - 40,000)/2 = 662.5 cal.

(b) $q_P = 2(5.000)(300 - 200) = 1,000$ cal.

(c) $\Delta C_P = [2(5.000)] - [6.000 + 2.500(10^{-3})T]$, so by the Kirchhoff relation $\Delta H_{300} - (-10,000) = \int_{200}^{300} [4.000 - 2.500(10^{-3})T]\,dT = 337.5$ or $\Delta H_{300} = -9,663$ cal.

(d) (i) $\Delta H = 662.5 - 9,663 = -9,000$ cal.

(ii) $\Delta H = -10,000 + 2(5.000)(100) = -9,000$ cal.

6. $q_P = q_V + nRT$, so $10,000 = q_V + 1(1.99)(298)$ or $q_V = 9,410$ cal.

7. $C_2H_5OH(l) + 3O_2(g) \longrightarrow 2CO_2(g) + 3H_2O(l)$ and $q_P = q_V + \Delta nRT$, so $q_P = -326,106 + (-1)(1.987)(298) = -326,698$ cal. $-326,698 = 2(-94,052) + 3(-68,317) - \Delta H_f$. Therefore $\Delta H_f = -66,357$ cal.

8. One Cl—Cl and one C—H bond are broken whereas one C—Cl and one H—Cl are formed. Therefore $58 + 99 = 157$ kcal are required and $77 + 103 = 180$ kcal are released, giving a net heat evolved of 23 kcal, or $\Delta H = -23$ kcal.

9. For every mole of water formed 13,500 cal are evolved. Since $50(0.10) = 5.0$ meq or 0.0050 moles of water are formed, $0.0050(13,500) = 67$ cal are evolved. But heat capacity of salt solution is 1.00 cal deg^{-1} g^{-1} or 100 cal deg^{-1} for the 100 g, so temperature rise = $67/100 = 0.67°$.

10. $\Delta H = [-52.3 + 4(-68.3) + 5(-11.4)] - [-123.9 + 5(-21.0) + 8(0)] = -153.6$ kcal.

11. (a) $(\partial \overline{V}/\partial T)_P = \overline{V}\alpha = 97.1(12.4)(10^{-4}) = 0.1204$ cm^3 deg^{-1} mole^{-1}. Therefore $\overline{C}_P - \overline{C}_V = 3340(0.1204) + 1(0.1204) = (402 + 0.120)$ cm^3 atm deg^{-1} mole^{-1} = 9.72 cal deg^{-1} mole^{-1}.

(b) The fraction 0.120/402, or 0.000299, represents work of expansion against the atmosphere. The remaining fraction (nearly 100%) represents expansion against intermolecular forces.

12. In a $4m$ solution there are 13.89 moles of water to every mole of solute. So we may write:

$$NaOH(s) + 13.89H_2O(l) \longrightarrow NaOH \cdot 13.89H_2O; \qquad \Delta H_{293} = -10,235 \text{ cal}$$

and

$$NaOH(s) + \infty \ H_2O(l) \longrightarrow NaOH(aq); \qquad \Delta H_{293} = -10,100 \text{ cal}$$

Subtracting gives:

$$NaOH \cdot 13.89H_2O + \infty \ H_2O(l) \longrightarrow NaOH(aq); \qquad \Delta H_{293} = 135 \text{ cal}$$

Thus when 1 mole NaOH in $4m$ solution is diluted indefinitely 135 cal are absorbed; when 4 moles in $4m$ solution are diluted indefinitely 4(135) cal or 540 cal are absorbed and $\Delta H_{293} = 540$ cal.

13. For $\frac{1}{2}H_2(g) + \frac{1}{2}Cl_2(g) \longrightarrow HCl(g)$, $\Delta H^\circ_{298} = -22.063$ kcal. Expressing ΔC_P° as $\Delta a + \Delta b T + \Delta c T^2$ we have $\Delta a = 6.7319 - \frac{1}{2}(6.9469) - \frac{1}{2}(7.5755) = -0.5293$; similarly, $\Delta b = -0.6797(10^{-3})$ and $\Delta c = 6.118(10^{-7})$.

Therefore $\Delta H_{328} = -22,063 + \displaystyle\int_{298}^{328} [-0.5293 - 0.6797(10^{-3}) T + 6.118(10^{-7}) T^2] dT = -22,084$ cal. (Cf. Example 1-33.)

CHAPTER 2

1. (a) If the engine is reversible $\eta = \dfrac{(300 + 273) - (273 + 0)}{300 + 273} = 0.52$.

Since $0.47 \neq 0.52$ the engine is not reversible.

(b) $w/q_2 = w/4000 = 0.47$, so $w = 1880$ cal.

2. (a) Let final temperature be t°. Since heat lost by brick = heat gained by H_2O, $500(200 - t) = (900/18.0)(1440) + (900/18.0)(18.0) \times (t - 0)$. Solving gives $t = 20°$.

(b) $\Delta S_{brick} = 500 \ln (293/473) = -239$ eu. $\Delta S_{H_2O} = (900/18.0) \times (1440/273) + (900 \times 18.0/18.0) \ln (293/273) = 327$ eu. $\Delta S_{total} = -239 + 327 = 88$ eu > 0.

3. Under these conditions $q = 6200$ cal, so $\Delta S_{surr} = -6200/298 = -20.8$ eu. But $\Delta S_{system} = 5870/298 = 19.7$ eu, so $\Delta S_{total} = -20.8 + 19.7 = -1.1$ eu, so the change is forbidden.

4. (a) Since, for ideal gases, H is independent of P, the change in H will be the result of the temperature change only, so $\Delta H = C_P \Delta T = 5(6.95)(400 - 300) = 3475$ cal.

(b) Since conditions are not those under which $q = \Delta H$, q will have to be found from w and ΔE. Now $V_1 = 5(0.0821)(300/1) = 123.1$ liters and, similarly, $V_2 = 32.8$ liters. Therefore $w = 5(32.8 - 123.1) = -451.5$ liter-atm $= -10,934$ cal. But $\Delta E = C_V \Delta T = 5(6.95 - 1.99) \times (400 - 300) = 496$ cal. Therefore $q = \Delta E + w = 496 - 10,934 = -10,438$ cal. This means that 10,438 cal were given to the surroundings. It follows that $\Delta S_{surr} = 10,438/400 = 26.1$ eu. $\Delta S_{total} = -6.0 + 26.1 = 20.1$ eu.

(c) Yes, since $20.1 > 0$.

5. (a) If the isothermal step is at 300°K we may restore the initial state by the following scheme:

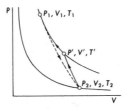

(b) We have:

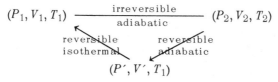

where $P_1 = 20$ atm, $V_1 = 2.46$ liters, $T_1 = 300°K$, and $P_2 = 10$ atm, $V_2 = 3.94$ liters, $T_2 = 240°K$. Solving $P'V' = 2(0.08205)(300)$ and $P'V'^{4.987/1.987} = 10(3.94^{4.987/1.987})$ for P' and V' gives $P' = 17.4$ atm and $V' = 2.83$ liters.

(c) $q = 2(1.987)(300)(2.303)\log(2.46/2.83) = -167$ cal $= q_{rev}$.

(d) ΔS for restoration $= -167/300 = -0.56$ eu, since the entropy changes only in the isothermal step. This result is equal numerically but opposite in sign to the answer to Ex. 2-11.

(e) q cannot be greater than zero for then work would have been done in a cyclic process using only one reservoir. q cannot equal zero for this would imply that the initial and final states of the original change have the same entropy.

Note If the temperature of 240°K had been chosen for the isothermal step the value of q would have been different but the value of ΔS would have been the same. *Any* temperature could have been chosen for the isothermal step, but then more than one adiabatic return step would have been needed.

6. (a) $V_1 = 1(0.0821)(300/6) = 4.10$ liters and $V_2 = 1(0.0821)(290/2) = 11.90$ liters. $w = 2(11.90 - 4.10) = 15.60$ liter-atm $= 377.5$ cal. $\Delta E = C_V \Delta T$ for ideal gas $= 3.00(290 - 300) = -30.0$ cal. $q = \Delta E + w = -30.0 + 377.5 = 347.5$ cal.

(b) $\Delta E = -30.0$ cal, as shown above. $\Delta H = \Delta E + \Delta(PV) = -30.0 + [2(11.90) - 6(4.10)]24.2 = -49.4$ cal. $\Delta S_{gas} = nR \ln (V_2/V_1) + n\bar{C}_V \ln (T_2/T_1) = 1.99(2.303)\log(11.90/4.10) + 3.00(2.303)\log(290/300) = 2.09$ eu. $\Delta S_{surr} = -347.5/290 = -1.20$ eu. $\Delta S_{total} = 2.09 - 1.20 = 0.89$ eu.

(c) Yes, because $\Delta S_{total} > 0$.

7. (a) Since $C_6H_6(l)$ and $C_6H_6(g)$ are in equilibrium at $80°$ and 1 atm, ΔS under these conditions is $7353/353 = 20.83$ eu, i.e. $\Delta S^\circ_{353} = 20.83$ eu. Since $(\partial \Delta S/\partial T)_P = \Delta C_P/T$, we have:

$$\int_{343}^{353} d\Delta S = \Delta S^\circ_{353} - \Delta S^\circ_{343} = \int_{343}^{353} (20.3 - 36.2)\, dT/T$$

and so $20.83 - \Delta S^\circ_{343} = -15.9 \ln (353/343) = -0.45$, or $\Delta S^\circ_{343} = 21.28$ eu. (b) For $C_6H_6(g, 70°, 1 \text{ atm}) \longrightarrow C_6H_6(g, 90°, 1 \text{ atm})$, $\Delta S = 20.3 \ln (363/343) = 1.15$ eu. Therefore ΔS for $C_6H_6(l, 70°, 1 \text{ atm}) \longrightarrow C_6H_6(g, 90°, 1 \text{ atm}) = 21.28 + 1.15 = 22.43$ eu.

CHAPTER 3

1. $\bar{S}^\circ(g, 350°K) = 0.195/3 + \int_{15}^{200} [(0.0085T + 0.00030T^2)/T]\,dT +$

$1800/200 + \int_{200}^{300} [(14.50 + 0.0043T)/T]\,dT + 7050/300 +$

$\int_{300}^{350} (12.00/T)\,dT = 0.06 + 0.0085(200 - 15) + 0.00015(200^2 - 15^2) +$

$9.00 + 14.50 \ln (300/200) + 0.0043(300 - 200) + 23.50 + 12.00 \ln (350/300) = 48.26$ eu. This is the entropy at $350°K$ and 1 atm. In expanding to 0.5 atm there will be another gain of $R \ln (P_1/P_2)$ or $1.98(2.303) \log 2 = 1.38$ eu. Therefore $\bar{S}(g, 350°K, 2 \text{ atm}) = 48.26 + 1.38 = 49.64$ eu mole^{-1}.

2. (a) $\Delta S^\circ_{298} = (15.2 + 17.3) - (12.2 + 19.8) = 0.5$ eu. $\Delta S^\circ_0 = 0$ by the third law, since it is an all-solid system.
(b) $q_{rev} = T\Delta S = 298(0.5) = 150$ cal.
(c) Nothing. If, as is implied, the change were isothermal and isobaric, there would be energy transferred to or from the surroundings, the entropy change of which could not be calculated because we are not told ΔH. The value of q_{rev} cannot be used for ΔH, as the latter is for an irreversible process. (Actually, ΔH is $+5.943$ kcal so ΔS_{surr} would be $-5943/298 = -19.9$ eu if the surroundings were at $298°K$. This would give $\Delta S_{total} = 0.5 - 19.9 = -19.4$ eu, so the isothermal, isobaric process is forbidden.)

3. (a) Since $V = f(P, T)$, $dV = (\partial V/\partial P)_T dP + (\partial V/\partial T)_P dT$. For changes at fixed volume this becomes $0 = (\partial V/\partial P)_T(\partial P/\partial T)_V + (\partial V/\partial T)_P$ or $(\partial P/\partial T)_V = -(\partial V/\partial T)_P/(\partial V/\partial P)_T = (1/V)(\partial V/\partial T)_P/-(1/V)(\partial V/\partial P)_T = \alpha/\beta$.
(b) From the third law $\lim_{T \to 0} (\partial P/\partial T)_V = \lim_{T \to 0} \alpha/\beta = 0$, which is consistent with the above relation regardless of the value of β.

4. (a) W for N_A indistinguishable molecules in N_1 cells $= N_1^{N_A}/N_A! = W_A$, and W for N_B indistinguishable molecules in N_2 cells $= N_2^{N_B}/N_B! = W_B$, as shown in the text, since $N_1 \gg N_A$ and $N_2 \gg N_B$. For the mixture we wish to find the number of ways we can place $N_A + N_B$ molecules in $N_1 + N_2$ cells. There will be $(N_1 + N_2)(N_1 + N_2 - 1) \times (N_1 + N_2 - 2) \ldots (N_1 + N_2 - N_A + 1)/N_A!$ ways of placing the N_A molecules of A. For each of these ways there will be $(N_1 + N_2 - N_A) \times (N_1 + N_2 - N_A - 1)(N_1 + N_2 - N_A - 2) \ldots (N_1 + N_2 - N_A - N_B + 1)/N_B!$ ways of placing the N_B molecules of B. The product of these last two expressions, viz. $(N_1 + N_2)(N_1 + N_2 - 1)(N_1 + N_2 - 2) \ldots (N_1 + N_2 - N_A - N_B + 1)/N_A!N_B!$, can be approximated by $(N_1 + N_2)^{(N_A + N_B)}/N_A!N_B!$ as usual. This is the value of W_{AB}. Therefore $\Delta S = k \ln W_{\text{final}} - k \ln W_{\text{initial}} = (k \ln W_{AB}) - (k \ln W_A + k \ln W_B) = k \ln [(N_1 + N_2)^{(N_A + N_B)}/ N_A!N_B!] - [k \ln (N_1^{N_A}/N_A!) + k \ln (N_2^{N_B}/N_B!)] = -k \ln [(N_1^{N_A}N_2^{N_B}/ (N_1 + N_2)^{(N_A + N_B)}]$.

(b) This expression for ΔS may be modified as follows:

$$\Delta S = -k \ln \left[\left(\frac{N_1^{N_A}}{(N_1 + N_2)^{N_A}} \right) \left(\frac{N_2^{N_B}}{(N_1 + N_2)^{N_B}} \right) \right] = k \ln (X_A^{N_A} X_B^{N_B})$$

$$= -k (N_A + N_B) \ln (X_A^{N_A} X_B^{N_B})^{1/(N_A + N_B)}$$

For 1 mole of mixture $N_A + N_B = N_0$, the Avogadro number. Furthermore $R = kN_0$, so $\Delta S = -R \ln (X_A^{X_A} X_B^{X_B}) = -R (X_A \ln X_A + X_B \ln X_B)$.

5. All four substances have the same molecular weight and are at the same temperature and pressure, so we may compare entropies by comparing states of aggregation and symmetries. The only liquid, ethylbenzene(l), should have the least entropy. Of the remaining three gases p-xylene is the most symmetrical and ethylbenzene(g) the least. This suggests the following order of increasing entropy: ethylbenzene(l), p-xylene(g), o-xylene(g), ethylbenzene(g).

Note The actual values are 60, 84.2, 84.3 and 86.2 eu mole^{-1}, respectively.

CHAPTER 4

1. Even if TS, A and PV are all in the same units, e.g. calories, the actual values of only TS and PV can be found. The absolute value of A, like that of E, H and G, is not known, so the *size* of the area denoted by A has no significance. The sizes of TS and PV will vary with the substance and the conditions of P and T, but TS is nearly always greater than PV.

2. The change to be considered is $H_2S(g) + Br_2(g) \longrightarrow 2HBr(g) + S(s)$. Since P and T are constant the criterion of spontaneity is conveniently the sign of ΔG.

$$\Delta G^\circ_{298} = [(2)(-12.72) + 0] - [-7.89 + 0.75] = -18.30 \text{ kcal}$$

The change is therefore spontaneous and $Br_2(g)$ should oxidize $H_2S(g)$ under these conditions.

3. (a) The entropy of $I_2(s)$ should change very little with pressure because it is a solid.

(b) $(\partial S/\partial P)_T = -(\partial V/\partial T)_P$. But $\alpha = (1/V)(\partial V/\partial T)_P = 2.64(10^{-4})$ deg^{-1}. For 1 mole $\overline{V} = 254/4.94 = 51.4 \text{ cm}^3 \text{ mole}^{-1}$, so $2.64(10^{-4}) = (1/51.4)(\partial \overline{V}/\partial T)_P$, giving $(\partial \overline{V}/\partial T)_P = 0.01357 \text{ cm}^3 \text{ deg}^{-1} \text{ mole}^{-1} = -(\partial S/\partial P)_T$ or $d\overline{S}_T = -0.01357 \, dP_T$. Integration yields $\overline{S}$ at 100 atm $- \overline{S}$ at 1 atm $= -0.01357(100 - 1) = -1.34 \text{ cm}^3 \text{ atm deg}^{-1} \text{ mole}^{-1} = -3.25(10^{-2}) \text{ eu mole}^{-1}$. Therefore $\overline{S}_{298}$ at 5 atm $= 27.9 - 0.0323 = 27.9 \text{ eu mole}^{-1}$.

4. $\overline{S}^\circ_{id} - \overline{S}^\circ_{act} = \overline{S}^\circ_{id} - 53.23 = \displaystyle\int_0^1 \left(\frac{R}{P} + \frac{27RT_c^3}{32P_cT^3} - \frac{R}{P} \right) dP = \frac{27RT_c^3}{32P_cT^3}$

$$= \frac{27(1.987)(417.2)^3}{32(76.1)(298.2)^3} = 0.06$$

Hence $\overline{S}^\circ_{id} = 53.23 + 0.06 = 53.29 \text{ eu mole}^{-1}$.

5. By integration of Eq. (4-28), $\Delta G_T = nRT \ln (P_2/P_1)$ for ideal gases. Therefore $\Delta G_T = (10/2)(1.99)(400)(2.303) \log 10 = 9200 \text{ cal}$, so the free energy increases by 9200 cal. The work content changes by the same amount since $\Delta A = \Delta G - \Delta(PV)$, and $\Delta(PV)$ is zero (isothermal change of volume of ideal gas). Alternatively, by Eq. (4-37) $dA_T = -(nRT/V)dV$ or $\Delta A_T = nRT \ln (V_1/V_2) = nRT \ln (P_2/P_1)$.

6. (a) By Eq. (4-29) $d\Delta G_T = \Delta V dP$. But $\Delta V \cong \overline{V}_{CO_2} = RT/P$. Therefore $d\Delta G_T = RT \, d \ln P$. Integration gives ΔG at 0.010 atm $- \Delta G$ at 1 atm $= RT \ln (0.010/1.0) = -2720 \text{ cal}$. But ΔG at 1 atm $= 31,100 \text{ cal}$, so ΔG at 0.010 atm $= 28,400 \text{ cal}$.

(b) By Eq. (4-33) $d\Delta G_P^\circ = -\Delta S^\circ dT_P$. Integration between 298° and 308°K gives $\Delta G^\circ_{308} - \Delta G^\circ_{298} = -38.4(308 - 298) = -384 \text{ cal}$. Since $\Delta G^\circ_{298} = 31.1 \text{ kcal}$, $\Delta G^\circ_{308} = 31,100 - 384 = 30,700 \text{ cal}$.

7. (a) $\Delta G = 0$ because $H_2O(l)$ and $H_2O(g)$ are in equilibrium under these conditions. $\Delta A = \Delta G - \Delta(PV)$. The volume of 1 mole of $H_2O(l)$ is $18.0/1.00 = 18.0 \text{ cm}^3 \text{ mole}^{-1} = 0.0180 \text{ liter mole}^{-1}$; the volume of 1 mole of $H_2O(g) = RT/P = 0.0821(355/0.500) = 58.3 \text{ liters}$. Therefore $\Delta(PV) = 0.500(58.3) - 0.500(0.0180) = 29.15 \text{ liter-atm} = 706 \text{ cal}$, so $\Delta A = 0 - 706 = -706 \text{ cal}$.

(b) Consider that the change occurred via vaporization at 82° and 0.500 atm in order to utilize the fact that under these conditions $\Delta G = 0$, i.e., regard the overall change as the sum of the following steps:

$H_2O(l, 25°, 1.000\ atm) \xrightarrow{(1)} H_2O(l, 82°, 1.000\ atm) \xrightarrow{(2)}$

$H_2O(l, 82°, 0.500\ atm) \xrightarrow{(3)} H_2O(g, 82°, 0.500)atm) \xrightarrow{(4)}$

$$H_2O(g, 82°, 0.250\ atm)$$

To find ΔG in (1), which involves a temperature change, we need to know S as a function of T (cf. Example 4-19). Now $\overline{S}_T^\circ$ for $H_2O(l)$ will equal $\overline{S}_{298}^\circ$ + increase in $\overline{S}$ in heating it from 298 to $T°K$. The latter will be $\overline{C}_P \ln (T/298)$ so $\overline{S}_T^\circ = 16.72 + 18.0 \ln (T/298) = 18.0 \ln T -$ 85.7 eu mole^{-1}. Since $(\partial G/\partial T)_P = -S$, $dG = -(18.0 \ln T - 85.7) dT$. Integration between 298 and 355°K gives $\overline{G}_{355}^\circ - \overline{G}_{298}^\circ = \Delta G$ in (1) = -1060 cal.

ΔG in (2), by Eq. (4-28) = $\displaystyle\int_{1.00}^{0.500} (0.0180)\,dP = -0.009$ liter-atm = -0.22 cal.

ΔG in (3) = 0 as in part (a).

ΔG in (4) = $\displaystyle\int_{0.500}^{0.250} \overline{V}dP = nRT \ln (0.250/0.500) = -490$ cal.

$\Delta G_{overall} = -1060 - 0.22 + 0 - 490 = -1550$ cal.
To find $\Delta A_{overall}$ we use $\Delta A_{overall} = \Delta G_{overall} - \Delta(PV)_{overall}$. Initial $PV = 1.000(0.0180)(24.2) = 0.436$ cal. Final $PV = RT = 1.987(355) =$ 705 cal. Therefore $\Delta(PV)_{overall} = 705 - 0.436 = 705$ cal. $\Delta A_{overall} = -1550 - 705 = -2260$ cal.

8. (a) The maximum "useful" work is given by $-\Delta G$. $\Delta G_{298.15}^\circ = \Delta H_{298.15}^\circ - (298.15)\Delta S_{298.15}^\circ$ and $\Delta S_{298.15}^\circ = 16.716 - [31.211 + \frac{1}{2}(49.003)] = -38.997$ eu. Therefore $\Delta G_{298.15}^\circ = -68,317 - (298.15)(-38.997) = -56,690$ cal. The maximum useful work is thus 56,690 cal.
(b) $\Delta A_{298.15}^\circ = \Delta G_{298.15}^\circ - \Delta(PV) = \Delta G_{298.15}^\circ - P\Delta V$. Ignoring the volume of the $H_2O(l)$, $P\Delta V$ is given by $\Delta n_{gases}RT = (-3/2)(1.987)(298.2) = -889$ cal. Therefore $\Delta A_{298.15}^\circ = -56,690 + 889 = -55,801$ cal. The maximum work obtainable is thus 55,801 cal.
(c) Since $(\partial \Delta G^\circ/\partial T)_P = -\Delta S^\circ = 38.997$ eu, ΔG° increases by 38.997 cal per degree rise in temperature in the neighborhood of 298°K. Therefore $\Delta G_{299.15}^\circ = -56,690 + 38.997 = -56,651$ cal.
(d) Since $(\partial \Delta G^\circ/\partial P)_T = \Delta V^\circ \cong \Delta V_{gases} = \Delta nRT/P = (-3/2)(1.987) \times (298.15)/P = -888.6/P$ cal atm^{-1}, we have, on integrating between 1 and 2 atm, $\Delta G_{298.15}$ at 2 atm $- \Delta G_{298.15}$ at 1 atm $= \displaystyle\int_1^2 -(888.6/P)\,dP = -(888.6)(2.303)\log(2/1) = -616$ cal, or $\Delta G_{298.15}$ at 2 atm $- (-56,690) = -616$ or $\Delta G_{298.15}$ at 2 atm $= -57,306$ cal.

9. (a) $\Delta S_{298.2}^\circ = \Delta[(\overline{H}_{298.2}^\circ - \overline{H}_0^\circ)/298.2 - (\overline{G}_{298.2}^\circ - \overline{H}_0^\circ)/298.2] = [(2073/298.2) + 40.25 + (2194/298.2) + 45.93] - [(3075/298.2) + 57.50] = 32.68$ eu.

(b) $\Delta H^\circ_{298.2} = \Delta(\overline{H}^\circ_{298.2} - \overline{H}^\circ_0) + \Delta(\Delta\overline{H}^\circ_0) = (2.073 + 2.194 - 3.075) + (-27.202 + 0 + 52.06) = 26.05$ kcal.

(c) $\Delta G^\circ_{298.2} = \Delta H^\circ_{298.2} - (298.2)\Delta S^\circ_{298.2} = 26,050 - (298.2)(32.68) = 16,305$ cal.

(d) $\Delta G^\circ_{800} = 800\{\Delta(\Delta H^\circ_0)/800 - \Delta[-(\overline{G}^\circ_{800} - \overline{H}^\circ_0)/800]\}$. The values of $-(\overline{G}^\circ_{800} - \overline{H}^\circ_0)/800$ are obtained by interpolation as follows:

for CO: $43.86 + 0.6(4.91) = 46.81$
for Cl_2: $49.85 + 0.6(5.58) = 53.20$
for $COCl_2$: $63.33 + 0.6(9.46) = 69.01$

Therefore $\Delta G^\circ_{800} = 800[(0 - 27,202 + 52,060)/(800) - (46.81 + 53.20 - 69.01)] = 58$ cal.

(e) The reaction is still forbidden at $800°K$ so there is no reversal of the spontaneity.

10. (a) $\Delta a = (7.219 + 7.5755) - [2(6.7319) + \frac{1}{2}(6.0954)] = -1.717$. Similarly $\Delta b = 2.307(10^{-3})$, $\Delta c = -9.29(10^{-7})$. Therefore $\Delta C^\circ_P = -1.717 + 2.307(10^{-3})T - 9.29(10^{-7})T^2$. Using Eq. (1-18) and integrating between $T = 298°$ and $T = T°K$ gives $\Delta H^\circ_T = -13,672 - 1.717(T - 298) + 1.153(10^{-3})(T^2 - 298^2) - 3.10(10^{-7})(T^3 - 298^3) = -13,254 - 1.717T + 1.153(10^{-3})T^2 - 3.10(10^{-7})T^3$.

(b) We are now in a position to find ΔG°_{1000} from ΔG°_{298}. Using Eq. (4-35) we have $d(\Delta G^\circ/T) = \{[13,254 + 1.717T - 1.153(10^{-3})T^2 + 3.10(10^{-7})T^3]/T^2\}\,dT$. Integrating between $T = 298°$ and $T = 1000°K$ gives $\Delta G^\circ_{1000}/1000 - \Delta G^\circ_{298}/298 = 32.7$, or $\Delta G^\circ_{1000}/1000 = 32.7 - 30.5 = 2.2$, or $\Delta G^\circ_{1000} = 2200$ cal.

(c) Confirmation using Table 4-1:

$$\Delta G^\circ_{1000} = 1000\left[\frac{(-57,107 + 0) - (-44,038 + 0)}{1000}\right.$$
$$\left. - (47.01 + 55.43 - 92.32 - 25.35)\right] = 2161 \text{ cal}$$

This is in satisfactory agreement with 2200 cal calculated in (b).

11. By Eq. (4-44), $(\partial E/\partial V)_T = T(\partial P/\partial T)_V - P$. Consequently the internal pressure $= 293(12.67) - 1 = 3710$ atm.

CHAPTER 5

1. On passing from the liquid to the solid state at the freezing point $\overline{PV}$ would decrease and $\overline{A}$ would increase.

2. For $K(s) \longrightarrow K(l)$, $\Delta V = 1/0.830 - 1/0.851 = 0.030$ cm^3 g^{-1}. Substitution in Eq. (5-2) gives $1/0.0167 = \Delta H/(63.7 + 273.2)(0.030)$ or $\Delta H = 600$ cm^3 atm g$^{-1} = 14.5$ cal g^{-1}.

3. Substitution in Eq. (5-6) gives $\log(10.0/1.00) = (\Delta H_s/2.303R)[31.1/405.6(436.7)]$. Using the value for R in cal deg^{-1} mole^{-1} gives $\Delta H_s = 26,060$ cal mole^{-1}. Similarly $\log(100.0/40.0) = (\Delta H_v/2.303R)[24.5/$

465.2(489.7)] gives ΔH_v = 16,930 cal mole^{-1}. Then $\Delta H_f = \overline{H}_1 - \overline{H}_s =$ $(\overline{H}_g - \overline{H}_s) - (\overline{H}_g - \overline{H}_1)$ = $\Delta H_s - \Delta H_v$ = 26,060 − 16,930 = 9130   cal mole^{-1}.

To find the coordinates of the triple point we find the intersection of the log P vs. $1/T$ line for the solid with that for the liquid by finding the equation for each line. This has the form of Eq. (5-5). We have, therefore, log $P = (-26,060/2.303R)(1/T) + A$ and log $P = (-16,930/2.303R)(1/T) + B$ for these two lines, respectively, where A and B are constants. These constants are determined by substituting the coordinates of points known to lie on the lines, such as 436.7°K, 10.0 mm for the first and 465.2°K, 40.0 mm for the second, thus:

log 10.0 = $(-26,060/2.303R)(1/436.7) + A = -5695(1/436.7) + A,$

and

log 40.0 = $(-16,930/2.303R)(1/465.2) + B = -3700(1/465.2) + B.$

Solving gives A = 14.04 and B = 9.56. The equations for the two lines are then:

$$\log P = -5695(1/T) + 14.04 \text{ for the solid}$$

and

$$\log P = -3700(1/T) + 9.56 \text{ for the liquid,}$$

where P is in mm. The point of intersection is found by solving these two simultaneous equations, yielding T = 445°K and P = 17 mm.

4. If ΔC_P and H are independent of pressure $(\partial \Delta H/\partial T)_P$ = $d\Delta H/dT$ = ΔC_P, and $\Delta H = \Delta H_I + \Delta C_P T$. Then $dP/dT = \Delta H/T\Delta V \cong (\Delta H_I + \Delta C_P T)/T\overline{V}_g$. Furthermore, replacing $\overline{V}_g$ by RT/P gives d ln P/dT = $(\Delta H_I + \Delta C_P T)/RT^2$. Integration gives ln $P = -\Delta H_I/RT + (\Delta C_P/R)$ ln T + constant or log $P = -\Delta H_I/2.303RT + (\Delta C_P/R)$ log T + constant′.

Note Vapor pressure data are commonly expressed in this form, viz. log $P = -A/T + B$ log $T + C$, where A, B and C are constants.

5. Slope = -1693.3 = $-7400/(2.303z)(1.987)(1)$, so z = 0.955.

6. Since $\overline{V} = 24.055P^{-1} - 4.8678(10^{-2}) + 8.956(10^{-5})P + 10.486(10^{-10})P^3$ and RT = 0.08206(293.15) = 24.055 liter-atm, $b = \overline{V} - RT/P$ may be readily found as a function of P. Substitution in Eq. (5-13) followed by integration between P = 0 and P = 300 atm gives f = 211.2 atm.

7. (a) Since dP/dT = 2.3026 P d log P/dT, the given function for log P is differentiated giving:

$$dP/dT = 2.3026P\,[(477.3/T^2) - 0.064129 + 5.1822(10^{-4})T]$$

If $P = 1$ atm and $T = 81.61°K$ then we obtain:

$$dP/dT = 2.3026(1)[(477.3/6660.2) - 0.064129 + 422.92(10^{-4})]$$
$$= 0.11473 \text{ atm deg}^{-1}$$

But this equals $\Delta H/T\Delta V$ and $\Delta H = 1444$ cal mole^{-1} or 59,620 cm^3 atm mole^{-1}, so we have:

$$0.11473 = 59,620/81.61 \, \Delta V$$

or

$$\Delta V = 6368 \text{ cm}^3 \text{ mole}^{-1} = \overline{V}_g - \overline{V}_l = \overline{V}_g - 35.$$

Therefore $\overline{V}_g = 6403$ cm^3 mole^{-1}. The ideal value, $\overline{V}_{id}$, is $RT = 82.06(81.61) = 6697$ cm^3 mole^{-1}, a difference of about 5%.
(b) $P_{id} = RT/\overline{V} = 82.06(81.61)/6403 = 1.046$ atm, so $f = P^2/P_{id} = 1^2/1.046 = 0.956$ atm, and f/P, the activity coefficient $= 0.956/1 = 0.956$.

8. $\ln(f/300) = [9(190.7)(300.0)/128(45.8)(293.2)][1 - 6(190.7^2)/293.2^2] = -0.4608$. Therefore $f = 189.3$ atm.
   This is about 10% smaller than the more accurate value of 211.2 atm and illustrates the approximate nature of Eq. (5-17).

9. In general $\overline{V}$ is small for liquids and solids but large for gases. Hence in Eq. (5-21) the rate of change of $\ln f$ (and therefore of f) with P will be small for the former and large for the latter. On the other hand, $\overline{H}^* - \overline{H}$ is large for liquids and solids (because it includes enthalpy of vaporization) but small for gases (which are already vaporized) so that in Eq. (5-22) the rate of change of $\ln f$ (and therefore of f) with T is large for the former and small for the latter.

10. Assuming that $\overline{H}^* - \overline{H}$ is independent of T in the given temperature range we have, on integration of Eq. (5-22) $\log(167.7/141.8) = [(\overline{H}^* - \overline{H})/2.303R][(260 - 240)/260(240)]$ from which $H^* - H$ is found to be 33 cal mole^{-1}.

11. $\overline{V}_l = 18.02/0.988 = 18.24$ cm^3 mole^{-1}. Eq. (5-23) then gives $\ln(p_2/92.51) = [18.24/82.06(323.2)](200 - 0.12)$ from which $p_2 = 106.2$ mm.

    Note The experimental value is 141 mm (!) showing how non-ideal the water vapor-nitrogen mixture really is. (The solubility of the gas in the water is too slight to cause the deviation.)

CHAPTER 6

1. (a) For $KCl(s) \longrightarrow KCl(4.42m)$, $\Delta G_{291} = 0 = \Delta H_{291} - 291(\Delta S_{291})$ by Eq. (4-13). But $\Delta H_{291} = 3.830$ kcal so $\Delta S_{291} = [3.830(1000)]/291 = 13.16$ eu. However $\Delta S = \overline{S}_{KCl(4.42m)} - \overline{S}_{KCl(s)} = \overline{S}_{KCl(4.42m)} - 19.76$. Therefore $\overline{S}_{KCl(4.42m)} = 13.16 + 19.76 = 32.92$ eu mole^{-1}.
   (b) Since, for the above change, $\Delta S > 0$, $(\partial \Delta G/\partial T)_P = -\Delta S < 0$. Therefore ΔG decreases with rise in temperature. The process to which ΔG refers is, as before, $KCl(s) \longrightarrow KCl(4.42m)$ and so, at a tempera-

ture slightly above 25°, the transfer of KCl from the solid state to the dissolved state *at a concentration of 4.42m* must be <0. To make $\Delta G = 0$ at this higher temperature (i.e. for the solution to be saturated) the chemical potential of the dissolved KCl must be larger and therefore the concentration must be larger. Hence the solubility must increase with rise in temperature.

Note The partial heat of solution in a saturated solution is sometimes called the **last heat of solution.** Observe that the entropy of the KCl in solution is over 60% greater than what it is when undissolved.

2. The mass of an arbitrary amount of solution, say 1 mole, is $0.375(46.07) + 0.625(18.02) = 28.54$ g, and its volume is $28.54/0.8859 = 32.21$ cm^3. By Eq. (6-6), $32.21 = 0.625\overline{V}_{H_2O} + 0.375(57.4)$ or $\overline{\overline{V}}_{H_2O} = 17.1$ cm^3 mole^{-1}.

3. (a) If a graph such as Fig. 6-1 be drawn, $\Delta\overline{H}_{H_2SO_4}$ may be found from the slope. For this purpose the data may be restated as in the first two columns of the following table:

ΔH (kcal mole H$_2$O^{-1}) "y"	$n_{H_2SO_4}/n_{H_2O}$ "x"	Δy	Δx	$\Delta y / \Delta x$
-5.01	0.5000			
-3.90	0.3333	1.11	-0.1667	-6.7
-3.23	0.2500	0.67	-0.0833	-8.0
-2.77	0.2000	0.46	-0.0500	-9.2
-2.42	0.1667	0.35	-0.0333	-10.5

The slope of the curve at a composition corresponding to H$_2$SO$_4$ · 4H$_2$O may be estimated by interpolation of $\Delta y/\Delta x$, yielding $(-8.0 - 9.2)/2 = -8.6$. The partial heat of solution of H$_2$SO$_4$ at the composition is thus $\Delta\overline{H}_{H_2SO_4} \cong -8.6$ kcal mole^{-1}. The total heat of solution, on the other hand, is $\Delta H = -12.92$ kcal mole^{-1}.

(b) H$_2$SO$_4$(l) $\longrightarrow$ H$_2$SO$_4$(in H$_2$SO$_4$ · 4H$_2$O) $\Delta H_{298} = -8.6$ kcal

H$_2$SO$_4$(l) + 4H$_2$O(l) $\longrightarrow$ H$_2$SO$_4$ · 4H$_2$O $\Delta H_{298} = -12.92$ kcal

4. (a) $\Delta\overline{\overline{H}}_{H_2SO_4} = \Delta H$ for H$_2$SO$_4$(l) $\longrightarrow$ H$_2$SO$_4$(1.1101m soln) so $\Delta H = \Delta L = \overline{L}_{H_2SO_4} - \overline{L}_{H_2SO_4(l)} = 6065 - 23{,}540 = -17{,}470$ cal.

(b) $\Delta H_{soln} = \Delta H$ for H$_2$SO$_4$(l) + 50H$_2$O(l) $\longrightarrow$ H$_2$SO$_4$ · 50H$_2$O so $\Delta H = \Delta L = L_{soln} - (\overline{L}_{H_2SO_4(l)} + 50\overline{L}_{H_2O(l)}) = [50(-5.70) + 1(6065)] - (23{,}540 + 0) = -17{,}760$ cal.

(c) The change to be considered is:

$$H_2SO_4 \cdot 15H_2O + 35H_2O(l) \longrightarrow H_2SO_4 50H_2O$$

$\Delta H = \Delta L = L_{H_2SO_4 \cdot 50H_2O} - [L_{H_2SO_4 \cdot 15H_2O} + 35\overline{L}_{H_2O(l)}] = [50(-5.70) + 1(6065)] - [15(-89.8) + 1(7896) + 35(0)] = -769$ cal.
Therefore 769 cal of heat are evolved.

5. (a) The change in question is

$$2(H_2SO_4 \cdot 25H_2O) + \infty H_2O(l) \longrightarrow 2(H_2SO_4 \cdot \infty H_2O)$$

for which $\Delta H = \Delta L = 0 - [50(-24.4) + 2(6681) + 0] = -12{,}142$ cal. Therefore 12,142 cal are evolved.

(b) $L_{soln} = 50(-24.4) + 2(6681) = 12{,}142$ cal.

6. (a) Since there are two components and three phases, presumably in equilibrium after the shaking, $\bar{\Im} = 2 - 3 + 2 = 1$. With the maintenance of constant temperature this reduces to $\bar{\Im} = 0$, so the system is invariant and therefore already defined.

(b) (i) μ_{ether} is the same in all three phases.

(ii) μ_{water} is the same in all three phases.

(iii) There is no relationship between μ_{ether} and μ_{water} (except as required by Eq. (6-11)).

7. (a) The required curve must begin at 18.1 and end at 13.7 cm^3 $mole^{-1}$. Since $d\bar{V}_{EtOH}/dX_{EtOH}$ is finite for the lowest alcohol contents $d\bar{V}_{H2O}/dX_{EtOH}$ must be zero. Since $d\bar{V}_{EtOH}/dX_{EtOH}$ is zero for the highest alcohol contents $d\bar{V}_{H2O}/dX_{EtOH}$ must be finite. Furthermore the slope of the line to be drawn must be opposite in sign to that of the given curve at the same value of X_{EtOH}. We are thus led to the following:

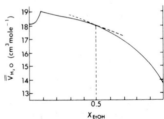

Note While this result is correct qualitatively, it is not correct quantitatively. For example, the maximum in the curve is actually less prominent than shown.

(b) Type 1.

CHAPTER 7

1. (a) (i) By Eq. (7-5), $\Delta G^\circ_{298} = \mu_{SnCl_4} - \mu_{SnCl_4}^\bullet = RT \ln X_{SnCl_4} = 1.987(298) \ln 0.60 = -303$ cal.

(ii) By Eq. (7-13) $\Delta G^\circ_{298} = \Delta G^M_{298} = R(298)(0.60 \ln 0.60 + 0.40 \ln 0.40) = -398$ cal.

(b) Since $\Delta H = 0$, $\Delta G = -303$ cal and $\Delta S = (\Delta H - \Delta G)/T$ by Eq. (4-13), so $\Delta S = 1.02$ eu.

2. (a) For 2A(g, 2 atm) $\longrightarrow$ 2A(g, 5 atm), $\Delta G_{273} = 2RT \ln (5/2) = RT \ln (5/2)^2$. For 3B(g, 3 atm) $\longrightarrow$ 3B(g, 5 atm), $\Delta G_{273} = 3RT \ln (5/3) =$

RT ln $(5/3)^3$. For 2A(g, 5 atm) + 3B(g, 5 atm) $\longrightarrow$ Mixture (g, $P =$ 5 atm), $\Delta G_{273} = \Delta G^M = 5RT(0.4$ ln $0.4 + 0.6$ ln $0.6)$.
Therefore ΔG_{273}(total) = RT ln $(5/2)^2 + RT$ ln $(5/3)^3 + 5RT[(2/5)$ ln $(2/5) + (3/5)$ ln $(3/5)] = 0$.
(b) Volume of 2 moles of A at 2 atm and $0° = 22.4$ liters. Volume of 3 moles of B at 3 atm and $0° = 22.4$ liters. Volume of 5 moles of mixture at 5 atm and $0° = 22.4$ liters. Therefore $\Delta V^M = 22.4 - (22.4 + 22.4) = -22.4$ liters.

3. By Eq. (7-15) $\Delta S^M = -R(0.714$ ln $0.714 + 0.286$ ln $0.286) = 1.19$ eu. But the absolute entropy of these quantities unmixed is $0.714(70.42) + 0.286(74.10) = 71.47$ eu. Therefore the entropy of the mixture = $71.47 + 1.19 = 72.66$ eu.

4. (a) For normal $\rightleftharpoons$ iso, $\Delta G^\circ_{298} = -4.296 - (-3.754) = -0.542$ kcal = 542 cal. Since $\bar{G}^\circ_n = 0$, $\bar{G}^\circ_{iso} = 0 - 542 = -542$ cal mole^{-1}.
(b) If unmixed, $G_{tot} = 0.300(-542) + 0.700(0) = -163$ cal mole^{-1}.
(c) By Eq. (7-13) $\Delta G^M = R(298)$ 0.300 ln $0.300 + 0.700$ ln $0.700 = -362$ cal. Therefore $\bar{G}_{soln} = -163 - 362 = -525$ cal mole^{-1}.
(d) $\mu_{iso} = \mu^\circ_{iso} + RT$ ln $X_{iso} = -542 + R(298)$ ln $0.300 = -1255$ cal mole^{-1}. Similarly $\mu_n = 0 + R(298)$ ln $0.700 = -211$ cal mole^{-1}.
(e) By Eq. (7-23), $-542 = -R(298)$ ln K_p or $K_p = 2.50$. But since $\Delta n = 0$, $K_p = K_X = 2.50 = X_{iso}/X_n = X_{iso}/(1 - X_{iso})$, the solution of which is $X_{iso} = 0.714$, so $X_n = 0.286$. This is the composition of the equilibrium mixture. It is independent of total pressure, for K_X is independent of pressure, since $\Delta n = 0$.
(f) $\mu_{iso} = \mu_n = 0 + R(298)$ ln $0.286 = -742$ cal mole^{-1}.
(g) $\bar{G}_{soln} = -742(0.714) - 742(0.286) = -742$ cal mole^{-1}.

5. (a) By Eq. (7-26) $K_p = 0.570 = K_c[0.0821(2000)]^1$ since $\Delta n = 1$, so $K_c = 0.00347$. By Eq. (7-28), $0.570 = K_X(2)^1$, so $K_X = 0.285$. K_p and K_c are true equilibrium constants, but not K_X.
(b) The required ΔG is ΔG° when the standard state is 1 mole liter^{-1} so, by Eq. (7-27), $\Delta G^\circ = -1.987(2000)$ ln $0.00347 = 22,500$ cal.

6. Let there be n_o moles of H_2O initially. Then we have:

	H_2O	H_2	O_2
Initial	n_o	0	0 moles
Decrease	αn_o	—	— moles
Increase	—	αn_o	$\alpha n_o/2$ moles
Final	$n_o(1 - \alpha)$	αn_o	$\alpha n_o/2$ moles

$$n_t = n_o(1 + \alpha/2) \text{ and } \Delta n = 1$$

Therefore

$$K_p = 6.9(10^{-15}) = \frac{(\alpha n_o)^2(\alpha n_o/2)}{[n_o(1 - \alpha)]^2}(2^1)[n_o(1 + \alpha/2)]^{-1}$$

$$= \frac{\alpha^3}{(1 - \alpha)^2(1 + \alpha/2)}.$$

Complete solution of this equation for α is involved and unnecessary. The smallness of K_p indicates that α is very small, so we may ignore α and $\alpha/2$ compared to unity in the factors of the denominator and write $6.9(10^{-15}) = \alpha^3$ from which we obtain $\alpha = 1.9(10^{-5})$ or 0.0019%.

7. (a) By Eq. (7-36), $21,800 = -R(298) \ln K_p'$ which gives $K_p' = 1.07(10^{-16})$ (atm). But $K_p' = \mathcal{P}_{H_2O}^{10}$ so $\mathcal{P}_{H_2O} = 0.0253$ atm or 19.23 mm.

(b) A partial pressure of water equal to 19.23 mm.

(c) K_p' and therefore $\mathcal{P}_{H_2O}$ is independent of pressure so $\mathcal{P}_{H_2O}$ will remain constant.

8. (a) $K_p = \alpha^2 P/(1 - \alpha^2) = 0.80^2(1)/(1 - 0.80^2) = 1.78$ (atm). $n_t = 0.20 + 0.80 + 0.80 = 1.80$ moles, so $V = 1.80(0.0821)(523)/1 = 77.2$ liters. $c_{PCl_5} = 0.20/77.2 = 0.0026$ mole liter^{-1}; $c_{PCl_3} = c_{Cl_2} = 0.80/77.2 = 0.0104$ mole liter^{-1}.

(b)

	PCl$_5$	PCl$_3$	Cl$_2$	
Initial	0.20	0.80	1.30	moles
Decrease	—	x	x	moles
Increase	x	—	—	moles
Final	$0.20 + x$	$0.80 - x$	$1.30 - x$	moles

$$n_t = 2.30 - x \text{ moles} \quad \text{and} \quad \Delta n = 1$$

Therefore $[(0.80 - x)(1.30 - x)/(0.20 + x)]1^1(2.30 - x)^{-1} = 1.78$, giving $x = 0.04$. Therefore the new quantities present are 0.24 moles of PCl$_5$, 0.76 moles of PCl$_3$ and 1.26 moles of Cl$_2$. The new $n_t = 2.26$ moles, the new volume is $2.26(0.0821)(523)/1 = 97.0$ liters and the new concentrations are $c_{PCl_5} = 0.24/97.0 = 0.0025$ mole liter^{-1}, $c_{PCl_3} = 0.76/97.0 = 0.0078$ mole liter^{-1} and $c_{Cl_2} = 1.26/97.0 = 0.0130$ mole liter^{-1}.

(c) If no shift had occurred the volume would have been $2.30(0.0821)(523)/1 = 98.8$ liter and $c_{Cl_2} = 1.30/98.8 = 0.0132$ mole liter^{-1}.

9. (a) $K_p = \alpha^2 P/(1 - \alpha^2) = 0.718^2(1)/(1 - 0.718^2) = 1.064$ (atm).

(b) (i) Since K_p is independent of pressure $K_p = 1.064$ (atm) at 10 atm.

(ii) At 10 atm $1.064 = \alpha^2(10)/(1 - \alpha^2)$ giving $\alpha = 0.310$ or 31.0%.

10. Combination of the heat capacity data gives $\Delta a = 7.581$, $\Delta b = -20.435(10^{-3})$, $\Delta c = 131.76(10^{-7})$ and $\Delta d = -2.751(10^{-9})$. Substitution of these values in Eq. (1-22), with an extra term, $(\Delta d/4)T^4$, and making the substitutions $T = 298.2$ and $\Delta H_{298}^\circ = 41,220.4$ cal gives $\Delta H_I^\circ = 39,757.4$ cal. But $\Delta G_{298}^\circ = 28,644.0$ cal from which $\ln K_p$ at this temperature is found to be -48.344 from Eq. (7-23). Substitution of this value in Eq. (7-44), with the addition of the term $(\Delta d/12R)T^3$, yields $I = -1.540$. Therefore we obtain:

$$\ln K_p' = -\frac{39,757.4}{RT} + \frac{7.581}{R} \ln T - \frac{20.435(10^{-3})}{2R} T + \frac{131.76(10^{-7})}{6R} T^2$$

$$-\frac{2.751(10^{-9})}{12R} T^3 - 1.540$$

Substitution of $T = 1000$ in this result gives $\ln K_p' = 0.654$ or $K_p' = 1.923$ at $1000°K$. From Eq. (7-36), $\Delta G°_{1000} = -1300$ cal. (This value may be confirmed by calculation from the data of Table 4-1.)

11. Integration of Eq. (7-45) and substitution gives:

$$\log \frac{2.44(10^{-2})}{5.48(10^{-3})} = \frac{\Delta E°}{2.303\ R} \left[\frac{318 - 298}{318(298)} \right]$$

from which we find that $\Delta E° = 14,100$ cal.

12. Consider 1 mole of starting mixture and let x be the number of moles of NH_3 formed in it. This gives:

	H_2	N_2	NH_3	Ar	
Initial	0.762	0.235	0	0.003	moles
Decrease	$3x/2$	$x/2$	—	—	moles
Increase	—	—	x	—	moles
Final	$0.762 - 3x/2$	$0.235 - x/2$	x	0.003	moles

The final n_t per mole of starting mixture $= 0.762 - 3x/2 + 0.235 - x/2 + x + 0.003 = 1.000 - x$ moles. But 15.11% of this equals x, i.e. $0.1511(1.000 - x) = x$, the solution of which is $x = 0.1313$. Moreover $\Delta n = -1$, so we have:

$$K_p = [0.1313/(0.762 - 0.3939/2)^{3/2}(0.235 - 0.1313/2)^{1/2}]$$
$$\times (50)^{-1}(1.000 - 0.1313)^{+1} = 1.31(10^{-2})(\text{atm}).$$

CHAPTER 8

1. By Eq. (8-5) $P = 760(1 - 0.300) + 560(0.300) = 532 + 168 = 700$ mm. $Y_B = 168/700 = 0.240$.

2. (a) $P = 23.8 + 11.5 = 35.3$ mm. $Y_{C_6H_5Cl} = 11.5/35.3 = 0.326$. (b) By Eq. (8-12) $Y_{C_6H_5Cl} = 0.700 = 11.5/P$, so $P = 16.4$ mm.

3. We may solve this problem by finding $p^•$ for each component as a function of T and then P for the mixture as a function of T. Let A stand for C_6H_5Cl and B for H_2O. For A, by Eq. (5-6), since $p_A^• = 1$ atm at $T = 404°K$, $\log p_A^•$ at $T°$ is $= \frac{8730}{2.303R} \left(\frac{T - 404}{404T} \right)$ where $p_A^•$ is in atm. This rearranges to:

$$\log p_A^• = 4.72 - 1908(1/T) \qquad (1)$$

Similarly for B, since $p_B{}^{\bullet} = 1$ atm at $T = 373°$K, we obtain:

$$\log p_B{}^{\bullet} = 5.69 - 2124(1/T) \qquad (2)$$

From (1) we may find that when $T = 350$, e.g., $\log p_A{}^{\bullet} = -0.73$ and $p_A{}^{\bullet} = 0.19$ atm. Log $p_A{}^{\bullet}$ vs. $1/T$ may now be plotted since we have two points on the straight line. From (2), similarly, we may find that when $T = 350$, e.g., $\log p_B{}^{\bullet} = -0.38$ and $p_B{}^{\bullet} = 0.42$ atm. Log $p_B{}^{\bullet}$ may now also be plotted vs. $1/T$. From these two plots $p_A{}^{\bullet}$ and $p_B{}^{\bullet}$ may be read off at several temperatures to give, e.g.:

$T(°$K$)$	350	373	404
$p_A{}^{\bullet}$(atm)	0.19	0.40	1.00
$p_B{}^{\bullet}$(atm)	0.42	1.00	2.80
P (atm)	0.61	1.40	3.80

and P may then be found for each T by the addition of $p_A{}^{\bullet}$ and $p_B{}^{\bullet}$. Finally a third plot, P vs. T, gives a curve from which it is found that $P = 1.00$ atm when $T = 363°$K or $90°$C, the normal boiling point of the two-liquid system.

4. Using Eqs. (8-15) and (8-16) we have:

$$\log(X_A/Y_A) = \frac{4908}{(2.303)(1.987)} \left[\frac{350 - 360}{350(360)} \right]$$

from which $X_A/Y_A = 0.822$ and:

$$\log(X_B/Y_B) = \frac{4484}{2.303(1.987)} \left[\frac{350 - 338}{(350)(338)} \right]$$

from which $X_B/Y_B = 1.257$. However, $X_A + X_B = 1$ and $Y_A + Y_B = 1$, so $X_B = 0.486$, $Y_B = 0.409$. The mole fraction of p-C_6H_4BrCl in the liquid and solid phases is therefore 0.486 and 0.409, respectively.

5. (a) Let A stand for C_6H_6 and B for p-$C_6H_4Cl_2$ in Eqs. (8-17) and (8-18). Since here the solid phase is B we substitute in Eq. (8-18) to give:

$$\log X_B = \frac{4340}{2.303(1.987)} \left[\frac{300.0 - 326.3}{300.0(326.3)} \right] = -0.255$$

or $X_B = 0.556$ which is the ideal solubility of p-$C_6H_4Cl_2$(s) in C_6H_6(l).   (b) Since here the solid phase is A we substitute in Eq. (8-17) to give

$$\log(1 - 0.091) = \frac{2370}{2.303(1.987)} \left[\frac{T - 278.6}{278.6T} \right]$$

the solution of which is $T = 273.2°$K, the freezing point of the solution.

CHAPTER 9

1. (a) If p_A be calculated for any of the solutions using Raoult's law it will be found to be less than the observed value. For example, when $X_B = 0.1016$, $X_A = 0.8984$ and $p_A(\text{ideal}) = 0.8984(173.09) = 155.04 < 158.45$. Similarly p_B (ideal) for this solution $= 0.1016(258.84) = 26.30 < 95.32$, so the system exhibits positive deviations from ideality.

(b) (i)

X_B	0	0.0212	0.0356	0.1016	0.1638
X_A	1.0000	0.9788	0.9644	0.8984	0.8362
p_A	173.09	169.41	167.34	158.45	150.97
ΔX_A		0.0212	0.0144	0.0660	0.0622
Δp_A		3.68	2.07	8.89	7.48
$\Delta p_A / \Delta X_A$		173.6	143.8	134.7	120.3

The approach of $\Delta p_A / \Delta X_A$ to the value for $p_A{}^\bullet$, viz. 173.09 indicates the approach to Raoult's law behavior. (The fact that $173.6 > 173.09$ is the result of a small experimental error.)

(ii)

X_B	0	0.0212	0.0356	0.1016	0.1638
p_B / X_B	—	1100	1076	938	828

The approach of p_B / X_B to a finite nonzero limiting value indicates the approach to Henry's law behavior.

(c) $f_B^\circ = 1135$ mm.

(d) (i) Henry's law does not hold in this range so we must use $\Delta G_{318.2} = RT \ln (f_B / f_B') = RT \ln (p_B / p_B') = 1.987(318.2) \ln (38.31 / 95.32) = -577$ cal.

(ii) By Eq. (9-12) $\Delta G_{318.2} = \mu_B^\circ - \mu_B = -1.987(318.2) \ln 0.0212 = 2437$ cal.

(iii) Since Henry's law holds for $X_B = 0.0212$, $\overline{\overline{H}}_B = \overline{\overline{H}}_B^\circ$ by Eq. (9-15) so $\Delta H_{318.2} = 0$. By Eq. (9-16) $\Delta S = \overline{\overline{S}}_B^\circ - \overline{\overline{S}}_B = 1.987 \ln 0.0212 = -7.66$ eu.

(iv) Since $\overline{\overline{H}}_B^\circ = \overline{\overline{H}}_B$ at infinite dilution, $\Delta H_{318.2} = 0$.

(e) *If* Henry's law is valid Eq. (9-12) applies to both initial and final states so $\Delta G_{318.2} = 1.987(318.2) \ln (0.0356/0.1016) = -663$ cal.

Note This value differs by about 15% from the more correct value in (d) (i).

2. By the Gibbs-Duhem relation $X_A d\mu_A + X_B d\mu_B = 0$ at constant T and P, or $d\mu_B = -(X_A / X_B) d\mu_A$. But, since $\mu_A = \mu_A{}^\bullet + RT \ln X_A$ wherever Raoult's law holds, $d\mu_A = RT\, d \ln X_A$, so $d\mu_B = -(X_A / X_B) RT\, d$

$\ln X_A = -(RT/X_B)dX_A$. But $X_A + X_B = 1$ so $dX_A = -dX_B$. Therefore $d\mu_B = (RT/X_B)dX_B = RT\, d\ln X_B$. Integration at constant T and P gives $\mu_B = RT\ln X_B + $ constant. But, by definition, $\mu_B = RT\ln f_B + $ constant'. Therefore $f_B \propto X_B$ wherever Raoult's law holds.

3. (a) Differentiation of Eq. (9-11) gives $(\partial\mu_A/\partial X_A)_{P,\,T} = (\partial\mu_A{}^\circ/\partial X_A)_{P,\,T} + RT/X_A$. But $\partial X_A = -\partial X_B$ since $X_A + X_B = 1$. Moreover $\mu_A{}^\circ$ is independent of X_A. Therefore $(\partial\mu_A/\partial X_B)_{P,\,T} = -RT/(1 - X_B)$ so $\lim\limits_{X_B\to 0} (\partial\mu_A/\partial X_B)_{P,\,T} = -RT$. Differentiation of Eq. (9-12) gives, similarly, $(\partial\mu_B/\partial X_B)_{P,\,T} = RT/X_B$ so $\lim\limits_{X_B\to 0} (\partial\mu_B/\partial X_B)_{P,\,T} = \infty$.

Chemical potential is thus seen to fall into the first of the two categories, where $\overline{\overline{J}}_1$ stands for μ_A, $\overline{\overline{J}}_2$ for μ_B and X_2 for X_B. (b) Differentiation of Eq. (7-19) applied to solvent (A) gives $(\partial\overline{\overline{S}}_A/\partial X_A)_{P,\,T} = (\partial\overline{\overline{S}}_A/\partial X_A)_{P,\,T} - R/X_A$ or $(\partial\overline{\overline{S}}_A/\partial X_B)_{P,\,T} = R/(1 - X_B)$ so $\lim\limits_{X_B\to 0} (\partial\overline{\overline{S}}_A/\partial X_B)_{P,\,T} = R$. Differentiation of Eq. (9-16) gives, similarly, $(\partial\overline{\overline{S}}_B/\partial X_B)_{P,\,T} = -R/X_B$ so $\lim\limits_{X_B\to 0} (\partial\overline{\overline{S}}_B/\partial X_B)_{P,\,T} = -\infty$, so partial molar entropy falls in the second category, where $\overline{\overline{J}}_1$ stands for $\overline{\overline{S}}_A$, $\overline{\overline{J}}_2$ for $\overline{\overline{S}}_B$ and X_2 for X_B.

4. In the derivation of Eq. (9-21) it is assumed that the solute is involatile, so the vapor is 100% solvent. It is this fact that permitted replacing $(\mu_A)_v$ by $(\mu_A{}^\bullet)_v = (\mu_A^\circ)_v$ at 1 atm. *Depression* of boiling points occurs only with volatile solutes (but not with all volatile solutes).

5. Although Eq. (9-28) was developed for solutions of difficultly soluble solids in liquids it applies to difficultly soluble gases at constant pressure by almost identical arguments. $\Delta H_B'$ is then the required heat of solution at infinite dilution. Since enthalpy of gases is virtually independent of pressure and since enthalpy of solutes is independent of concentration (as long as Henry's law holds) and virtually independent of pressure, the heat of solution will also be independent of concentration and pressure if these are small enough. We first find X_{H_2}'/X_{H_2} for a given constant pressure, 1 atm, e.g.. Since, at $20°$, $p_{H_2} = k_{H_2}X_{H_2} = 6.85(10^4)X_{H_2}$, $X_{H_2} = p_{H_2}/6.85(10^4) = 1/6.85(10^4)$ or $1.46(10^{-5})$ when $p_{H_2} = 1$ atm. Similarly, at $40°$, $X_{H_2} = 1/7.63(10^4)$ or $1.31(10^{-5})$ when $p_{H_2} = 1$ atm. We then have:

$$\log\,[1.46(10^{-5})/1.31(10^{-5})]. = \frac{\Delta H_{H_2}'}{2.303\,R}\left[\frac{293 - 313}{293\,(313)}\right]$$

the solution of which is $\Delta H_{H_2}' = -970$ cal mole^{-1}.

6. (a) Since $X_B = 0.00029$ when $X_A = 0.99971$ both quantities refer to the same solution. The freezing point is therefore $-0.0300°$ and the depression is $0.0300°$.

(b) By Eq. (9-21), $\Delta T_b = 1.99\,(373)^2\,(0.00029)/9720 = 0.0083°$. The normal boiling point is therefore $100.0083°$.

(c) Since, at the normal boiling point, $P_{solvent} = 760.00$ mm, Eq. (9-18) becomes $(P_{solvent} - P_{solution})/760.00 = 0.00029$ or $P_{solvent} - P_{solution} = 0.22$ mm $=$ lowering of the vapor pressure.

(d) By Eq. (9-30) $\pi = 0.0821\,(373)\,(0.00029)/0.01880 = 0.47$ atm.

7. The fugacity of water in the solution would become greater than that of the pure solvent and water would flow from the solution into the solvent ("reverse osmosis").

Note This concept offers the possibility of desalting sea water.

8. (a) Substitution in Eq. (8-18) gives:

$$\log X_B = \frac{600}{2.303\,R}\left[\frac{298 - 317}{298\,(317)}\right]$$

from which it is found that $X_B = 0.941$.

Note The high ideal solubility might have been anticipated from the nearness of $25°$ to the melting point, $44°$.

(b) Assuming Henry's law to hold for B we may use Eq. (9-28):

$$\log\,(X_B'/0.0124) = \frac{4100}{2.303\,R}\left[\frac{313 - 298}{313\,(298)}\right]$$

from which it is found that $X_B' = 0.017$.

9. Before the addition of I_2 to the KI solution $2\,(0.125) = 0.250$ moles of I^- were present. After 0.05945 moles of I_3^- had been formed in the approach to equilibrium after the addition of the aqueous KI, 0.05945 moles of I^- must have disappeared, so the final c_{I^-} must have been $(0.250 - 0.05945)/2.00 = 0.096$ mole liter^{-1}. The final c_{I_2} was $0.00639/2.00 = 0.00320$ mole liter^{-1}. The final $c_{I_3^-}$ was $0.05945/2.00 = 0.0297$ mole liter^{-1}. Therefore $K_c = 0.0297/(0.00320)\,(0.096) = 97$.

10. (a) $c_{(W)}/c_{(bz)} = 0.246, 0.1139, 0.0747$ and 0.0555 in the four runs, respectively. It is clearly not constant. This is because $c_{(bz)}$ includes two different species.

(b) To find $c_{(bz)}'$ we note that $c_{(bz)} = 2c_{(bz)}'' + c_{(bz)}'$ so $c_{(bz)}' = c_{(bz)} - 2c_{(bz)}''$. In the first run, then, $c_{(bz)}' = 0.1449 - 2\,(0.0470) = 0.0509$ mole liter^{-1}. In the remaining three runs, similarly, $c_{(bz)}' = 0.1439, 0.2323$ and 0.3212 mole liter^{-1}.

(c), (d) and (e) The required quotients are readily seen to be as follows:

Run	$c_{(W)}/c_{(bz)}{}'$	$c_{(W)}/c_{(bz)}{}''$	$c_{(W)}/c_{(bz)}{}''^{1/2}$
1	0.701	0.760	0.1645
2	0.700	0.272	0.1656
3	0.700	0.167	0.1649
4	0.700	0.120	0.1646

$c_{(W)}/c_{(bz)}{}'$ *is* constant: it is the partition coefficient for $HB_{(bz)} \rightleftharpoons HB_{(W)}$.

$c_{(W)}/c_{(bz)}{}''$ is *not* constant because there is no equilibrium $(HB)_{2(bz)} \rightleftharpoons HB_{(W)}$.

$c_{(W)}/c_{(bz)}{}''^{1/2}$ *is* constant: it is the equilibrium constant for $\frac{1}{2}(HB)_{2(bz)} \rightleftharpoons HB_{(W)}$.

CHAPTER 10

1. By Eq. (5-18) $\ln (f/200) = [9(126.1)(200)/128(33.5)(273.2)][1 - 6(126.1^2)/273.2^2]$, where f is the fugacity of pure $N_2(g)$ at 200 atm and 0.0°. A value of 189.4 atm is found from this expression. Therefore, according to the Lewis and Randall rule, the fugacity of the N_2 in the gas mixture = 189.4(0.400) = 75.8 atm. Ex. 10-1 gives a value of 81.2 atm, showing the inadequacy of the Berthelot equation and/or the Lewis and Randall rule.

Note Since the actual fugacity of pure N_2 at 0.0° and 200 atm is 194.2 and not 189.4 atm, and since 194.2(0.400) ≠ 81.2 atm it is seen that *both* the Berthelot and Lewis and Randall relations are approximations.

2. (a) If p_B be calculated (from PY_B) for any of the solutions it will be found to be greater than the corresponding Raoult's law value of $p_B^\circ X_B = 172.76 X_B$. Similarly, p_A, calculated from $P(1 - Y_B)$ will be found to be greater than $p_A^\circ(1 - X_B) = 433.54(1 - X_B)$. The system therefore shows positive deviations from ideality.

(b) $a_A = p_A/p_A^\circ = p_A/p_A^\bullet = PY_A/433.54 = P(1 - Y_B)/433.54$ and $\gamma_A = a_A/X_A = a_A/(1 - X_B)$. These quantities are tabulated below. Values of $\log \gamma_A$ and X_A/X_B are also included.

X_B	P(mm)	Y_B	a_A	γ_A	$\log \gamma_A$	X_A/X_B
0	433.54	0	1	1	0	∞
0.0443	448.49	0.0681	0.9641	1.0088	0.0038	21.57
0.4595	425.28	0.2297	0.7556	1.3980	0.1455	1.176
0.8740	249.92	0.6026	0.3974	3.154	0.4989	0.1442
0.9288	214.44	0.7533	0.2467	3.465	0.5397	0.07666
0.9524	199.62	0.8283	0.1717	3.607	0.5571	0.04998

0.9811	182.63	0.9284	0.0716	3.789	0.5785	0.01926
0.9843	180.96	0.9400	0.0600	3.822	0.5823	0.01595
1	172.76	1	0	—	—	0

(c) $a_B = p_B/p_B^\circ = p_B/p_B^\bullet = Y_B P/172.76 = 0.7533(214.44)/172.76 = 0.9350$. $\gamma_B = a_B/X_B = 0.9350/0.9288 = 1.0067$.

(d) To find p_A° on this basis the limiting slope of the Henry's law line for A must be determined. For the solutions low in A content we have:

X_B	0.8740	0.9288	0.9524	0.9811	0.9843
X_A	0.1260	0.0712	0.0476	0.0189	0.0157
p_A (mm)	99.32	52.90	34.27	13.08	10.86
p_A/X_A (mm)	788	743	720	692	692

It appears, therefore, that $\lim_{X_A \to 0} (p_A/X_A) = 692$ mm $= p_A^\circ$ so, when $X_B = 0.9288$ $a_A = 52.90/692 = 0.0764$ and $\gamma_A = 0.0764/0.0712 = 1.073$ on *this* basis.

(e) By Eq. (10-29) log γ_B at $X_B = 0.9288$ is given by the negative of the area under the curve obtained when log γ_A is plotted vs. X_A/X_B between $X_B = 1$ and $X_B = 0.9288$. The necessary data are included in the table in the answer to (b) part. The curve resembles Fig. 10-3 (a). The area so found is about -0.00199 so log $\gamma_B = 1.005$. The value found in (c) on the same basis is 1.0067, in satisfactory agreement.

3. By Eq. (10-14) $\Delta G_{298} = 2.00(1.99)(298) \ln [0.0100(12.3)/0.200(3.12)] = -1920$ cal.

4. (a) When $X_A = 0.660$, $\gamma_A = 1.04$ so $a_A = 1.04(0.660) = 0.686 = p_A/7.48$. Therefore $p_A = 5.13$ mm. Similarly $a_B = 0.93(0.340) = 0.316 = p_B/2.36$ so $p_B = 0.75$ mm. The total pressure is therefore $5.13 + 0.75 = 5.88$ mm.

(b) Over a range of composition A shows positive deviations from Raoult's law while B shows negative deviations.

5. (a) Denoting quantities referring to infinite dilution by an asterisk, $(a_B)_X/(a_B^*)_X = (a_B)_m/(a_B^*)_m$. But, since the reference state for both bases is infinite dilution, $(a_B^*)_X = X_B^*$ and $(a_B^*)_m = m^*$. Therefore $(a_B)_X/(a_B^*)_X = (a_B)_X/X_B^*$ and $(a_B)_m/(a_B^*)_m = (a_B)_m/m^*$, so $(a_B)_X/X_B^* = (a_B)_m/m^*$ or $(a_B)_X = (a_B)_m X_B^*/m^*$. But $X_B^* = m^* M_A/1000$ so $(a_B)_X = (a_B)_m m^* M_A/1000 m^* = (a_B)_m M_A/1000$.

(b) Using the result in part (a): $(a_B)_X = 0.427 = (a_B)_m (50.0)/1000$ or $(a_B)_m = 8.54$, which agrees with the value in Table 10-2.

6. At high dilution a_A can be replaced by $X_A = 1 - X_B$ and $\ln (1 - X_B) \cong -X_B$ when $X_B \ll 1$. Therefore $\theta = -1000(-X_B)/m M_A$. But $X_B =$

$m/(m + 1000/M_A)$. As m approaches zero X_B approaches $m/(1000/M_A) = mM_A/1000$. Hence, in the limit, $\phi = -1000(-mM_A/1000)/mM_A = 1$.

7. (a) By Eq. (10-43) $\Delta G^M = 1.99(298)[0.9000 \ln 0.9000(1.05) + 0.1000 \ln 0.1000(6.05)] = -60$ cal per mole of solution.

(b) By Eq. (10-44) $\Delta G^E = 1.99(298)(0.9000 \ln 1.05 + 0.1000 \ln 6.05) = 130$ cal per mole of solution.

8. (a) Since the solution is regular, $\Delta S^E = 0$ so $\Delta G^E = \Delta H^E = 26$ cal per mole of solution.

(b) Measurements of a_A and a_B at several temperatures could be made. These would enable one to find ΔG^E at several temperatures from which $(\partial \Delta G^E/\partial T)_P = -\Delta S^E$ could then be calculated.

9. By Eq. (10-38) we have:

$$\int_{T=298}^{T=308} d \log \gamma_B = -\int_{T=298}^{T=308} \frac{453}{2.303RT^2} dT$$

But γ_B at $298°K = 1.435$ so $\log \gamma_B$ at $308°K$ is:

$$0.1567 - \frac{453}{2.303R}\left(\frac{1}{298} - \frac{1}{308}\right)$$

which gives γ_B at $308°K = 1.399$.

CHAPTER 11

1. Computation of a_{CaCl_2}/m, a_{CaCl_2}/m^2 and a_{CaCl_2}/m^3 gives:

m	0.0001	0.0005	0.001	0.005
a_{CaCl_2}/m	$3.56(10^{-8})$	$7.72(10^{-7})$	$2.79(10^{-6})$	$4.80(10^{-5})$
a_{CaCl_2}/m^2	$3.56(10^{-4})$	$1.54(10^{-3})$	$2.79(10^{-3})$	$9.60(10^{-3})$
a_{CaCl_2}/m^3	3.56	3.09	2.79	1.92

The data in the last row show the best approach to constancy.

2. The cell reaction is $\frac{1}{2}H_2(g) + AgCl(s) \longrightarrow HCl(0.500m) + Ag(s)$ and $a_{HCl} = [0.500(0.757)]^2 = 0.2865$. Since H_2 is assumed to be ideal $a_{H_2} = p_{H_2} \approx 0.500$ atm. By Eq. (11-27) $\mathscr{E} = 0.222 - 0.05916 \log (0.2865/0.500^{1/2}) = 0.245$ volt.

3. Set up a cell (without transport) in which the zinc electrode is coupled to an electrode reversible with respect to Cl^- ion, e.g.

$$Zn \mid ZnCl_2(m) \mid AgCl \mid Ag$$

The cell reaction is $Zn(s) + 2AgCl(s) \longrightarrow ZnCl_2(m) + 2Ag(s)$. Measure $\mathscr{E}$ at $25°$ for various values of m down to as low a concentration as possible. Since $\mathscr{E} = \mathscr{E}° - (RT/2\mathscr{F}) \ln (m_{\pm}\gamma_{\pm})^3$ we may write:

$$\mathscr{E} + 3(RT/2\mathscr{F}) \ln m_{\pm} = \mathscr{E}° - (3RT/2\mathscr{F}) \ln \gamma_{\pm}$$

where $m_{\pm} = m(1^1 2^2)^{1/3}$ and $T = 298.2°K$. We now plot the left-hand member of this equation vs. $m^{1/2}$ and extrapolate to $m^{1/2} = 0$. This intercept equals $\mathscr{E}°$ since there $\gamma_{\pm} = 1$. Knowing $\mathscr{E}°$ for the Ag-AgCl electrode, $\mathscr{E}°$ for the zinc-zinc ion electrode is readily calculated.

4. For $1.5m$ $FeCl_2$, $\gamma_{\pm} = 0.637$; for $0.5m$, $\gamma_{\pm} = 0.460$. $\mathscr{E}° = 0$ as for all concentration cells so, using Eq. (11-27),

$$\mathscr{E} = 0 - (0.05916/2) \log [0.5(1^1 2^2)^{1/3}(0.460)/1.5(1^1 2^2)^{1/3}(0.637)]^3$$

$$= 0.0549 \text{ volt}$$

5. (a) Maximum electrical work $= - \Delta G° = 94,260$ cal.
(b) If a mole of $CO_2(g)$ were formed by combustion 94,052 cal of heat would be released. If this were used as the heat source for a reversible heat engine the work done would be $w = q_2(T_2 - T_1)/T_2 = 94,052(800 - 250)/800 = 64,662$ cal which would yield 64,662 cal of electrical work if there were no energy losses.
(c) Process (a) is far more efficient.

Note This suggests the desirability of having the galvanic cell indicated in (a). No such cell has yet been devised.

6. (1) For $H_2(g) + \frac{1}{2}O_2(g) \longrightarrow H_2O(l)$, $\Delta G° = - 56,690$ cal.
(2) For $H_2O(l) \rightleftharpoons H^+(aq) + OH^-(aq)$, $\Delta G° = - RT \ln K_a = -1.987(298.2)\ln [1.002(10^{-14})] = 19,099$ cal.
(3) For $H^+(aq) + e \longrightarrow \frac{1}{2}H_2(g)$, $\Delta G° = 0$.
Multiplying (2) by 2 and (3) by 2 and adding the results to (1) gives:

$$H_2O(l) + \frac{1}{2}O_2(g) + 2e \longrightarrow 2OH^-(aq) \ \Delta G° = -18,492 \text{ cal}$$

But, by Eq. (11-23), $-18,492 = -2\mathscr{E}°(23,061)$ or $\mathscr{E}° = 0.401$ volt for reduction. The standard oxidation potential is therefore $- 0.401$ volt.
7. (a) The half-cell reactions are:

$$Zn(s) \longrightarrow Zn^{+2}(aq) + 2e$$

and
$$I^-(aq) + Ag(s) \longrightarrow AgI(s) + e$$

Subtraction, after doubling the second equation, gives:

$$Zn(s) + 2AgI(s) \longrightarrow ZnI_2(aq) + 2Ag(s)$$

(b) $\Delta S° = [- 25.45 + 2(26.14) + 2(10.21)] - [9.95 + 2(27.6)] = - 17.9$ eu.
(c) Substitution of $\Delta G° = -n\mathscr{E}\mathscr{F}$ in the Gibbs-Helmholtz equation, $(\partial\Delta G°/\partial T)_P = - \Delta S°$, gives $(\partial\mathscr{E}/\partial T)_P = \Delta S°/n\mathscr{F}$. In the present case $(\partial\mathscr{E}°/\partial T)_P = - 17.9/2(23,061) = - 3.88(10^{-4})$ volt deg^{-1}.
(d) By Eq. (11-25), $\Delta H° = 2(23,061)[298.2(-3.88 \times 10^{-4}) - 0.610] = -33480$ cal.
8. $m_{H^+} = m_{Ac^-} = 0.0500(0.0188) = 0.000940$. $m_{Ca^{2+}} = 0.01000$ and $m_{Br^-} = 0.02000$. Therefore $\mu = \frac{1}{2}[0.000940(1^2) + 0.000940(1^2) + 0.01000(2^2) + 0.02000(1^2)] = 0.03094$.

9. By Eq. (11-41), $\phi = 2(0.796)(0.897)/5(0.565) = 0.505.$

10. (a) Integration of Eq. (11-38) gives:

$$\int_{\gamma_\pm = \gamma'_\pm}^{\gamma_\pm = \gamma_\pm} d \ln \gamma_\pm = \int_{\phi = \phi'}^{\phi = \phi} d\phi - \int_{m = 0.1}^{m = m} \frac{1 - \phi}{m} dm$$

or:

$$\ln (\gamma_\pm/\gamma'_\pm) = \phi - \phi' - \int_{0.1}^{m} \frac{1 - \phi}{m} dm = -[(1 - \phi) - (1 - \phi')]$$

$$- \int_{0.1}^{m} \frac{1 - \phi}{m} dm$$

Replacing dm by $2m^{1/2}dm^{1/2}$ gives:

$$\ln (\gamma_\pm/\gamma'_\pm) = -[(1 - \phi) - (1 - \phi')] - 2 \int_{0.1^{1/2}}^{m^{1/2}} \frac{1 - \phi}{m^{1/2}} dm^{1/2}$$

(b) The following data are required for plotting:

m	0.1	0.2	0.3	0.4	0.5
$m^{1/2}$	0.3162	0.4472	0.5477	0.6325	0.7071
$1 - \phi$	0.207	0.184	0.141	0.095	0.045
$(1 - \phi)/m^{1/2}$	0.655	0.411	0.257	0.150	0.064

m	0.7	1.0	1.2	1.4
$m^{1/2}$	0.8367	1.0000	1.095	1.183
$1 - \phi$	-0.057	-0.231	-0.349	-0.469
$(1 - \phi)/m^{1/2}$	-0.068	-0.231	-0.319	-0.396

The integral is evaluated by plotting $(1 - \phi)/m^{1/2}$ vs. $m^{1/2}$ between $m^{1/2} = 0.3162$ and $m^{1/2} = 1.095$ and finding the area under the curve, which is 0.0775 units. Therefore $\ln (\gamma_\pm/\gamma'_\pm) = -(-0.349 - 0.207) - 2(0.0775) = 0.401$, so $\gamma_\pm/\gamma'_\pm = 1.493.$

11. (a) For electrolytes (B), since $a_B = (m_\pm \gamma_\pm)^\nu$, $\ln a_B = \nu \ln m_\pm + \nu \ln \gamma_\pm$ and $(\partial \ln a_B/\partial T)_{P,X} = \nu (\partial \ln \gamma_\pm/\partial T)_{P,X}$ since $m_\pm$ is constant at constant composition. Therefore Eq. (10-37) becomes:

$$(\partial \ln \gamma_\pm/\partial T)_{P,X} = -\overline{\overline{L}}_B/\nu RT^2$$

Eq. (10-38), as it stands, is therefore not correct for electrolytes if γ is replaced by $\gamma_\pm$.

(b) Integration of the above equation between $T = T'$ and $T = T''$, assuming $\overline{\overline{L}}_B$ independent of T, gives:

$$\ln \gamma_\pm \text{ at } T'' - \ln \gamma_\pm \text{ at } T' = \frac{\overline{\overline{L}}_B}{2R} \left(\frac{T' - T''}{T' T''} \right)$$

Letting $T' = 298°K$ and $T'' = 308°K$ we have $\ln \gamma_\pm$ at $308°K - \ln 0.656 = [-186/2(1.987)][-10/298(308)]$, or $\gamma_\pm$ at $308°K = 0.659.$

Note Relative partial molar enthalpies are usually temperature-sensitive so they should not be regarded as constant when the temperature range is large.

12. Activities do not pass through a minimum with increase in concentration but rise continuously. Since $a_B = (m_{\pm} \gamma_{\pm})^{\nu}$ any decrease in $\gamma_{\pm}$ with increase in m is more than counteracted by the accompanying increase in $m_{\pm}$. Decrease in a_B with increase in concentration would lead to $\Delta G > 0$ for a transfer of solute from a higher to a lower concentration.

13. $\mu = \frac{1}{2}[0.0100(2^2) + 0.0100(2^2)] = 0.0400$ so log $\gamma_{\pm} = -0.511(2)(2) \times (0.0400)^{1/2} = -0.409$, or $\gamma_{\pm} = 0.390$. Table 11-4 gives $\gamma_{\pm} = 0.387$, in unexpectedly good agreement considering that $ZnSO_4$ is a higher valence type.

14. (a) Here $\mu = m = 1.41(10^{-2})$, so log $\gamma_{\pm} = -0.511(1)(1)(0.0141)^{1/2} = -0.0608$ or $\gamma_{\pm} = 0.869$. Therefore $K_{sp} = [(0.869)(0.0141)]^2 = 1.50(10^{-4})$.
(b) As a first approximation $\mu = 0.0141 + 0.0500 = 0.0641$, so log $\gamma_{\pm} = -0.511(1)(1)(0.0641)^{1/2} = -0.129$, or $\gamma_{\pm} = 0.743$. Therefore $K_{sp} = 1.50(10^{-4}) = (0.743s)^2$ where s is the solubility of TlCl, so $s = 1.65(10^{-2})$. Second approximation: $\mu = 0.0165 + 0.0500 = 0.0665$, so log $\gamma_{\pm} = -0.511(1)(1)(0.0665)^{1/2} = -0.132$, or $\gamma_{\pm} = 0.738$. Therefore $K_{sp} = 1.50(10^{-4}) = (0.738s)^2$, or $s = 1.66(10^{-2})$. Further repetition of this process makes no appreciable change in s.

Note The result is still approximate, even if there were no error in the original solubility figure, because we have used the *limiting* law.

15. $\Delta S^\circ = (\Delta H^\circ - \Delta G^\circ)/298.2$. Since the infinitely dilute solution is the standard state for enthalpies, $\Delta H^\circ = -17{,}960$ cal. There remains to find ΔG°.
(1) For HCl(g, 1 atm) $\longrightarrow$ HCl(g, $6.974(10^{-5})$) atm),

$$\Delta G = 1.987(298.2) \ln [6.974(10^{-5})/1] = -5671 \text{ cal.}$$

(2) For HCl(g, $6.974(10^{-5})$) atm) $\longrightarrow$ HCl($5m$),

$$\Delta G = 0.$$

(3) For HCl($5m$) $\longrightarrow$ HCl($a = 1$),

$$\Delta G = 1.987(298.2) \ln [1/5(2.38)]^2 = -2935 \text{ cal.}$$

Addition of (1), (2) and (3) gives, for HCl(g, 1 atm) $\longrightarrow$ HCl($a = 1$), $\Delta G = -8606$ cal. Therefore $\Delta S^\circ_{298.2} = [-17{,}960 - (-8606)]/298.2 = -31.37$ eu.

Note This illustrates in more detail how ΔS° was obtained for use in finding $\overline{\overline{S}}_{Cl^-}$ in the last section of Chapter 11.

16. (a) For

$$Fe^{2+}(aq) \longrightarrow Fe^{3+}(aq) + e, \quad \mathcal{E}° = -0.77 \text{ volt}$$

and for

$$Sn^{2+}(aq) \longrightarrow Sn^{4+}(aq) + 2e, \quad \mathcal{E}° = -0.14 \text{ volt}$$

Doubling the first of these equations and subtracting gives:

$$2Fe^{2+}(aq) + Sn^{4+}(aq) \longrightarrow 2Fe^{3+}(aq) + Sn^{2+}(aq), \quad \mathcal{E}° = -0.63 \text{ volt}$$

Therefore, by Eq. (11-24), $\ln K_a = 2(-0.63)(23,060)/1.99(298)$, or $K_a = 5.1(10^{-22})$ and K_a for the reverse reaction, the reduction of $Fe^{3+}(aq)$ by $Sn^{2+}(aq)$ is $1/5.1(10^{-22}) = 1.96(10^{21})$.

(b) $\Delta G° = [0.7 + 2(-20.30)] - [2(-2.53) + (-6.27)] = -28.57 \text{ kcal} = -1.987(298.2) \ln K_a$ so $K_a = 1.0(10^{21})$. This is in satisfactory agreement with the result in (a) considering the variety of independent methods used to determine the data.

17. (a) For KBr(s) $\longrightarrow$ KBr(5.75m), $\Delta G = 0$. Moreover, since in 5.75m solution, $m_{\pm} = 5.75$ and $\gamma_{\pm} = 0.645$, $a_{KBr} = [5.75(0.645)]^2 = 13.76$, so for KBr(5.75$m$) $\longrightarrow$ KBr($a = 1$), $\Delta G = 1.987(298.2) \ln (1/13.76) = -1553 \text{ cal}$. By adding these two results we find that for KBr(s) $\longrightarrow$ KBr($a = 1$), $\Delta G = 0 - 1553 = -1553 \text{ cal}$.

For the latter change, however, $\Delta H = \Delta H° = 4790 \text{ cal}$ since the enthalpy of KBr(aq) in its standard state ($a = 1$) is that in the infinitely dilute solution. Hence $\Delta S° = (\Delta H° - \Delta G°)/T = (4790 + 1553)/298.2 = 21.27 \text{ eu}$.

(b) $\Delta S° = \bar{\bar{S}}°_{K^+} + \bar{\bar{S}}°_{Br^-} - \bar{S}_{KBr(s)}$, or $21.27 = 24.5 + \bar{\bar{S}}°_{Br^-} - 23.05$ which gives $\bar{\bar{S}}°_{Br^-} = 19.8 \text{ eu mole}^{-1}$.

18. (a) By Eq. (11-57), $a_{H^+} = 10^{-1.085} = 0.0822$. Hence by Eq. (11-3) $\gamma_{H^+} = 0.0822/0.100 = 0.822$ and by Eq. (11-59) $a_{OH^-} = 1.002(10^{-14})/0.0822 = 1.219(10^{-13})$.

(b) If pH is defined as $-\log c_{H^+}$ then pH $= -\log 0.100 = 1.00$.

1. What, if anything, does the second law of thermodynamics have to say about desegregation of the human races?

2. Detect the fallacy in the following argument. By the Gibbs-Helmholtz equation $(\partial G/\partial T)_P = -S$ so, since $S > 0$ for H_2O, G decreases with rise in temperature. Cold water therefore has more free energy than hot water. A sealed inverted U-tube contains cold water in one leg and hot water in the other. The total pressure is constant throughout the tube since both legs are in contact. Since the cold water has the greater free energy it will have the greater fugacity so liquid will distil from the colder into the warmer leg.

3. If, for $A(g) \rightleftharpoons 2B(g)$, $K_P = 4\alpha^2 P/(1 - \alpha^2)$, state the dimensions of α and P and reconcile with the dimensionless quality of K_P.

4. In the section on the effect of addition at constant pressure of inert gas to a system at equilibrium in Chapter 7 it was assumed that the volume underwent an increase. Is it conceivable that a shift of equilibrium occurs, decreasing the total number of *reacting* molecules by more than the increase caused by the added inert gas, thereby causing a *decrease* in n_t of Eq. (7-32) and a consequent decrease in volume?

5. Detect the fallacy in the following. A system of $N_2(g)$, $H_2(g)$ and $NH_3(g)$ is in equilibrium according to $N_2(g) + 3H_2(g) \rightleftharpoons 2NH_3(g)$. The system is compressed isothermally. This causes more NH_3 to be formed at the expense of some of the N_2 and H_2. The partial pressure of NH_3 increases, therefore, and the partial pressures of N_2 and H_2 both decrease. Since $K_P = \mathscr{P}_{NH_3}{}^2/(\mathscr{P}_{N_2})(\mathscr{P}_{H_2})^3$, K_P will decrease.

6. A certain mixture of $N_2(g)$, $H_2(g)$ and $NH_3(g)$ which is at equilibrium at $723°K$ and a total pressure of 420 atm according to:

$$N_2(g) + 3H_2(g) \rightleftharpoons 2NH_3(g)$$

has the following composition: $X_{N_2} = 0.600, X_{H_2} = 0.200, X_{NH_3} = 0.200$. If more $N_2(g)$ be added to this mixture, maintaining both the total pressure and the temperature constant, a new equilibrium mixture is attained in which X_{N_2} is now *less than* 0.600. The equilibrium has thus shifted to the *left*. How is this reconciled with the Le Chatelier principle?

7. Experimentally a hydrate is stable at a given temperature in contact with $H_2O(g)$ over a *range* of pressure of water vapor. For $CuSO_4 \cdot 5H_2O$ at 50°, e.g., this range is about 40 mm. If the fugacity of the water vapor in this stable system can vary by this much how can it remain in equilibrium with $CuSO_4 \cdot 5H_2O$, the fugacity of water vapor from which is presumably fixed at a given temperature?

8. Suppose we write the equilibrium between $H_2(g)$, $I_2(g)$ and $HI(g)$ as:

$$H_2(g) + I_2(g) \rightleftharpoons HI(g) + HI(g)$$

If, initially, we have 1 mole of $H_2(g)$ and 1 mole of $I_2(g)$ and equilibrate the mixture so that x moles of HI are formed we have:

$$K_n = K_P = x^2/(1 - x)^2$$

If, on the other hand, we had written the reaction:

$$H_2(g) + I_2(g) \rightleftharpoons 2HI(g)$$

then we would have had:

$$K_n = K_P = (2x)^2/(1 - x)^2 = 4x^2/(1 - x)^2$$

Why do the two approaches give different results?

9. Detect the fallacy in the following argument. For a homogeneous equilibrium involving ideal gases, Eq. 7-27 gives:

$$-RT \ln K_c = \Delta G_c^\circ$$

where ΔG_c° is the value of ΔG when each gas is at a concentration of one mole per liter. It follows that $\Delta G_c^\circ/T = -R \ln K_c$. Differentiating this with respect to temperature at constant total pressure P gives:

$$[\partial(\Delta G_c^\circ/T)/\partial T]_P = -R \, (\partial \ln K_c/\partial T)_P$$

Using the Gibbs-Helmholtz relation and recognizing that K_c is independent of P gives:

$$d \ln K_c/dT = \Delta H_c^\circ/RT^2$$

where ΔH_c° is the enthalpy change when each substance is at 1 mole liter^{-1}. The latter equation is contrary to Eq. (7-45).

10. For component A in solution, $\mu_A = \mu_A^\circ + RT \ln a_A$. As X_A approaches zero, a_A approaches zero and μ_A approaches $-\infty$. If A is negligibly soluble in component B its chemical potential in solution will then be large and negative. That of pure A, however, is more positive, so, for:

$$A \longrightarrow A \text{ (in B)}$$

ΔG will be negative. Why, then, does A not dissolve in B?

11. For

$$Fe(s) \longrightarrow Fe^{2+}(aq) + 2e, \quad \mathcal{E}_{298}^\circ = 0.440 \text{ volt}$$

and for

$$Fe^{2+}(aq) \longrightarrow Fe^{3+}(aq) + e, \quad \mathcal{E}_{298}^\circ = -0.771 \text{ volt}$$

Therefore, by addition, we have:

$$Fe(s) \longrightarrow Fe^{3+}(aq) + 3e, \quad \mathcal{E}_{298}^\circ = -0.331 \text{ volt}$$

The tabulated value, however, is 0.036, not -0.331 volt. Reconcile.

12. The entropy of a system is commonly described as a measure of its randomness or "mixed-upness" so that isolated systems become more "mixed up" in the process of equilibration. Reconcile this with the fact that a supersaturated solution of sodium thiosulfate, on being isolated in a Dewar flask, equilibrates by depositing crystals of the solid solute which, being crystalline, are highly ordered.

13. Two involatile solids, A and B, form an eutectic system such as that of Fig. 8-8. When A and B are heated separately at 1 atm they melt at T_A and T_B, respectively. When mixed and then heated they begin to melt at T_E. Why does the mere proximity of the two pure solids in the mixture affect the melting behavior?

Index

LOGARITHMS

Natural Numbers	0	1	2	3	4	5	6	7	8	9	PROPORTIONAL PARTS								
											1	2	3	4	5	6	7	8	9
10	0000	0043	0086	0128	0170	0212	0253	0294	0334	0374	4	8	12	17	21	25	29	33	37
11	0414	0453	0492	0531	0569	0607	0645	0682	0719	0755	4	8	11	15	19	23	26	30	34
12	0792	0828	0864	0899	0934	0969	1004	1038	1072	1106	3	7	10	14	17	21	24	28	31
13	1139	1173	1206	1239	1271	1303	1335	1367	1399	1430	3	6	10	13	16	19	23	26	29
14	1461	1492	1523	1553	1584	1614	1644	1673	1703	1732	3	6	9	12	15	18	21	24	27
15	1761	1790	1818	1847	1875	1903	1931	1959	1987	2014	3	6	8	11	14	17	20	22	25
16	2041	2068	2095	2122	2148	2175	2201	2227	2253	2279	3	5	8	11	13	16	18	21	24
17	2304	2330	2355	2380	2405	2430	2455	2480	2504	2529	2	5	7	10	12	15	17	20	22
18	2553	2577	2601	2625	2648	2672	2695	2718	2742	2765	2	5	7	9	12	14	16	19	21
19	2788	2810	2833	2856	2878	2900	2923	2945	2967	2989	2	4	7	9	11	13	16	18	20
20	3010	3032	3054	3075	3096	3118	3139	3160	3181	3201	2	4	6	8	11	13	15	17	19
21	3222	3243	3263	3284	3304	3324	3345	3365	3385	3404	2	4	6	8	10	12	14	16	18
22	3424	3444	3464	3483	3502	3522	3541	3560	3579	3598	2	4	6	8	10	12	14	16	17
23	3617	3636	3655	3674	3692	3711	3729	3747	3766	3784	2	4	6	7	9	11	13	15	17
24	3802	3820	3838	3856	3874	3892	3909	3927	3945	3962	2	4	5	7	9	11	12	14	16
25	3979	3997	4014	4031	4048	4065	4082	4099	4116	4133	2	3	5	7	9	10	12	14	15
26	4150	4166	4183	4200	4216	4232	4249	4265	4281	4298	2	3	5	7	8	10	11	13	15
27	4314	4330	4346	4362	4378	4393	4409	4425	4440	4456	2	3	5	6	8	9	11	13	14
28	4472	4487	4502	4518	4533	4548	4564	4579	4594	4609	2	3	5	6	8	9	11	12	14
29	4624	4639	4654	4669	4683	4698	4713	4728	4742	4757	1	3	4	6	7	9	10	12	13
30	4771	4786	4800	4814	4829	4843	4857	4871	4886	4900	1	3	4	6	7	9	10	11	13
31	4914	4928	4942	4955	4969	4983	4997	5011	5024	5038	1	3	4	6	7	8	10	11	12
32	5051	5065	5079	5092	5105	5119	5132	5145	5159	5172	1	3	4	5	7	8	9	11	12
33	5185	5198	5211	5224	5237	5250	5263	5276	5289	5302	1	3	4	5	6	8	9	10	12
34	5315	5328	5340	5353	5366	5378	5391	5403	5416	5428	1	3	4	5	6	8	9	10	11
35	5441	5453	5465	5478	5490	5502	5514	5527	5539	5551	1	2	4	5	6	7	9	10	11
36	5563	5575	5587	5599	5611	5623	5635	5647	5658	5670	1	2	4	5	6	7	8	10	11
37	5682	5694	5705	5717	5729	5740	5752	5763	5775	5786	1	2	3	5	6	7	8	9	10
38	5798	5809	5821	5832	5843	5855	5866	5877	5888	5899	1	2	3	5	6	7	8	9	10
39	5911	5922	5933	5944	5955	5966	5977	5988	5999	6010	1	2	3	4	5	7	8	9	10
40	6021	6031	6042	6053	6064	6075	6085	6096	6107	6117	1	2	3	4	5	6	8	9	10
41	6128	6138	6149	6160	6170	6180	6191	6201	6212	6222	1	2	3	4	5	6	7	8	9
42	6232	6243	6253	6263	6274	6284	6294	6304	6314	6325	1	2	3	4	5	6	7	8	9
43	6335	6345	6355	6365	6375	6385	6395	6405	6415	6425	1	2	3	4	5	6	7	8	9
44	6435	6444	6454	6464	6474	6484	6493	6503	6513	6522	1	2	3	4	5	6	7	8	9
45	6532	6542	6551	6561	6571	6580	6590	6599	6609	6618	1	2	3	4	5	6	7	8	9
46	6628	6637	6646	6656	6665	6675	6684	6693	6702	6712	1	2	3	4	5	6	7	7	8
47	6721	6730	6739	6749	6758	6767	6776	6785	6794	6803	1	2	3	4	5	5	6	7	8
48	6812	6821	6830	6839	6848	6857	6866	6875	6884	6893	1	2	3	4	4	5	6	7	8
49	6902	6911	6920	6928	6937	6946	6955	6964	6972	6981	1	2	3	4	4	5	6	7	8
50	6990	6998	7007	7016	7024	7033	7042	7050	7059	7067	1	2	3	3	4	5	6	7	8
51	7076	7084	7093	7101	7110	7118	7126	7135	7143	7152	1	2	3	3	4	5	6	7	8
52	7160	7168	7177	7185	7193	7202	7210	7218	7226	7235	1	2	2	3	4	5	6	7	7
53	7243	7251	7259	7267	7275	7284	7292	7300	7308	7316	1	2	2	3	4	5	6	6	7
54	7324	7332	7340	7348	7356	7364	7372	7380	7388	7396	1	2	2	3	4	5	6	6	7